D1592897

MINES AND MINERALS
OF THE
GREAT AMERICAN RIFT
(COLORADO-NEW MEXICO)

MINES AND MINERALS
OF THE
GREAT AMERICAN RIFT
(COLORADO-NEW MEXICO)

**Richard Walker Holmes and
Marrianna B. Kennedy**

VNR VAN NOSTRAND REINHOLD COMPANY
NEW YORK CINCINNATI TORONTO LONDON MELBOURNE

Copyright © 1983 by Van Nostrand Reinhold Company Inc.

Library of Congress Catalog Card Number: 81–23975
ISBN: 0–442–28038–6

Manufactured in the United States of America

Published by Van Nostrand Reinhold Company Inc.
135 West 50th Street, New York, N.Y. 10020

Van Nostrand Reinhold Publishing
1410 Birchmont Road
Scarborough, Ontario M1P 2E7, Canada

Van Nostrand Reinhold Australia Pty. Ltd.
17 Queen Street
Mitcham, Victoria 3132, Australia

Van Nostrand Reinhold Company Limited
Molly Millars Lane
Wokingham, Berkshire, England

15 14 13 12 11 10 9 8 7 6 5 4 3 2 1

Library of Congress Cataloging in Publication Data

Holmes, Richard Walker.
  Mines and minerals of the Great American Rift
(Colorado-New Mexico).

  Bibliography: p.
  Includes index.
  1. Mines and mineral resources—Colorado.
2. Mines and mineral resources—New Mexico.
I. Kennedy, Marrianna B. II. Title. III. Title:
Great American Rift.
TN24.C6H74   553'.09788   81–23975
ISBN 0–442–28038–6   AACR2

DEDICATION

We dedicate this book to the concept that all possible steps should be taken to preserve our mineral heritage, whether in physical form as irreplaceable specimens, as information of their formation, or background of their occurrence. Our part of saving this heritage has been enjoyable and our wish is to share past experiences and information.

Space will not permit recognition of all the dedicated workers who have advanced our understanding of the Great American Rift. The scientific literature carries voluminous listings. To say our work drew heavily from all is a gross understatement. Where else is the information available? If this work can be considered a tribute to them, we would be pleased.

We assume no credit for their work, only for pertinent omissions and possible misinterpretations. We hope these are few.

This work is also dedicated to the early miners and prospectors whose dreams and visions, not to mention their determination and perseverance, hammered out of the frontier wilderness a mineral industry; and to past, present and future mineral collectors, whether in vaulted halls or humble miner's shacks. Their appreciation of symmetrical beauty in naturally formed objects binds them together in a single brotherhood. These we salute.

WARNING

Most mineral properties are in private ownership and permission to enter must be obtained to prevent trespass. Old mine workings are dangerous and entering underground openings without an authorized person can end in disaster.

My wholehearted appreciation goes to my wife, Wanda, who by her patience and understanding over many years, made my mineral collecting possible and by ably handling the grim logistics of everyday living made time available for writing and research.

R.W.H.

PREFACE

The purpose of this book is to preserve information about the mines and minerals of the Great American Rift in New Mexico and Colorado. Great American Rift is the name we use for a major continental rift that extends from Mexico along the Rocky Mountain Front to possibly the North Slope of Alaska. In New Mexico and Colorado, this rift zone is between the stable plates, or large blocks of the earth's crust, of the Great Plains and the Colorado Plateau. This rift zone contains the mines that have produced most of the mineral wealth for which these states are noted.

Information about many of the mines and their minerals is becoming scattered or lost to the mineral collector and hobbyist. Many sources are no longer available.

We hope we have recovered and preserved some of this information for the future. We also hope to introduce to the reader the concept of a great split or rift in the earth's crust that was responsible, directly or indirectly, for the many mineral deposits it exposed.

Richard Walker Holmes
Marrianna B. Kennedy

ACKNOWLEDGMENTS

Many people contributed directly and indirectly to the contents of this book as well as to its physical accomplishment. Their help is deeply appreciated.

Major thanks go to all, but especially to the following who contributed greatly of their time and respective talents:

Research Assistant: Gary D. Streetman

Director of Photography: Jack R. Morrison

Contributing Photographers: Tom E. Carpenter

Wanda H. Holmes

C. E. Withers

All photographs except those listed by initials of the contributing photographers are the work of Jack R. Morrison.

All specimens photographed were from the collections of the authors, with the exception of the rhodochrosites of the Sweet Home Mine, Alma, Colorado, which were loaned for photography by Norman L. Bennett.

CONTENTS

MINES AND MINERALS
OF THE
GREAT AMERICAN RIFT
(COLORADO-NEW MEXICO)

CHAPTER 1
THE GREAT AMERICAN RIFT

GENERAL

A rift is a large fissure (split) in the earth's crust that can be traced for some distance along the surface. A fault is a similar fissure, usually smaller, and it does not have certain rift characteristics. Rifting is a tectonic event because it changes the crust of the earth along the rift for a long period of geologic time. Movement of magma under a rift is caused by the release of crustal pressure.

Some of the criteria for determining if an active rift exists are seismic activity and abnormal heat flow. These conditions may indicate emplacement at shallow depth of igneous rock masses or pending volcanic activity. Thermal springs frequently occur along rifts. Visible surface evidence is the occurrence of rift valleys that trace the rift as a depression, usually of steep profile, graben valleys and rift valley lakes. Indications of former volcanic activity and the formation of calderas, large collapsed structures due to removal of material from the underlying magma chamber, are significant of rift activity. Large varieties and quantities of igneous rocks are usually found along rift zones.

Continental rifts are large enough to extend the length or width of a continent. The East African rift, in Ethiopia, is 600 miles wide, but the innermost or main rift is smaller. It is usually the most recently active part of a rift.

Rock material from the walls of a rift fall in to form the valley floor. In desert areas where there is insufficient alluvium to fill the rift valley, a deep gorge may develop between the steep and narrow walls. This is another topographic feature that defines a rift. Where there is more rainfall and more runoff from the surrounding area the rift will be filled with alluvium and it may be more difficult to identify. Rift valley lakes are a distinctive feature of rifts and often they are unusually deep. Lake Baykal, in the Baykal Rift of central Asia, is the world's deepest lake (5315 feet); Lake Tanganyika (over 5000 feet) and Lake Nyasa, both formed in the Great Rift Valley of East Africa, rank with the world's deepest.

The crust of the earth is separated from the mantle, at a depth of about 21.0 miles on land and about 6.0 miles under the oceans, by the Mohorovicic Discontinuity. This discontinuity marks a radical change in composition of the rocks from a more solid state to a more plastic state. Under the deeper oceans the crust is composed of basalt and rifts occur under the oceans as well as on the continents. Basalt, a dark to black heavy igneous rock, is composed principally of iron and magnesium (ferromagnesian) minerals. On continents, the crust is made of less dense rocks rich in silica (silicic) such as granitic rocks and transported rocks. Transported rocks also occur offshore near the continents.

If longer and wider blocks of the earth's crust slip down into the rift, more or less as a unit, a graben valley is formed. A large graben valley, such as the Rhine Graben of Europe, may also be a rift system. Walls of a graben are formed by near-vertical or normal faults. These faults are also called graben faults and often remain as scarps along the graben.

Areas above the fault scarps are called horst blocks. They continue to rise (or horst) as the graben block continues to sink into the less dense magma along and under the rift zone. Auxiliary faults along the rift may be shallow or deep-seated; however the graben faults extend to a depth where rock is becoming plastic and can flow. (Fig. 1–1).

Plastic magma moving toward the rift, where pressure has been lessened by the original break or rift, tends to make the area, in general, rise and this stretching of the crust makes it thinner. Many rift-related events, therefore, take place along the rift but at a distance from it. The phonolite plugs and other intrusive forms along the East African Rift occur as far as 75 miles from the rift, yet they are rift related.

Phonolite is a name used for igneous rocks of the phonolite–nepheline syenite group. Soda orthoclase is the principal mineral and carbonic acid is present in many magmas. It is thought to be formed from assimilated carbonate rocks. The name was suggested from the characteristic sound it makes when struck with a steel object.

Along a rift, the general overall effect is for the area, especially the horst blocks, to continue to rise as the graben continues to sink deeper into the rift. If graben filling keeps pace with sinking, the structure may be difficult to determine.

It could be expected that the activity along a continental rift although it extends over varying geologic time, would not be uniform. Batholiths, large

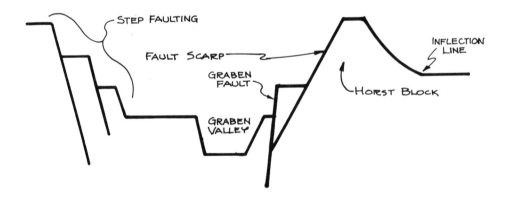

Fig. 1–1.   Horst and graben faults in cross section.

masses of generally silicic material lighter and more fluid than the larger mass of ferromagnesian material below, rise into the crust. The top or roof of a batholith tends to stope its way upward by cracking the overlying rock and forcing it into the magma. This rock, called xenoliths if smaller and roof pendants if larger masses, sinks to where the density of the magma will support it and generally it is assimilated into the melt, thereby changing the composition of its host. This process is called magmatic stoping. As conditions vary, the roof is not at the same elevation over the batholith. Some parts of the magma may be more fluid and rise faster to form cupolas that are rounded, vault-like structures.

Frequently, cupolas spawn smaller forms of igneous intrusives such as stocks, plugs, sills, dikes, laccoliths, pipes, chimneys, and less common forms. (Fig. 1–2)

If magma reaches the surface, volcanic activity produces ash, tuff, agglomerate, breccia, or other forms of pyroclastic materials. Lava flows may occur. After prolonged activity, which may extend over millions of years, large

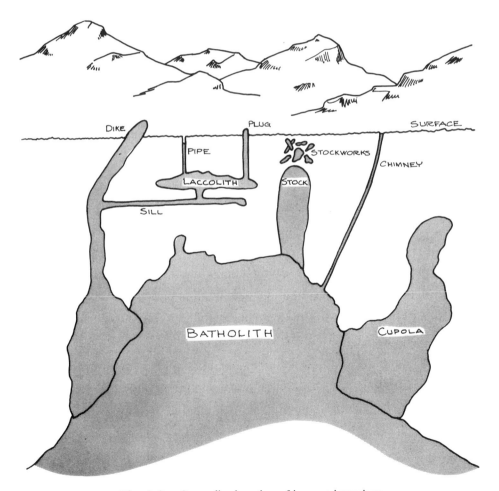

Fig. 1–2.   Generalized section of igneous intrusions.

relatively circular areas around the vent collapse to form a caldera. Should one side not fall all the way in and a hinge develop, the resulting structure would be called a pocket-book or hinged caldera. The Silverton caldera in Colorado is such a structure.

Rifts occur all over the world, on land and under the oceans. They are most numerous in the oceans and some of the largest rifts are found in the Mid-Ocean Ridge of the Indian Ocean and the Mid-Atlantic Ridge of the Atlantic Ocean. The ridges seem to form a line of expelled magma connecting the cross-cutting rifts. They may be special expressions of rifts themselves. The Dead Sea, Red Sea, and Gulf of Aden all occupy large rift valleys.

The largest continental rift is the Great Rift Valley of East Africa. It extends from the Red Sea Rift along the east side of Africa to South Africa. In Kenya, Uganda, Burundi, and Tanzania it forms two parts around Lake Victoria, which may occupy a depression that is rift-related. The more concentrated rift system, composed of parallel fault swarms, goes west around the lake and the largest, or at least widest, part goes around the east side. It is called the Eastern Rift System. Kilimanjaro, 19,340 feet high and the highest point in Africa, is a volcano in the Eastern Rift System. Lake Tanganyika is in the west part of the rift. The Great Dike of Southern Rhodesia extends through the Limpopo Belt and Bushveld Complex, two highly mineralized areas of the rift, to the vicinity of Kimberly, in South Africa. It is almost 1000 miles long and considered to be rift-related.

Baykal Rift in Central Asia and the Rhine Valley Graben in Europe are other well known continental rifts. Continental rifts are part of a global system of crustal movement that involves the ocean spreading of continents. This is the science of plate tectonics.

The following is our understanding of the formation of continental rifts.

Tensional breaks occur in the earth's crust because it is weak in some places and not strong enough to sustain itself in large segments. It breaks into large plates and continental rifts occur where these plates meet. There is a tendency for rifts to occur where older zones of weakness existed. Rifts are said to be cross-cutting structures; however, they might be considered as joining together a series of such older and smaller zones of weakness like the break that occurs in a piece of flagstone when a series of hammer blows are made in a straight line to break it.

All major metallic ore deposits are near and related to large silicic masses of intrusive rocks. Smaller centers of mineralization were formed in smaller centers of igneous intrusives. The old prospector's maxim that porphyry, a spotted rock by his terminology, was the mother of gold, actually helped him to find the Bonanzas (big, rich mineral deposits) of the West.

Rift zones have deep-seated faults through which igneous rocks can rise into the crust. These intrusives formed channelways through which the hydrothermal solutions rose to where they were deposited as ores.

The more common forms of igenous intrusives found along rift zones are: (Fig. 1-1)

Older batholiths:	Often exposed by erosion or mining.
	Often intruded by younger igneous rocks.
Stocks:	Column-like, generally rounded, large masses.
Pipes:	Smaller than stocks but also column-like and rounded or circular.
Chimneys:	Smaller, in general, than a pipe; however, pipes a few feet in diameter are known.
Plugs or stubs:	Usually filling an old crater, also a rounded mass.
Dikes:	Near vertical to vertical sheets formed between fault walls.
Sills:	Near horizontal to horizontal sheets usually formed between sedimentary bedding planes or other zones of weakness.
Laccoliths:	Mushroom-shaped masses usually with a flat bottom or floor and usually with a dike, pipe or chimney as a feeder conduit; found in sedimentary rocks where resistance of overlying beds forced the magma from the feeder conduit to spread laterally.
Lopoliths and chonoliths:	Irregular forms, not symmetrical in any respect.

These intrusive forms all have one thing in common. They follow zones of weakness and form their own zones of weakness. By cracking up the enclosing rocks they form breccia (crushed rock) zones, and may themselves be brecciated, to form stockworks, by fresh surges of intrusives from below. Brecciated stocks, pipes, and chimneys are common forms.

Hydrothermal (from water + heat) solutions are formed in the magma at great depth. Pressure and heat are high as it is a confined system within the magma chamber. Superheated ground water with metallic content may join the system as it moves into the crust. Metallic ions of gold, silver, manganese, copper, lead, zinc, iron, molybdenum, tin, tungsten, uranium, and less common ones are deposited in the crust as primary sulfides, oxides, carbonates, and less common forms. Breccias and other zones of weakness are the hosts for these minerals, which form the ores of commerce and minerals for collectors.

The part that rifting plays in exposing mineral deposits is extremely important. Erosion and changes in drainage patterns have exposed many of the metalliferous deposits of New Mexico and Colorado.

In the Leadville district of Colorado (Fig. 1–3), an area about four miles long was step-faulted down into the rift so as to expose bonanza mineralization at different elevations. Step-faulting into the rift is also common in the East African Rift System. We feel that rifting in New Mexico and Colorado is responsible for most of the mineral wealth represented by the metal deposits of these two states. This rifting reoccurred along zones of weakness that existed for a long span of geologic time.

Van Alstine found in his studies of continental rifting that fluorine, as

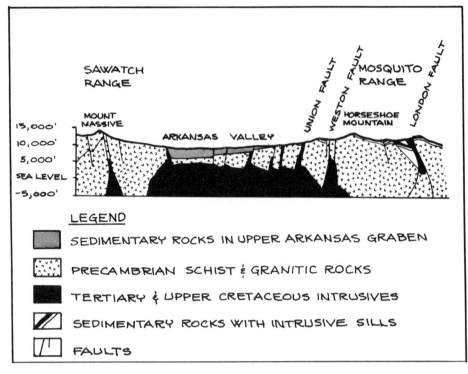

Fig. 1–3. East-west cross section of Upper Arkansas Valley near Leadville, Lake County, Colorado. Adapted from U.S.G.S., P.P. 726–c, 1972.

fluorspar, the impure fluorite of commerce, occurs consistently along continental rifts in North America and Africa. Thermal springs in the rift zones contain fluorine and some are depositing fluorspar. The world's largest concentration of fluorspar occurs in the Bushveld Complex in the Eastern African Rift System, in South Africa.

CARBONATITES: A SPECIAL RIFT-RELATED IGNEOUS ROCK FORM

A carbonatite is a rock derived from deep magmatic sources; it is rich in carbonate material. Carbonatites occur in the same forms as other igneous rocks and may form as large volcanoes or as small dikes and associated veinlets. Although they are not exclusively rift-related, they are most numerous and most often found along rifts. The Eastern Rift System of Africa has by far the largest number of them. Their composition is not constant.

Kimberlite is primarily a matrix of serpentine and carbonate material and the diamond pipes near Pretoria have carbonatite dikes in them. Kimberlite is considered a form of carbonatite.

Phonolite, nepheline syenites, and alkalic rocks, such as Bostonite porphyry, a common rock of the Colorado Front Range mineral districts, are forms of carbonatites.

It is thought that carbonatites are formed by recrystallization of modified or original magma; from hydrothermal solutions, or by remobilized carbonate rocks or material. They are considered to be of secondary or remelted crustal material.

Fluorite occurs with many of the African carbonatites, such as with those of the Bushveld Complex. It is being mined commercially as fluorspar from carbonatite sources. Carbonatite ash beds are being considered for commercial fluorspar mining.

At Phalabora, Transvaal, Africa, a carbonatite contains a major copper deposit. It is radioactive from baddeleyite and uranoan thorianite and two stages of fracturing introduced chalcopyrite and other copper minerals.

Carbonatites have a distinctive suite of minerals that includes thorium and the rare-earth minerals. Other than fluorite—barium, titanium, strontium, zirconium, iron, and copper are often present in varying amounts.

In a caldera near Pretoria, South Africa, in the rift zone, a salt pan contains a soda lake with the salts introduced by volcanic vapors. It is associated with a carbonatite body and dolomite–calcite matrix cements material ejected from a former vent. A layer of gaylussite occurs in the bottom of the lake below a layer of mud and chalcedonic concretions. Similar carbonatite–related deposits occur at Lake Magodi, where nahcolite, natural baking soda, occurs, and at other rift-related lakes and thermal springs along the rift system of Eastern Africa.

Heinrich presents an interesting speculation that the Eocene carbonate–rich evaporite deposits of the Green River Formation of northwestern Colorado and adjacent Utah and Wyoming may have been formed as a result of volcanic activity. The volcanic rocks of the Leucite Hills (rift-related carbonatite) were erupted through the Green River beds. Ash beds are found in this shale and evaporite formation. Trona, nahcolite, and shortite are the principal carbonate minerals of these shale beds that are also oil bearing. At least 21 other carbonate minerals have been identified.

It has been estimated, by C. Mains, that 29 billion tons of nahcolite and 10 billion tons of dawsonite are in the evaporite beds of the Piceance Basin of Colorado. This area is only a small part of the extensive oil shale beds. Such a concentration of carbonate material is unknown elsewhere. The minerals are considered primary in this inland lake deposit.

In the Great American Rift in New Mexico, one- to two-foot dikes of carbonatite cut an oval explosion breccia body, about a third of a mile long, in Precambrian (Fig. 1-4) rocks. This occurrence is in the Lemitar Mountains at Mount Largo, about 22 miles north of Albuquerque. One such dike was found to contain fine-grained calcite, dolomite, magnetite, apatite, phlogopite, and pyrite.

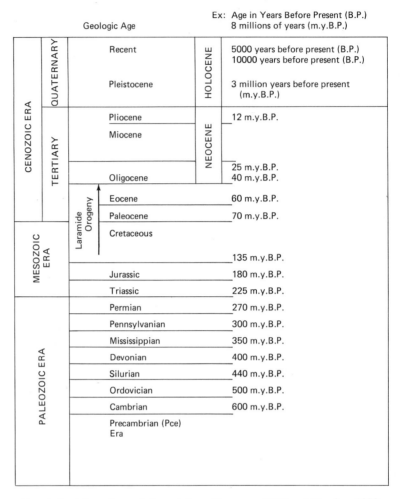

Fig. 1–4.   Time chart. Adapted from Newman, 1976 and Hawley, 1978.

In Colorado, carbonatite occurs in the Powderhorn district, at Iron Hill. Thorium and rare-earth minerals are present and a deposit of ilmenite has been prospected.

In the Wet Mountains, near the Pleasant Valley Graben, a rift-related structure, carbonatites occur in Precambrian (Pce) rocks and as three centers of alkalic intrusives known as the Democrat Creek stock, Gem Park stock, and McClure-Iron Mountain Complex. The area has been prospected extensively for thorium.

REFERENCES

G–12, H–15, J–2, J–3, J–27, J–29, J–33, J–47, J–52, 0–14 (Reiter), S–70, S–95, S–112, S–132, S–140, National Geographic Society Maps—Pacific Ocean Floor, Atlantic Ocean Floor, and Indian Ocean Floor.

DETAILS OF THE GREAT AMERICAN RIFT

The Rocky Mountain Trenchtintina, of the Desert Bolson zone north of Mexico City, is the lower part of a continental rift system that extends north up the Rio Grande of New Mexico and southern Colorado, continues north through the central part of Colorado into Wyoming, extends through Idaho and Montana into Canada, and goes on to the North Slope of Alaska. We call this rift system the Great American Rift. Our primary interest and mineral collecting experience has been in New Mexico and Colorado and this book is primarily concerned with the rift in those states.

The Western Great Plains and the Colorado Plateau are two relatively stable blocks or plates and the area between them is considered the rift zone, an area in which great batholiths formed along with Pce faults that still exist. The rift zone was active in Pce time; in Pennsylvanian time; extremely active in the Laramide orogeny, and again in Neocene to Recent time. The Pce batholiths were repeatedly invaded by younger intrusives. It was in Neocene to Recent time that the latest rifting occurred.

Lower Rio Grande

At El Paso, Texas, the Walker or Texas lineament crosses the Lower Rio Grande part of the rift which is about 175 miles wide along this lineament. A lineament marks a change in geologic formations or a series of physical units aligned in one direction. The Walker lineament marks the south end of the Colorado Plateau, west of the Rio Grande, and continues on to the West Coast. (Figs. 1–5 and 1–6).

Three large basins, the Tularosa, Mesilla, and Mimbres, in this area are filled with deep deposits of sediments, all rift-related. North along the Rio Grande are the Jordana, Palomas, and San Marcial Basins, also rift-related deep basins filled with similar sediments.

East of Las Cruces the Organ Mountains, remnants of an old batholith, and northward the Caballo, Fra Cristobal, Sierra de los Uvas and Potrillo Mountains form a more or less continuous fault scarp and discontinuous horst blocks along the east side of the Rio Grande.

On the west side of the Rio Grande Valley, on the edge of the Colorado Plateau, the Central mining district is centered around Silver City and the Santa Rita Open Pit Copper Mine. It has been the most productive mineralized area in New Mexico.

Between Las Cruces and the Central mining district is the Good Sight-Cedar Hills volcanic–tectonic depression (39 to 33 m.y.B.P.–million years Before Present) which has over 2000 feet of rift-related fill material. Rifting in this area was evident by 26 m.y.B.P.

Two calderas occur in the Organ Mountains, the Dona Ana (37 to 33 m.y.B.P.) and the Organ (32 m.y.B.P.). About 9000 feet of ash-flow tuff has collapsed into the Organ batholith magma chamber, in the Organ caldera.

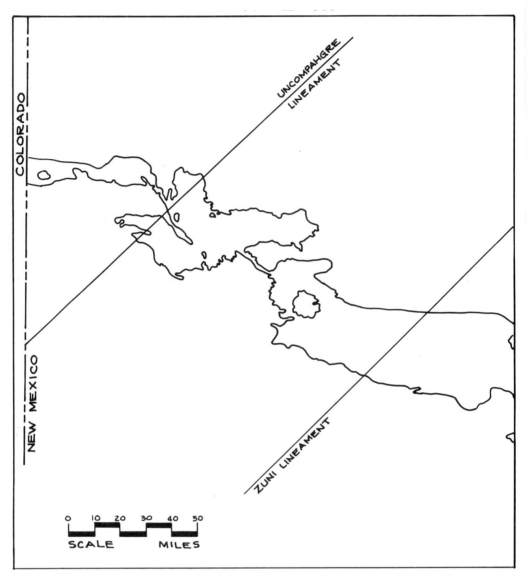

Fig. 1-5. Neogene to Holocene sedimentary rocks contemporaneous with rifting in the Great American Rift Zone, in New Mexico. (Areas shown in outline)

Tuff is volcanic material which solidifies on cooling to form thick beds of porous rock. West of the Palomas Basin, the Emory caldera (33.4 ± 1.0 m.y.B.P.) was the source of the Kneeling Nun tuff of the Central mining district to the south. Near Hillsboro an andesite of Cretaceous age has been intruded by a porphyry-copper stock (73.4 m.y.B.P.). Porphyry-copper stocks have been the source of ore for all the large open pit copper mines of the West.

In the Socorro area four major calderas dating from 32 to 26 m.y.B.P. have been identified. Volcanic activity continued intermittently up to 4 m.y.B.P.

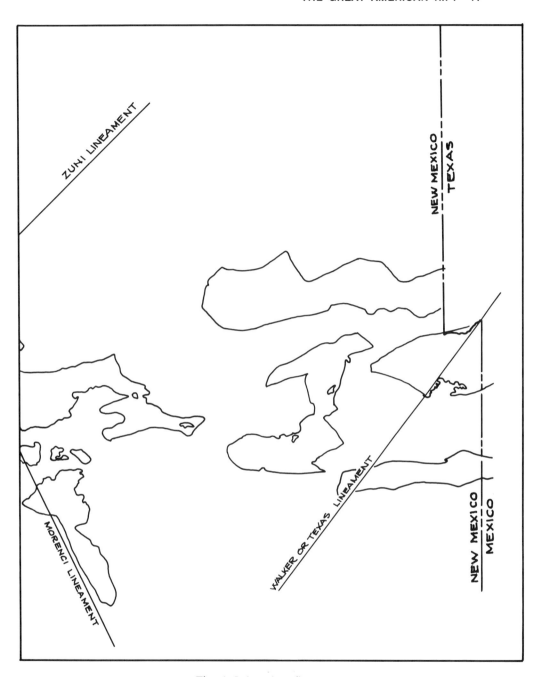

Fig. 1-5 (*continued*)

Flows of basalt in the Lower Rio Grande Valley have occurred as recently as 0.76 m.y.B.P.

Seismic evidence shows two magma bodies, one recent, having been emplaced under the Socorro area. Seismic activity and heat flow are abnormally high in the Socorro area and along the Rio Grande from Las Cruces to Albuquerque.

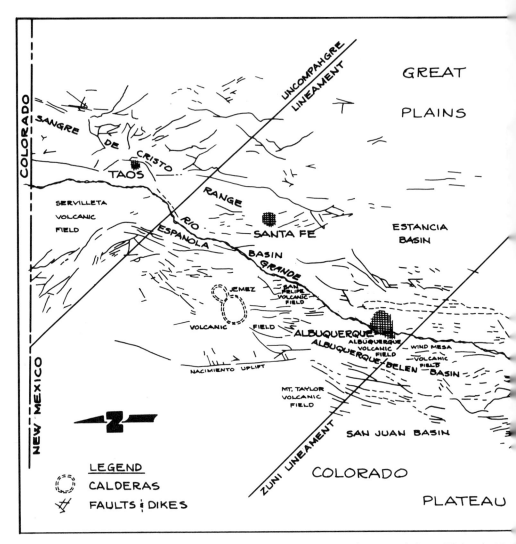

Fig. 1–6.   Fault, dike, and caldera pattern between the Colorado Plateau and Great Plains, in New Mexico. Base map adapted from Woodward *et al.*, 1978, Circ. 163, Sh–2 with additions from Kelly 1955.

REFERENCES

J–2, J–37, J–77, L–1969, L–1970, 0–14 (Hawley), 0–14 (Lovejoy), 0–14 (Sanford), 0–14 (Woodward), 0–29, 0–30, P–4 Kuellmer (Sanford), P–4 Kuellmer (Weber), P–6 Woodward (Elston), S–87, S–93, S–94, S–125.

Upper Rio Grande Valley

North of Socorro the Albuquerque-Belen Basin is a maximum of 25 miles wide and goes north along the rift for 100 miles. This basin has subsided about

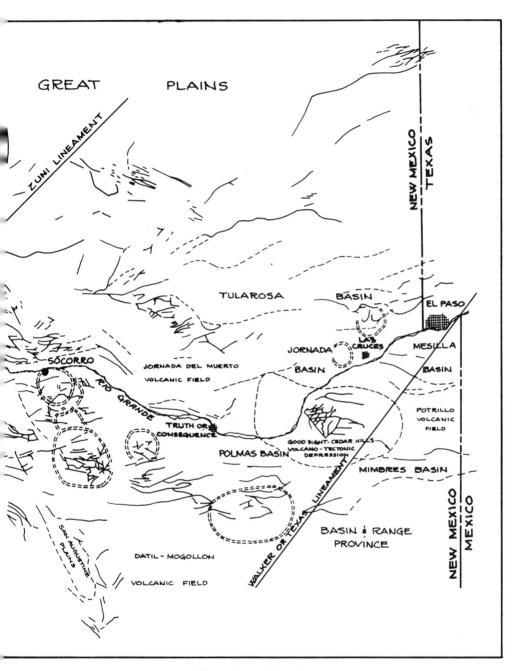

Fig. 1-6 (*continued*)

26,000 feet in relation to the crest of the Sandia Mountains. The Sandia–Manzano Mountains form a fault scarp along the east side of the basin almost to Santa Fe. As much as 20,000 feet of rift-related material has been deposited in the basin at this location of the Great American Rift.

In Pliocene and Pleistocene time many volcanic fields developed in the basin and within a 65 mile radius of Albuquerque there are 270 volcanic stubs and cones. San Felipe volcanic field has 20 volcanic cones and Cat Hills volcanic field has 23 cinder cones. West of Albuquerque the Mt. Taylor volcanic field and a number of north-trending, parallel faults separate the rift valley from the Colorado Plateau. This is the center of uranium mining in New Mexico.

Espanola Basin is north of the Albuquerque-Belen Basin. Near Santa Fe the Cerrillos volcanic field is a mineralized horst block in the rift. Pleistocene age basalts of the Hinsdale volcanic series of the San Juan Mountains moved down the upper end of the Espanola Basin from the San Luis Valley in flood-type flows.

North of Santa Fe the Sangre de Cristo Mountains form a continuous fault scarp to the head of the San Luis Valley in Colorado.

West of the Espanola Basin is the Jemez volcanic field in which the Valles and the Toledo calderas are nested in a great volcanic pile. A million years ago these calderas were the source of about 50 cubic miles of welded tuff and ash that was spread over the adjacent area. Pumicite, windblown fine pumice, that occurs in the Republican River Valley of Nebraska, is thought to have come from this eruption. An old lake bed at Ingham, Furnas County, contains up to 25 feet of white pumicite under 50 feet of loess from the Pleistocene glacial stage. A large intrusive mass is under this compound caldera, which is one of the world's largest. Subsidence of the Valles caldera was analogous in form to the Creede caldera collapse in Colorado. An elongate central resurgent dome formed and was cut by longitudinal and radial grabens.

East of the Jemez volcanic field the rift is filled with up to 15,000 feet of rift-related sediments. The Nacimiento Uplift separates the Jemez Mountains from the Colorado Plateau to the west.

In the San Luis Valley, in New Mexico, the Taos Plateau, and Servilleta volcanic field occupy the rift between the Sangre de Cristo Mountains and the Brazos Uplift. The Questa volcanic area is a mineralized area in the Sangre de Cristo Mountains that is part of the rift. In this area the flood-type basalts, up to 800 feet thick, that flowed into the Espanola Basin were themselves covered with thick sediments. A Quaternary basalt flow in this area has been cut by recent faulting.

The olivine tholeiitic basalts (4.5 to 3.6 m.y.B.P.) that flowed down the rift in large quantities were from Los Mogotes Volcano, in the Servilleta volcanic field. These tholeiites have almost a glassy texture and they are thought to have come from 9 to 12 miles in depth while more alkalic basalts of the area along the rift possibly came from depths of 20 to 42 miles. This indicates magma has moved up into the upper part of the rift zone.

REFERENCES

C-9, 0-14, (Bailey), (Baltz), (Bridwell), (Renault), (Sanford), (Woodward), 0-21, 0-22, 0-23, 0-35, 0-36, P-1 Johnson (Kelley), P-2 Rosenzweiz (Kelley), (Baldwin), P-6 Woodward (Elston), (Budding), (Kelley), P-7 James (Butler), (Chapin), (Mickelson), P-8 Kelley (Northrup), P-9 Siemers (Woodward), (Jiracek), (Judo), S-4, S-109, S-125, S-149.

LOCATION IN COLORADO

San Luis Valley

The San Luis Valley is a large half graben structure with a floor that dips east to rift faults along the west side of the Sangre de Cristo Mountains (Figs. 1-7 and 1-8). Except for a horst block that goes north up the center of the valley at a depth of about a mile, valley fill is believed to be about 20,000 feet deep in places.

The Rio Grande River enters the San Luis Valley as a perennial stream at Del Norte, Colorado. It has formed a large alluvial fan and migrated south along this fan leaving the north part of the valley a closed basin. Large amounts of sand from this fan have blown up against the fault-scarp Sangre de Cristo Mountains to form Sand Dunes National Monument. To the south end of the valley the Rio Grande has cut a deep gorge through flood-type volcanic flows. This gorge is 50 miles long and up to 1500 feet deep.

Along the west side of the valley, in the San Juan volcanic field, at least eight major ash falls formed sheets in the period between 28 to 26 m.y.B.P. At least seven major calderas formed. LaGarita caldera (27.8 m.y.B.P.) is one of the world's largest. The Creede caldera (27.8 to 26.7 m.y.B.P.) formed within this caldera and graben valleys extend from the San Luis Valley to the Creede caldera.

Hot springs occur in the north end of the San Luis Valley and movement has occurred along faults bordering the Sangre de Cristo Mountains within the last 10,000 years. Sag ponds occur along streams flowing from the Sangre de Cristos where recent faults formed and the lower block of the fault moved up to form a dam.

On the northwestern end of the valley the Bonanza Mountains mark the northern extension of the San Juan volcanic field. Bonanza caldera may have formed 34.2 to 33.4 m.y.B.P. These volcanics are on the southeastern end of the Sawatch Mountains, a remnant of a Laramide-age anticline.

Rifting in the north end of the valley cut off the Sangre de Cristos from the Sawatch Mountains. Formations of the Paleozoic age that once dipped off the flank of the Sawatch Anticline, but have since been eroded away, are preserved in the Sangre de Cristo Mountains. Ancient or paleovalleys whose streams once flowed off the anticline into the area of South Park, to the east, are preserved in part in the Sangre de Cristo Mountains.

An area of low hills separates the San Luis Valley from the Upper Arkansas Valley in the Poncha Pass area. Until 1968 it was thought that the Rio Grande Rift terminated in this area; however, a fault trough at least 10,000 feet deep was found. Dry Union Formation, the Miocene–Pliocene age sediments that fill the Upper Arkansas Grabens, was in the trough along with large blocks (800 × 400 × 100 feet) of Paleozoic sediments that had been moved by gravity sliding into the rift zone. An ancestral Arkansas River was flowing into the San Luis Valley through this trough until it was probably directed east along graben cross faults at Salida.

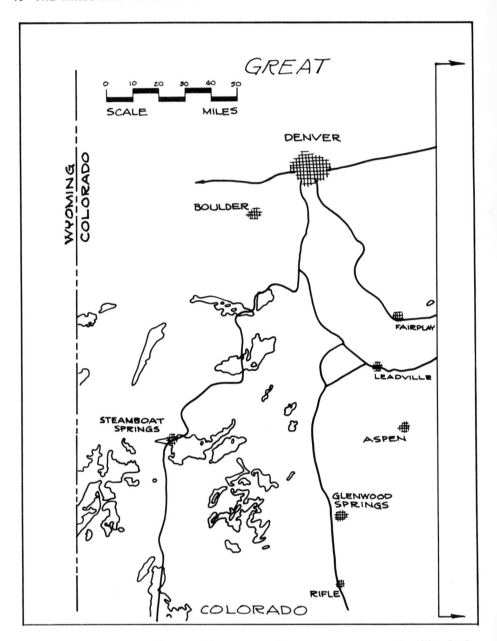

Fig. 1-7. Neogene to Holocene sedimentary rocks contemporaneous with rifting in the Great American Rift Zone, in Colorado. (Areas shown in outline)

East of the Sangre de Cristo Mountains

Raton Basin is a north-trending basin east of the Sangre de Cristo Mountains that formed during the Laramide orogeny as the San Luis Valley, the Sangre de Cristo Mountains, and the Sawatch anticline were rising. Sediments from these

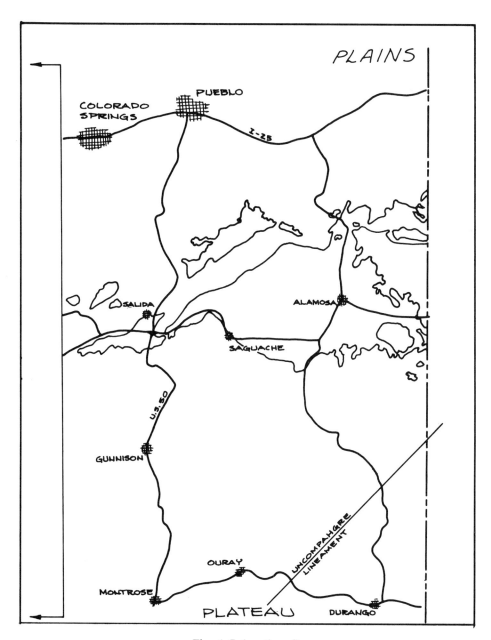

Fig. 1-7 (*continued*)

areas filled the Raton Basin to a depth of two miles. A band of Paleozoic to Mesozoic rocks is found between the basin sediments and the crest of the Sangre de Cristo Mountains.

Volcanic activity associated with rifting occurred in Neocene to Holocene time and the San Luis Valley formed a half graben and settled into the rift. Volcanic activity has continued into Quaternary time.

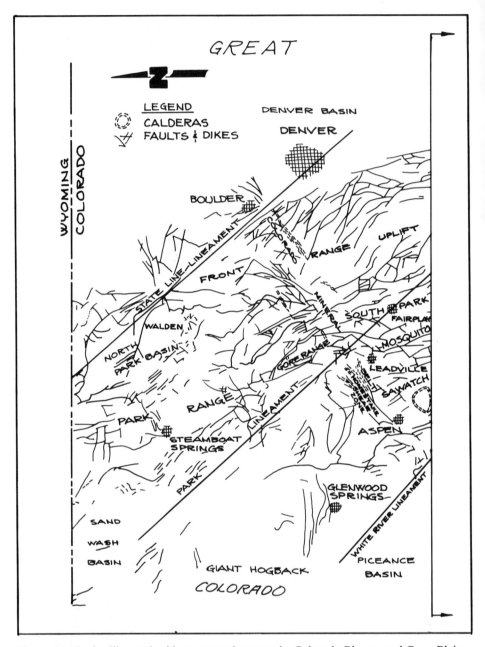

Fig. 1-8.   Fault, dike, and caldera pattern between the Colorado Plateau and Great Plains, in Colorado. Base map adapted from Tweto, 1978, Circ. 163, Sh-1 with additions from Kelly, 1955, and Stevens and Lipman, 1976.

Spanish Peaks

Two large porphyry stocks uncovered by erosion, known as the Spanish Peaks, occur east of the Sangre de Cristo Mountains near the deflection line where the Great Plains start to rise to the top of this range. Faulting along the east side of

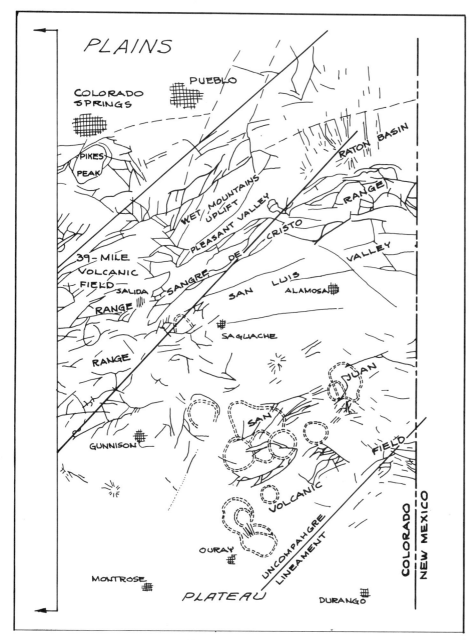

Fig. 1-8 (*continued*)

the San Luis Valley was associated with the formation of these peaks and several smaller ones. A threading of parallel dikes of gabbro porphyry, a granular igneous rock, extends south about eight miles and north about ten miles parallel to the crest of the Sangre de Cristos. A classic pattern of radial dikes or near radial dikes, some of which have been invaded several times, occupy zones of weakness dating back to the Precambrian era (Pce) time. They were reactivated in the Laramide orogeny and again in Eocene and Oligocene times. This area is south of the Pleasant Valley Graben of the Wet Mountain

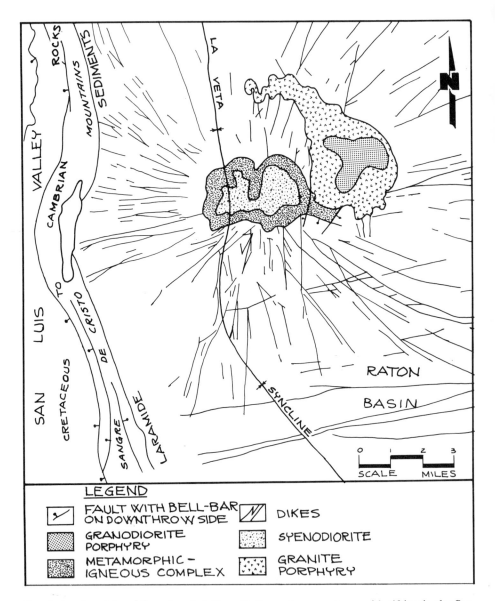

Fig. 1–9. Spanish peaks and radial dikes. Units contemporaneous with rifting in the San Luis Valley. Adapted from U.S.G.S., P.P. 594 G, 1968 and Circ. 163, Sh-1, 1978.

Valley, which is a structure of the Great American Rift. Active vulcanism occurred as late as Recent time in the Spanish Peaks area. (Fig. 1–9)

Pleasant Valley Graben

Pleasant Valley Graben is along the inflection line of the Sangre de Cristo Mountains in the Wet Mountain Valley. It extends from the West-cliff–Silvercliff area to Howard, on the east-flowing Arkansas River. A displacement of at least 1400 feet is indicated.

REFERENCES

A–3 A–5 Ridge (Tweto), C–9, J–4, J–12, J–34, J–35, J–42, J–44, 0–14 Hawley (Tweto) Gudel, (Davis), (Burroughs), (Tweto) map, P–6 Woodward (Knepper), P–7 James (Calkins), (Lochman-Balk), (Bruns), (Upson), (Burroughs), (Mickelson), (Knepper), (Bruns), (Buchanan), (Butler), (Chapin), (De Voto), P–9 Siemers (Burroughs), S–29, S–38, S–61, S–62, S–63, S–68, S–75, S–77, S–97, S–105, S–116, S–124, S–128, S–134, S–136, S–143.

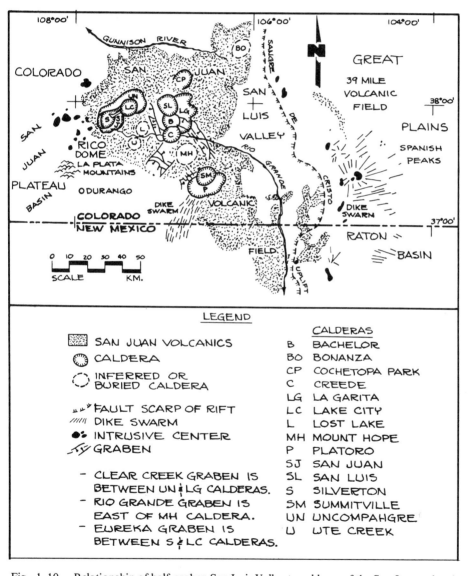

Fig. 1-10. Relationship of half-graben San Luis Valley to calderas of the San Juan volcanic field and to igneous and tectonic features of southwestern and central Colorado and adjacent New Mexico. Adapted from U.S.G.S. Jour. Res. vol. 1, no. 6, 1973 and U.S.G.S. P.P. 958, 1976.

San Juan Mountains

The San Juan Mountains and volcanic field extends from the Gunnison River Valley to Durango and almost to the Jemez Mountains in New Mexico. The Colorado Plateau borders it on the west and the San Luis Valley on the east.

At the close of Cretaceous time, sandstones and shales covered the San Juan area to a depth of 6000 to 8000 feet. Prior to about 65 m.y.B.P., a large dome 80 miles E–W by 40 miles N–S, centered in the Needle Mountains, rose to about 10,000 feet. Erosion accompanied this uplift and exposed intrusive porphyries,

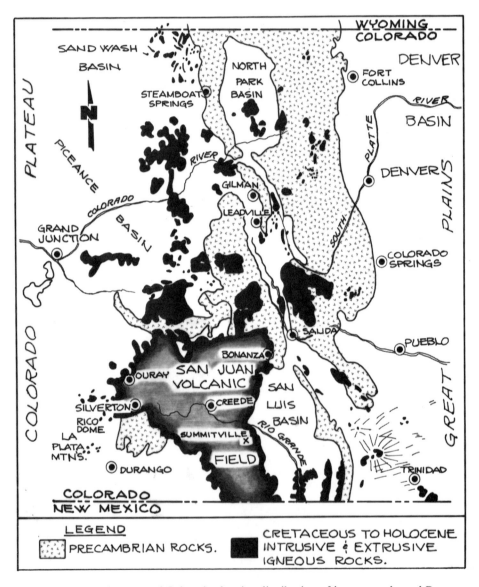

Fig. 1-11. Location map of Colorado showing distribution of igneous rocks and Precambrian rocks between the Colorado Plateau and the Great Plains. Adapted from U.S.G.S. Tectonic map of the U.S.A., 1961.

of the vent of the Ouray stock, and dome-like structures at Rico and La Plata. (Fig. 1–10)

An erosion surface with about 2000 feet of relief was developed over the area by the end of Eocene age (40 m.y.B.P.). The Telluride Conglomerate and Blanco Basin formations formed on this surface and conglomerate beds as thick as 2000 feet formed in the Mt. Wilson area, west of Telluride. A cluster of volcanoes developed in the western San Juan area and rhyolitic tuff breccia formed on top of the Telluride Conglomerate to a thickness of 3000 feet. This was the start of a volcanic field that was to become 1½ miles deep. These early volcanoes apparently collapsed to form the San Juan Depression. Early stratovolcanoes formed in the eastern San Juan, along the west edge of the San Luis Valley, and later volcanoes formed in both areas in Oligocene age, 40 to 26 m.y.B.P.

A large batholith was emplaced under the San Juan area during this time and 18 major ash-flow tuff sheets were deposited. Fifteen calderas and two postulated ones have been identified as the source of the ash-flow tuff. Depth to the top of this batholith ranges from 1.3 to 4.3 miles and the bottom may extend to 11.8 miles in depth. (Fig. 1–11)

The Clear Creek graben system formed between the eastern and western caldera areas. Volcanic flows of the Hinsdale series occurred in the Neocene, up to 4 m.y.B.P. This series has been cut by later rifting in places.

On the north end of the San Juan volcanic field near Powderhorn a carbonatite body occurs. It is partly pre-Jurassic in age, but a part of it has been dated at 58 to 52 m.y.B.P.

REFERENCES

E–3, E–4, J–64, P–3 Baldwin (Kottlowski), (Smith), (Wengerd), (Kelley) log, (Silver), (Baars), (Kelley) Tectonics, (Kelley) Ouray, Tectonic Map of United States of America, 1961, U.S. Geol. Survey, P–5 Shomaker (Molenaar) La Plata, (Eckel), (Chapin), (Pratt), (Engel), (Molenaar) Log, S–3, S–14, S–20, S–21, S–22, S–23, S–24, S–25, S–34, S–40, S–41, S–58, S–59, S–71, S–74, S–75, S–76, S–84, S–96, S–114, S–116, S–117, S–128.

Upper Arkansas Valley

At Salida the Arkansas River turns east through a valley that divides the Sangre de Cristo Mountains from the Mosquito Mountains that continue north to Climax. North of Trout Creek the Weston Fault forms the east fault scarp of the rift and north of Leadville it is formed by the Mosquito Fault. These Pce faults meet in the Leadville mining district. They were active in the Laramide orogeny and again in Neocene time.

The Upper Arkansas Valley, from Salida north almost to Climax, is formed by a series of graben sections divided by horst blocks that run transverse across the valley. On the west side of the Upper Arkansas Graben bordering faults may be covered by up to 300 feet of Recent gravel. The Sawatch Range is to the west all along this section and it continues north almost to the Eagle and Colorado Rivers. Fill in the rift in the Leadville area is up to 2000 feet deep. North of Leadville the Great American Rift is defined principally by a series of persistent faults.

At Leadville a zone about four miles long was broken by faults paralleling the Mosquito Fault. These faults stepped the outcrops of the productive ore replacement beds down into the graben. It was the Bonanza ore along these blocks that made the mining district famous.

Thirty-Nine Mile Volcanic Field

The Thirty-Nine Mile volcanic field is east of the Sangre de Cristo Mountains and west of Pike's Peak, a Pce granite batholith of the Front Range. It is south of South Park and north of the Arkansas Valley. Remnants occur in the Wet Mountains east of the Pleasant Valley Graben. Cripple Creek, a productive gold district, is an outlying part of this volcanic field. It is in a phonolite plug in a graben.

Calderas developed after large quantities of material were ejected. Volcanic units have been dated at 40, 36, 34, 29 to 28, and 19 m.y.B.P.

The Nathrop volcanics of the Arkansas River Valley were ejected from Ball Mountain, an old vent in the Sangre de Cristo Mountains, in 29 to 28 m.y.B.P. During Oligocene and early Miocene time as much as 3000 feet of volcanic rock of the Thirty-Nine Mile volcanic field series accumulated and changed the drainage system. A major graben below the surface contains Tertiary sediments.

Buffalo Peaks and Paleovalleys

From Salida north along the Sangre de Cristo Mountains ancient valleys or paleovalleys occur in a late Eocene erosion surface. Streams that occupied these valleys originated in the Sawatch Anticline and funneled ash-flow tuffs into South Park and as far east as the plains between Denver and Colorado Springs. Buffalo Peaks, East and West, are two landmarks capped by 34 m.y.B.P. andesite that preserves the paleovalleys. Faults along the rift have lowered sections of paleovalleys as much as 2200 feet. Subsidence of the rift zone had not cut off drainage from the Sawatch Anticline into South Park by 29 to 28 m.y.B.P.

Sawatch Range

The Sawatch Range is the largest mountain mass and the principal mountain massif of Colorado. It is a large cohesive mountain mass bounded by faults and flexures. At one time it covered a much larger area in the form of a great anticline. The remnant of this structure is still 80 miles N–S by 50 miles E–W. Some of the highest peaks in the state are in this range, part of which is called the Collegiate Range from the names of individual peaks named for famous universities.

The San Juan volcanic field is on the south end of the Sawatch Range. West Elk volcanic field is on the southwest; the Colorado Plateau on the west; and the Eagle Basin on the north and northwest. On the east the Sangre de Cristo, Mosquito, and Gore Ranges have been separated from the main anticlinal mass by the Great American Rift, which at this location is called the Upper Arkansas Graben.

In the West Elk volcanic field the Treasury Mountain pluton is the youngest known granitic mass (12 m.y.B.P.) in Colorado. On the northwest end of the Sawatch Range, in the Eagle Basin, at least five cinder cones and surface basalt flows have occurred within the last 1.5 m.y.B.P. At Dotsero, just east of the Glenwood Springs thermal area a cinder cone and small lava flow occurred 4000 years ago. Start of rifting in the San Luis Valley and Upper Arkansas Graben has been placed at 25 to 20 m.y.B.P. Pce rocks, including granite batholiths, form the core of the Sawatch Range, the largest, Mt. Princeton Batholith, is composed of seven units. Mt. Antero granite (30.8 $\pm$ 1.1 m.y.B.P.) is the youngest unit. This batholith, the Twin Lakes Batholith and the St. Kevin Batholith have mineralized veins and two mining districts, St. Kevin and Sugarloaf districts, were active. St. Kevin Batholith contains fluorite as one of it rock-making minerals.

South of Cottonwood Creek there is a quartz monzonite batholith that may have been the root of a caldera from which ash-flow tuff was ejected. This tuff clogged the paleovalleys that flowed eastward and are now preserved in the Mosquito and Sangre de Cristo Ranges and in South Park.

Sediments as old as the Cambrian dip away from the Sawatch Range. Although removed by erosion from the top part of the range in most areas, they are preserved in proper sequence in the horst blocks of the Gore, Mosquito and Sangre de Cristo Ranges; in the fault blocks of the Leadville mining district where they are stepped down into the rift zone; in the Monarch mining district as folded strata; and on the west side of the range in the Aspen, Tomichi, and Crested Butte mining districts. They dip under the Eagle Basin on the north and northwest.

REFERENCES

A-5 Ridge (Tweto) Sec. 27, (Tweto) Sec. 32, C-9, C-11, C-16, C-17, E-1, E-2, E-7, E-12, J-12, J-16, J-17, J-19, J-34, J-66, J-68, J-69, 0-14, Hawley (Tweto), P-6 Woodward (Knepper), P-7 James (Bruns) Bonanza, (Chapin) S-18, S-27, S-31, S-39, S-101, S-126, S-127, S-129, S-132, S-133.

Eagle Basin

Eagle Basin was filled with sea evaporites in Pennsylvanian and Permian time between the ancient Front Range Highlands and the Uncompahgre Uplift.

Near the shore of an ancient sea, coarse sediments were deposited while off-shore thick evaporite beds developed. Gore Range is part of the old Front Range Highlands and it is separate from the Eagle Basin by the Gore Fault. This Pce structure formed a fault scarp wall on the east side of the Eagle Basin in Pennsylvanian time.

Colorado Mineral Belt

Extent of the Colorado Mineral Belt has been given various interpretations; however, it is generally understood to be confined to intrusive porphyries of late Cretaceous and Middle Tertiary ages. These porphyries extend in a wide band through Boulder, Gilpin, and Clear Creek and through Summit, Park, Eagle and Lake Counties, to the Sawatch Range, including its west side.

Burbank called attention to a hinge line trending northeast from Rico to near Ouray along which Laramide intrusions are associated with mineral deposits. This was considered the southwest extension of the Colorado Mineral Belt.

In a broader interpretation, the central Colorado deposits and the whole San Juan mining area are included. Many outlines have been shown on Colorado maps but, at best, the Colorado Mineral Belt is slightly vague with some isolated districts included on some maps and omitted on others.

That part of the Mineral Belt from Boulder County to the Sawatch Range follows an old Pce lineament of faults and shear zones.

Gore Fault

Gore Fault runs north along the west side of the Gore Range to just north of the Colorado River where it is broken by a series of cross faults. The Colorado River flows between the Gore Range to the south and the Park Range to the north. A monoclinal fold, (Fig. 4–1) a bulge in the earth's crust with one side dipping steeply and one a gradual upsweep, seems to terminate the Gore Fault at this point. The south termination occurs in the Humbug Stock in the Ten-mile Range.

Faults and down-warped sedimentary rocks contemporaneous with rifting continue along the west side of the Gore Range into the Steamboat Springs thermal area and discontinuously to the Wyoming line. This line of rifting is between the Park Range to the east and the Sand Wash Basin, a Laramide structure, to the west. Sand Wash Basin is east of the Colorado Plateau.

North of Climax

The Mosquito Fault continues north along the Mosquito Range to Climax after leaving the Leadville mining district. It cuts the Climax stock, which is in the Pce rocks of the horst block of the Mosquito Range, and continues down the Ten Mile Range to the Humbug stock where it seems to junction and end the Gore Fault. Continuing down the Ten Mile Valley the Mosquito Fault merges the Blue River Fault near Frisco.

The Blue River Fault, like the Mosquito Fault, is an old Pce fault that was reactivated in Laramide time and possibly again in Holocene time. It also is a major unit of the rift zone in central Colorado. It can be traced along the Blue River Valley on the east side of the Ten Mile and Mosquito Ranges, over a divide into South Park and by a series of connecting faults, it may join the London Fault in South Park.

North of Frisco the Blue River Fault continues as a frontal fault of the Gore Range along the west side of the Blue River Valley. A series of frontal faults continue to the Colorado River. North of the river the cross faults that cut the Gore Fault on the west side of the Gore and Park Ranges seem to cut the frontal faults.

On the east side of the Park Range, which runs north along the west side of the Middle-North Park Basins, a series of frontal faults continue to the Wyoming line. They are mineralized with fluorspar west of Walden.

North and Middle Parks

North and Middle Parks were a single basin when they were formed in Laramide time; however, about 33 m.y.B.P. the volcanic Rabbit Ears Range, composed of over 2000 feet of andesite breccia, developed between them. The North and Middle Park Basins are bordered on the east by the Front Range. Thrust faults that terminate North Park to the north and both Parks to the east had movement in Neocene time.

REFERENCES

A–4 Burbank, A–5 Ridge (Tweto), Sec. 27 (Tweto), Sec. 32, C–9, D–1 (Burbank), E–11, E–13, J–48, J–49, J–50, J–61, J–69, 0–14 Hawley (Tweto) Guide 1, (Tweto) Map, S–6, S–8, S–32, S–36, S–43, S–49, S–51, S–60, S–81, S–83, S–89, S–92, S–110, S–126, S–130, S–131.

CHAPTER 2
TYPICAL DEPOSITS

Mineral deposits are not common because they require a unique combination of events and conditions to occur at the same place. This type of environment occurs only in places of crustal disturbances with a rift zone being one of the most favorable locations. Magma chambers that rise under rift zones extend a variety of igneous rocks into the crust and break it up to prepare a receptive host for the hydrothermal solutions that will follow.

One of the few things common to mineral deposits of a rift zone is that they are the result of hydrothermal activity. There are no typical deposits of a rift zone. Individual deposits of minerals are truly individual and must be examined as such. The parameters of their formation and of their minerals are too varied to fit a set pattern. Vein deposits in a limited area of replacement beds in the same formation and in a limited area might have some things in common; however, a change in the composition of ore solutions or other factors can make adjacent deposits dissimilar.

A brief review of some of the mines and minerals of New Mexico and Colorado along the Great American Rift will show how impossible it is to have a typical deposit.

In the Organ Mountains of New Mexico, quartz, calcite, barite, and fluorite were the common gangue minerals. Gold and molybdenum occurred in veins; lead, zinc and silver minerals replaced limestone beds, and copper occurred in tactite deposits. These deposits are metamorphosed carbonates into which a complex mineralogy has been introduced by hydrothermal solutions.

Four types of veins and a porphyry copper deposit have been recognized in the Burro Mountains. The Tyrone Pit ore body is a porphyry copper deposit in a laccolith. The Santa Rita Pit across the rift in the Central mining district is also a porphyry copper ore body but here the similarity ends. Santa Rita deposit is in a stock and contains significant molybdenum that the Tyrone ore lacks. There are four types of vein deposits, and some less important types, in the Burro Mountains. They are 1) quartz–pyrite, 2) quartz–specularite, radioactive, 3) silver or silver–lead, and 4) turquoise. There are six different types of ore deposits in the Central mining district. Magnetite and sphalerite both occur in large replacement beds. The Ground Hog and some other adjacent veins are primarily sphalerite deposits.

Differing mineral suites indicate individual surges or pulses of hydrothermal activity. Some deposits may have more than one stage of mineralization. None are known to have all stages in any one district.

San Pedro Mine, in the New Placers district of Santa Fe County, has massive replacement and tactite deposits, predominantly of copper ore. In a similar igneous environment, in the New Placers district to the north, a breccia deposit is being readied to open-pit mine for gold and tungsten ore.

In the San Juan Mountains of Colorado, the Sunnyside vein system of the Eureka Graben produced more mineral wealth from gold-base metal ore than all the Silverton area combined. The Shenandoah Dives vein system, on the other side of the Silverton caldera and in the ring-fault zone, probably produced the largest quantity of mill-grade base metal ore mined in the area.

Volcanic pipes of the ring-fault zone and Red Mountain Sag, of the Silverton caldera, produced Bonanza silver and copper ore. In the Dunmore Mine there was a hubnerite-bearing breccia pipe or chimney; a hematite chimney; and a copper-bearing chimney within the hematite chimney. At Lake City, in the Lake City caldera or closely associated with it, two distinct types of mineralization occur within a few miles of each other. High grade gold-telluride ore and base-metal sulfide ore both show multiple stages of mineralization along veins of this district.

Near Salida, the Sedalia Copper Mine is variously thought to be derived by magmatic replacement of noncarbonate schist and as a skarn. A skarn is a lime-bearing silicate in which large amounts of silicon, aluminum, iron, and magnesium were introduced by magmatic and possible hydrothermal activity.

The Orient Iron Mine, in the San Luis Valley and the manganese–iron deposits of Leadville and Battle Mountain were largely formed by primary siderite and carbonate manganese from hydrothermal solutions. Climax, a molybdenum ore deposit, is similar to the Henderson ore deposit in that an early mineral stage was followed by later surges of hydrothermal solutions that produced the main deposit. The Urad deposit, the early stage of the Henderson deposit, was mined almost to exhaustion before the deeper Henderson deposit was found. It is of interest that after two years of diamond drilling, Amax, the operating company, was ready to give up finding the ore body they suspected, when the drill hit ore in the last hole proposed to be drilled. It occurred in a porphyry of Oligocene age that had invaded the earlier Pce-age Silver Plume granite batholith and it was about 2400 feet below the Urad deposit. Conditions of formation of the base-metal sulfide minerals at Leadville, Eagle, and Kokomo were assumed to be similar; however, they were complexly different. Tactite bodies at Kokomo contained molybdenum in commercial quantities.

It was found in the early days of mining in Boulder, Gilpin, and Clear Creek counties of the Colorado Mineral Belt, that five stages and possibly seven stages of ore deposition occurred. There were few samples of ore that didn't show banding, crustification, brecciation, veining, or some other form that would indicate that a younger stage of ore deposition was present.

Possibly the only element that can be attributed directly to the rift is fluorine, which occurs as a gangue mineral in many of the ores, as fluorite and in large deposits as fluorspar, the impure ore of commerce.

Van Alstine focused attention on a great continental rift system, which we call the Great American Rift, when he traced it by fluorspar deposits through many of the famous Mexican mineral locations, such as Mapimi, Sonora, and Santa Eulalia, Chihuahua; along the Rocky Mountain front to Canada and to the North Slope of Alaska. Thermal springs occur near the fluorspar deposits in some areas of New Mexico and Colorado. Hot waters at Ojo Caliente, New Mexico, and Wagon Wheel Gap, Colorado, and depositing fluorspar at the present time.

Thermal rift-related brines of the Salton Sea and the Red Sea contain ionic lead, copper, zinc, and silver. With sufficient sulfur these ions could plate out of solution under the right condition to form the common sulfides of each element. Hydrothermally deposited minerals commonly found along the rift zone as primary ore are the sulfides of lead, zinc, copper, and iron.

The ages of most of the ores of the rift system are not yet dated by the K / Ar (potassium–argon) method; however, dates of 10 to 23 m.y.B.P. have been obtained for some. This puts their formation well within the period of rifting.

Agreement is not universal on the processes of ore formation and volumes have been written on the subject. Possibly the closest thing to a supposition that is accepted by a majority of people working in this field is that hydrothermal solutions associated with silicic magma form most ore deposits. One school of thought subscribes to the theory that the hydrothermal solutions, the minerals they contain and the pegmatite minerals come out of a magma, during the last stages of crystalization of an igneous rock mass from that magma. Temperatures and pressures are so high they are hard to imagine or to reproduce in the laboratory. We do know that it takes exceedingly high temperatures and pressures to form diamonds, for we can do it experimentally, and we know diamonds formed in the kimberlite pipes.

Hydrothermal solutions change as they leave the magma chamber and are expelled upward. The concept of minerals plating out and thereby raising the temperature and pressure of the resulting solution is an interesting one. We do not know the conditions that exist nor what materials might be added from the surrounding wall rocks in a hydrothermal system.

The other school of thought is that closed systems exist along veins and other host rock areas and that magmatic water gathers the metallic and other vein materials from surrounding country rock and deposits it as ore.

Studies of fluid inclusions have contributed a whole new concept of ore genesis. They have added to our understanding of the temperature, pressure and density of hydrothermal solutions. In the porphyry coppers, it was determined that many were emplaced at depths of over three miles. Temperatures ranged from under 200°C to 725°C and pressures from 500 to 2000 bars. Chlorine is important in transporting metals in the solutions. Major constituents of the fluids were sodium, potassium, calcium, and chlorine with water and carbon dioxide. Inclusions of small crystals within the inclusion fluids (daughter products) included sylvite, halite, anhydrite, hematite, and dawsonite.

Like any other science in an early stage there will probably be setbacks as well as successes. We applaud the effort and dedication of those involved.

REFERENCES

A-4 Lingren Volume (Schmitt), (Singewald), (Genetic), (Singleward), (Magmatic), (Knope), (McLaughlin), (Vanderwilt), (McKnight), (Nolan), (Burbank), (Hewitt), A-5 Ridge (Graton), (Ridge), C-6, C-7, C-8, C-12, D-1 Vanderwilt, D-2, D-3, E-14, H-2, H-7, H-9, H-10, H-12, H-13, J-1, J-7, J-29, J-46, J-65, J-70, M-1, 0-1, 0-2, 0-9, 0-12, 0-13, 0-15, 0-26, 0-28, 0-37, 0-40, P-6 Woodward (Gillerman), (Kolessar), (Nielsen), P-7 James (Bauer), R-7, R-25, S-5, S-7, S-9, S-10, S-13, S-42, S-44, S-47, S-54, S-55, S-57, S-64, S-65, S-67, S-73, S-80, S-91, S-141.

CHAPTER 3
NEW MEXICO MINES AND MINERALS

ORGAN MOUNTAINS

Small settlements started to form in southern New Mexico after the Treaty of Guadalupe Hidalgo in 1848, and the Gadsen Purchase of 1854. New Mexico became United States territory in 1850. Las Cruces, on the Rio Grande, had been established in 1846 at the site of an earlier Indian massacre of Hispanic settlers. Crosses marking the graves gave the town its name.

The Organ Mountains are in the southernmost part of a chain of fault-scarp, horst-block mountains that extend on the east side of the Rio Grande Valley from near El Paso, Texas, into central Colorado. This part of the chain is 5 to 15 miles wide and about 30 miles long in a north-south direction. Large rift-related desert valleys border the chain of fault-scarp mountains along their east side. San Augustine Pass, near the north end, leads from the Rio Grande Valley into the Tularosa Basin.

Antisell, who traveled through this area with the Pacific Railroad Survey in 1854, described the Organ Mountains and mentioned the silver–lead mines. These mines had been discovered in 1849 and he mentioned the Stevenson Mine was smelting argentiferous galena ore in adobe furnaces near Las Cruces. He also mentioned that the Barilla Mine (probably the Modoc) had been worked some years previously and argentiferous galena had been smelted in a furnace at the mine. Several lodges of Apaches camped close to the mine discouraged his visit to the area.

Paleozoic limestones, which have been intruded by quartz monzonite of batholithic proportion, form the range. On the northern end the limestones form an anticlinal-like structure over the core of the range.

Mineral deposits of the Organ Mountains occur as narrow quartz veins in the quartz monzonite near limestone contacts; replacement beds in the limestones; and tactite-type contact metamorphic deposits. The quartz veins in the Tertiary quartz monzonite contain gold and sparse molybdenite; most production of minerals came from the replacement beds, of which the Stevenson–Bennett ore bodies were the largest. Copper was the mineralization of most importance in the contact-metamorphic deposits.

Northrop listed the following minerals as among those furnished for museum specimens from the Organ Mountains:

Altaite, found at the Hilltop Mine
Calcite and aragonite, both in crystal and mammillary forms
Flos-ferri, an uncommon form
Cerussite, in large heart-shaped twin crystals
Orthoclase, as Baveno twins
Quartz, with chlorite phantoms
Thuringite

A deposit of high-grade rutile in granite was reported from the Organ Mountains in 1946.

Fleischer gives thuringite as a ferrian variety of chamosite, a member of the chlorite group. Thuringite pseudomorph of andradite and of idocrase (vesuvianite) occurred at the Excelsior Mine and as pseudomorph of andradite at the Merrimac Mine.

Stevenson-Bennett Mine

The Stevenson-Bennett Mine is 13 miles northeast of Las Cruces and 1-1/2 miles south of Organ, in the Organ Mountains. It is shown on some maps as the Empire Zinc Mine. First production of lead in New Mexico came from this mine in 1849. Ore was carried to the outside on the backs of laborers and by pack animals to adobe furnaces near Fort Fillmore, on the Rio Grande, for smelting. At first the lead was used only to collect the silver and was not saved.

Hugh Stevenson, a local resident, soon became a partner and later became owner of the mine. In 1858, he sold the mine to U.S. Army officers stationed at Fort Fillmore.

In the first ten years, the mine produced between $80,000 and $100,000 in lead and silver. The Army officers ordered new machinery; however, after it arrived in 1861 it was lost with the mine to the Confederate soldiers who had just captured Fort Fillmore. After the war, the mine was relocated and litigation resulted in the officers sharing the mine with the new locators.

The Bennett ore body was discovered in 1887 by a leasor named Cassera. Production in 1887-8 was said to be a quarter of a million dollars and by 1906 it was $0.6 million, about a third being produced in the interval 1890 to 1900. Lead was produced and not wasted in this period. This ore body was larger than the Stevenson ore body but contained less silver.

A third period of mining began in 1908 and lasted to 1920 when the mine was closed. Phelps-Dodge Corporation leased the property in 1916 but relinquished it in 1917. A 300 ton-per-day mill was built during the third period of activity but torn down in 1920 by A.S. & R. Company, who had leased the mine. In 1918, the mine produced 43, 328 pounds of molybdenum contained in wulfenite.

Production to 1935 was $1.2 million. The mine was reopened in 1946 and again in 1950 when some lead–silver ore was shipped. Ore from the dump was shipped in 1952.

In the Stevenson–Bennett Mine, a fault block about a mile long composed of limestone injected with quartz monzonite contained the replacement ore. In this block, a north-south fault zone with eleven faults was also mineralized and formed part of the ore bodies. The ore formed after the quartz monzonite was emplaced. Most of the early mining on the Stevenson ore body was from an open cut. A tunnel about 100 feet below the outcrop and later one 360 feet below developed the mine. A winze 150 feet below this second tunnel developed considerable water.

The early mining of the Stevenson–Bennett deposit followed two veins in the limestone and, although their outcrops were relatively barren, Bonanza deposits of secondary cerussite and anglesite occurred close to the surface. There was little zinc in these oxidized ores as it leached out and had been redeposited below as smithsonite and hemimorphite. Less common secondary minerals such as brochantite and silver halides occurred above the water table level. Copper carbonates, linarite, and chrysocolla were found in the upper part of the deposit. Wulfenite, in brown and yellow pseudocubic crystals, occurred in caverns in the limestone. Most crystals were opaque; however, transparent yellow crystals occurred.

Primary ore was galena, pyrite, sphalerite, and some molybdenite in a gangue of quartz, calcite, and barite. Caves contained masses of oxidized ore and some stopes contained mixed primary and secondary galena and cerussite ores.

The Stevenson ore body was made up chiefly of cerussite, quartz, green fluorite, smithsonite, and argentiferous galena.

The Bennett ore body did not reach the surface but was 10 feet wide by 500 feet long by 600 feet vertical. Minerals were aragonite, pale blue smithsonite, anglesite, limonite, cerussite, and wulfenite. Caves filled with limonite and cerussite occurred. The primary ore in the lower workings was pyrite, galena, sphalerite in quartz and silicified dolomite.

The smaller Page ore body was located between the Stevenson and the Bennett ore bodies. In the oxidized zone the ore was limonite, cerussite, and smithsonite. This changed to primary pyrite and galena below the water table level.

Small amounts of herrerite, smithsonite colored green by copper, were reported by Carter. Dana reports hemimorphite from this mine.

Modoc Mine

The Modoc Mine, probably the Barilla Mine of Antisell, developed the south end of the fault zone containing the Stevenson-Bennett ore bodies. The mine was probably worked before the Stevenson ore body. Between 1879 and 1905 about $200,000, mostly in lead, was produced.

JARILLA MOUNTAINS

Between U.S. Highway 54, Alamogordo to Orogrande, and the east side of the Organ Mountains, Otero County, a low range of mountains known as the Jarilla Mountains, rises above the rift-associated Tularosa Valley.

Placer gold was reported in this area in 1850 and there is evidence of prehistoric mining for turquoise. Quartz monzonite, possibly from the Organ Mountains batholith, is in contact with Paleozoic sedimentary rocks and has domed the limestones and quartzite. Contact metamorphic zones and replacement beds, similar to the mineralization in the Organ Mountains, occur. Iron ore and tungsten ore, which did not occur in the Organ Mountains, have been produced from this area. Pyrite and chalcopyrite with gold and silver values occurred in veins, and pipes.

Smoky quartz, orthoclase crystals, as Carlsbad, Baveno and Manebach twins, occur. Baveno twins up to four inches long have been found and it is thought that some specimens marked Organ Mountains actually came from this location (Fig. 3–1).

Mining has occurred from time to time and the Director of the Mint's report for 1884 gave a production of 5,000 ounces of gold and 45,000 ounces of silver for that year. Production of copper between 1915 and 1918 was over a million pounds, over 2,000 ounces of silver and the same amount of gold. Finley gave the cost of producing a quarter of a million dollars in ore as equal, or nearly so,

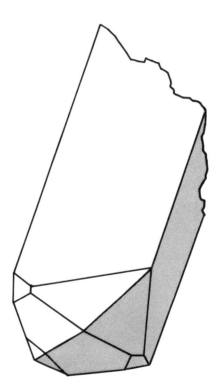

Fig. 3–1.   Orthoclase, Baveno Twin, Organ Mountains, New Mexico.

to the value of the ore produced. In the 1960s, a revived interest in copper resulted in the staking of numerous claims.

REFERENCES

A–4 Lindgren Volume (Henderson), (McKnight), F–3, G–1, G–2, G–3, G–6, G–7, G–10, G–11, I–6, I–15, J–23, J–46, J–54, J–57, J–60, K–7, K–10, L–1, 1948, 1950, 1952, N–15, 0–5, 0–9, 0–10, 0–17, 0–26, 0–28, 0–34, 0–37, 0–38, 0–39, P–7 James (Chapin), S–73.

SANTA RITA AREA AND THE CENTRAL MINING DISTRICT, GRANT COUNTY

The Santa Rita area and the Central mining district form an area bounded on the east and southeast by the Great American Rift (Rio Grande Graben at this location) with the Mimbres Fault making a sharp separation (Fig. 3–2). On

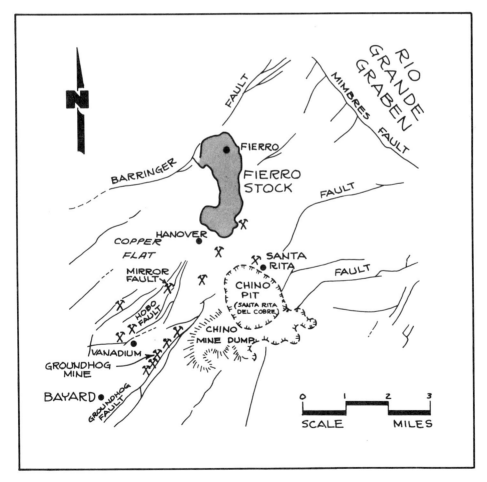

Fig. 3–2. Central mining district, Grant County, New Mexico. Adapted from U.S.G.S., P.P. 555, 1967 and NTIS Pub. PB–214–371, 1973.

the west and southwest the Basin and Range geologic province and on the northwest the Colorado Plateau limits the area. A roughly triangular synclinal block has been uplifted to form the Santa Rita horst. An eight mile segment of the Mimbres Fault, which may extend at least 35 miles, forms one side of this block. The Barringer Fault marks the northwest side and a zone of discontinuous faults mark the south side. The area of the horst is about forty square miles and it contains elongated arches, domes, small synclines, tight folds, and subsidiary minor horsts and grabens. These structural features date from the first igneous intrusions of late Cretaceous age and from later deformation during the Cenozoic Era.

Over 6,000 feet of Paleozoic and Mesozoic rocks in the Santa Rita horst have been faulted in late Cretaceous and again in Tertiary times. They were intruded by sills, dikes, laccoliths, stocks, and plugs.

In the Cretaceous time, doming and fracturing of the area was caused by emplacement of a batholith of grandiorite porphyry and accompanying stocks. More basic magma was forced into this complex in the form of dikes and sills. During Tertiary time flows of rhyolite covered the area but much of it was removed by erosion. Miocene volcanic breccia and Cenozoic gravels cover parts of the area.

Three mineralized stocks, the Santa Rita, Hanover–Fierro, and Copper Flats occur in the area. An age of 53 m.y.B.P. has been postulated for the emplacement of these stocks. Santa Rita granodiorite porphyry is dated at 63 m.y.B.P. and granodiorite of Santa Rita Mountains is dated at 68 m.y.B.P. Jones and others give a detailed account of how Laramide activity converted a series of flat-lying Paleozoic and late Cretaceous sediments into a scrambled complex mass. Hydrothermal minerals are considered to have been deposited from fluids rising along the margins of the stocks and extending along convenient faults. The Groundhog fault and the Mirror fault were the most important of these.

Limestones and dolomites around the north end of the Hanover-Fierro stock were massively replaced by tabular magnetite bodies and around the south end by sphalerite bodies. Magnetite replacement ores also occurred adjacent to the Santa Rita stock and sphalerite bodies were mined. Copper Flats stock contains hematite and sphalerite ores.

The Santa Rita stock, in which the Santa Rita pit is located, is a prophyry copper deposit. The ore body consists of disseminated copper minerals in granodiorite, quartz diorite and metamorphosed sediments that have been intensely fractured. Some ore is in limestone, sandstone, and shale. Most of the enriched ore has been mined from the South pit limestone; replacement ore was mined from the North pit. A large body of limestone replacement ore in the Lee Hill area, west of present pits, will be future ore. Most of the minerals chemically concentrated by ground water, secondary or supergene minerals, of the Central mining district had been mined by the turn of the century. These minerals included: malachite, chrysocolla, native copper, chalcanthite, mottramite, cuprite, cerussite, anglesite, smithsonite, hemimorphite, plumbojarosite, wulfenite, and pyromorphite, Vanadinite (var. endlichite) and descloizite were also reported.

Gangue minerals were: pyrite, pyrrhotite, jasper-silicified rock, quartz, calcite (commonly manganiferous), siderite, marble, serpentine, talc, apatite, wollastonite, pyroxenes; (including salite, hedenbergite, johannsenite, manganous-magnesian hedenbergite, manganous hedenbergite), amphiboles; (includes tremolite, ferro-tremolite, actinolite, cummingtonite), albite, orthoclase, garnet, epidote group; (includes zoisite, clinozoisite), pistacite (epidote), ilvaite, orthorhombic and monoclinic, rhodonite, chlorite, biotite, sericite, clays, (includes kaolinite, montmorillonite, illite, or hydromuscovite), alunite, and rhodochrosite.

Vein deposits extend southwest from the Hanover-Fierro and Santa Rita stocks along the southeast side of the Copper Flats stock. They carry lead, copper, and silver minerals and are associated with sills of Cretaceous age.

Ore minerals varied with the mines and with areas within the district. In the Chloride Flats area, where most of the deposits were mined in the early years, the ore minerals were: anglesite, argentite (acanthite), cerargyrite (chlorargyrite), embolite, cerussite, covellite, galena, magnetite, malachite, massicot, and silver. Barite, goethite, hematite, limonite, pyrite, and pyrolusite were common gangue minerals (Fig. 3–3). Age of the mineralization is not known but has been bracketed between late Cretaceous and Oligocene time.

Minerals formed by metamorphic processes, or metasomatic minerals associated with iron-oxide deposits in dolomitic rocks, were serpentine, wollastonite and idocrase; in shales and igneous rocks, epidote, and chlorite; and in limestone, andradite garnet. At the Union Hill Mine mountain leather or cork occurred. In some coarse crystalline marble, calcite grains up to two inches across were pseudomorphically replaced by magnetite. Quartz crystals with spire-like terminations (similar to the reversed scepters of the San Juan Mountains of Colorado) were found in vugs and cavities. Limonite after sphalerite was found to be brown and cellular in texture but limonite after salite (var. of diopside) maintained the radiating fibrous structure of salite and was porous and ocherous orange.

Thuringite and pyrite, in a granodiorite dike, formed poorly crystallized goethite. Cubanite occurred in massive iron-oxide replacement bodies.

In the Bullfrog Mine, near Bayard, the vein was enriched by gold and rhodochrosite occurred.

The Santa Rita quadrangle, an area mostly north of the Santa Rita pit, had some interesting mineral occurrences, which were recorded by Jones and others.

Some sphalerite occurred in a large block of magnetite, 300 feet in diameter and 70 feet thick, in the Pewabic Mine. Magnetite formed worm-like, vermiform, inclusions in the sphalerite. Calcite, dolomite, siderite, ankerite, and rhodochrosite were deposited after the sulfides, but also accompanied them. Away from the main ore conduits, manganiferous calcite preceded the sulfides.

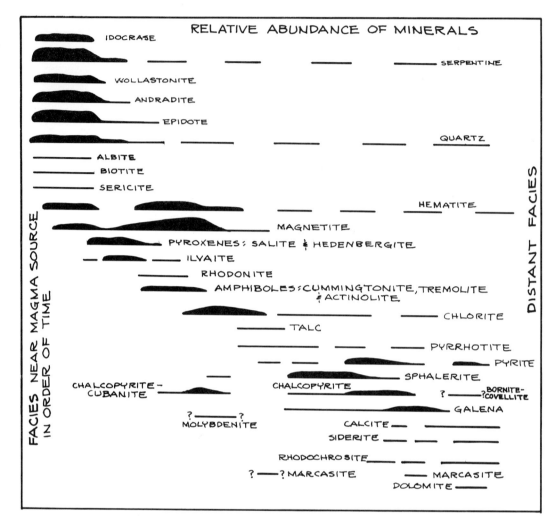

Fig. 3-3. Pyragenesis of minerals in areas close to main conduits adjacent to south lobe of Fierro stock, Central mining district, Grant County, New Mexico. Adapted from PB–214–371, 1973.

NOTES: Relative times and amounts of minerals are shown for a hypothetical place that contains the entire suite of minerals. This place does not exist due to conditions of temperature and distance from the source and it does not apply to the entire Central mining district. It does show the relative factors for the various minerals in relation to other minerals. Adapted from PB–214–371, 1973.

Mineral production from this district including iron, copper, lead, zinc, molybdenum, silver, gold, and minor metals has exceeded a billion dollars. It has produced far more of these minerals than all other districts of the state combined.

Santa Rita del Cobre

Santa Rita Pit, or Chino Mine as it is variously called, is the oldest of the large open-pit copper mines of North America. The deposit is a porphyry copper and is formed by disseminated minerals hydrothermally placed in the fractured Santa Rita stock.

Production of copper from the Santa Rita deposit prior to 1845 has been estimated at not less than 41 million pounds and from 1804 to 1934 over 1.3 billion pounds. From 1940 to 1964, yearly copper production dropped below 100 million pounds only twice, in periods of labor strikes.

Native copper may have been mined from the Santa Rita outcrops by the Aztecs as it is thought to be one of the places from which they and later native peoples obtained the metal. Ancient workings indicate that the Aztecs worked turquoise deposits in the Little Hachita Mountains of southern Grant, northern Hidalgo Counties. It is conceivable that they followed the high ridge of the Continental Divide northward to the Santa Rita pit area.

The Apaches were using copper from the Santa Rita deposit in the 17th century. Around 1800, a friendly chief showed the outcroppings to Colonel José Manuel Carasco, officer in charge of the Spanish military posts in New Mexico. Lacking the means to work the deposit, Carasco interested Don Manuel Francisco Elguea, a wealthy and influential merchant-banker of Chihuahua, Mexico, in the deposit's potential to produce wealth. Elguea obtained a grant, Santa Rita del Cobre, from the Spanish government and later obtained Carasco's interest in the deposit. Four years later, he began to develop the mine.

The Apaches did not remain passive and it was necessary to build a fort of adobe, with watchtowers and thick walls to keep them out. Armed forces protected the mule trains that packed the copper to Chihuahua and Mexico City, where it was used for coinage, and the return trip with supplies, which included a highly expendable commodity, slaves. The walls and guards not only kept the Apaches out but also kept the slaves in. They were convicts and Indian slaves borrowed from the government in Mexico. Mining was most primitive with the workers excavating as small openings and drifts as possible to work. Ore was picked out and put in rawhide bags with head straps, carried to the surface up notched poles (chicken ladders) and resorted for shipment to Mexico. Zebulon Pike, the explorer, recorded that the mine produced 20,000 mule loads of copper per year (about six million pounds). He was arrested and taken to Santa Fe, and later to Mexico in 1807.

Relics of this period found in the small one man openings (coyote holes) by later open pit mining included skeletons of workers, ore bags, chicken ladders, and other artifacts.

After Elguea's death in 1809 the mine was worked by Juan Onis. James Pattie, a trapper, hunter, and adventurer, was the first American to visit the mine. With his son he leased the mine for five years, at $1,000 per year, until 1827. A French resident of Chihuahua then operated the mine for a short period. In 1834 Robert McKnight assumed possession and worked the mine for about two years. Kit Carson was said to have been a teamster in his employ.

Lenardo Sesquieros took over the mine in 1840 and operated it until the late 1850s when Apache raids caused the mine to be abandoned. Under the Treaty of Guadalupe Hidalgo the territory became part of the United States in 1850 and a border survey group stayed at Santa Rita for a few months in 1851. The town of Santa Rita had grown up outside the walls of the fort in the early 1800s.

An unsuccessful attempt was made to work the mine in 1862 by Confederate forces from Texas. By this time a number of underground workings existed; rough smelting works had been built to reduce the black copper ore to metal and most of the rich surface ore had been mined.

M. B. Hayes, who was connected with some of the early Colorado smelters, began work at Chino in 1873 and sank a 248 foot shaft. A smelter was built but it was not a success. About 40 tons of imperfectly smelted copper and some hand sorted ore was hauled by team about 800 miles to a railroad in Colorado and shipped to the Revere Copper Works at Point Shirley, Massachusetts.

Hayes tried to get title to the mine from the U. S. Land Office but could not until heirs of the Elguea family in Mexico and Europe, were appeased. By October, 1873 he accomplished this and he also filed claims under U. S. mining laws.

J. P. Whitney bought the mine in 1881 and erected a stamp mill. Considerable diamond drilling, an advanced tool for prospecting at that time, was completed; however, locations of some of the holes were lost.

A railroad was completed to Hanover in 1891 and to Santa Rita in 1899.

Open pit mining of large bodies of low-grade copper ore was considered for Bingham Canyon in Utah, as early as 1898, but this porphyry copper ore body was not stripped until 1906. This new approach to mining large quantities of low grade ore began at Chino with extensive sampling of the ore body in 1906 to 1908, and by 1909 steam shovels were being used in the fast developing pit. Rail haulage was started in the pit and steam-driven churn drills were used for sampling and for blast holes. Black powder was the explosive used. First production came from the pit operation in 1914 and another porphyry copper mine was launched. The sampling and exploration program of 1906 to 1908 was carried out with principally churn drilling on a grid system. This showed the ore body to be about 9,000 feet in diameter. The Hurst pit was started in 1910 and Chino Copper Company was organized to work the deposit. After mergers in 1924, 1926, and 1933, Kennecott Copper Corporation became the owner and the present operator.

A gravity concentrating mill erected in 1911 was changed to part flotation in 1914 and to all flotation in 1925. Leaching the low grade dump material with water was started in 1920 and continued with acid leaching a little later. Circulating solutions for this purpose had increased to 15,000 gpm by 1965.

Molybdenum recovery was started in 1937 and the plant was replaced with a modern one in 1962. Silver and gold are other byproducts and a selenium slag was first produced as another byproduct in 1952. This was two years before the town of Santa Rita, which had developed outside of the old fort walls, had to be moved to keep it from falling into the expanding pit.

In the early 1930s it was not uncommon to find that actual ore removal could run up to 120 percent of estimated tonnage in an area and that this contained up to 123 percent of expected copper. Elaborate controls were set up so the ore could be blended and production tightly controlled. Millheads that contained

51.4 lbs. of copper/ton in 1911 now contained only 17 lbs. of copper/ton. Mining and milling technology had to keep pace with this trend.

After a history of almost 175 years of production, with much of it continuous operation, the present Chino Division of Kennecott Copper Corporation consists of an open pit 1,000 plus feet deep and over 1–1/4 miles wide with a modern mill and smelter at Hurley, ten miles from the pit. Modern equipment in the pit can move 95,000 tpd, about half of it ore. A modern sulfuric acid plant was built at Hurley to produce 500 tpd of acid in 1974. In that same year, the south Santa Rita pit and the Tyrone pit of the Phelps–Dodge Corporation, together produced $60.3 million in copper.

The granodiorite porphyry of the South pit has been dated at 63 m.y.B.P. and evidence indicates the original copper content was between 0.1 and 0.3 percent (Anderson).

Nash, in his fluid inclusion studies of porphyry copper deposits, found that all but 3 out of 37 deposits studied evolved through a hydrothermal stage having very high salinity (including Santa Rita). This generally amounted to about 35 weight percent sodium chloride equivalent. Temperature of the fluids ranged from 250 to 700 C and most systems boiled. He considered the parameters of these deposits to include epizonal (slight depths) intrusions emplaced at depths of from 6,000 to 10,000 feet with fluid pressures during mineralization to be less than 500 bars. He observed fluid inclusions in primary and secondary quartz.

There is compelling evidence that chloride is important for the transportation of metals. The porphyry coppers, as a class, have high salinity fluids associated with at least one stage of their formation.

Large amounts of native copper and cuprite occurred with malachite, azurite and chrysocolla in the upper part of the deposit. Gangue minerals were quartz, dioptase, kaolin, halloysite, and sericite. If Pike's assessment of the production was correct, the outcrop area must have originally resembled a pile of scrap copper.

Enrichment of disseminated chalcopyrite–pyrite bodies by chalcocite made the richest ore, the chalcocite–blanket, which was between the oxidized ore and the primary sulfides. Two enriched horizons occurred. The largest was up to 700 feet thick in places and extended as much as 1,200 feet downward. Two different periods of fluctuation in the ground water level caused this condition in the ore body.

Chalcocite, chalcopyrite, bornite, and molybdenite are the principal ore minerals. Magnetite, hematite, sphalerite, and minor gold (probably in pyrite) also occur in the deposit. Turquoise and libethenite also occur at Santa Rita.

Pyrite floaters, as pyritohedrons coated with chalcocite, occurred in the chalcocite blankets in clay pockets. They are rarely up to two inches in diameter. A floater is the name given to a crystal or group of crystals that are formed in a cavity within a vein or deposit without attachment to the enclosing rock or minerals. They are completely enclosed in crystal faces and do not have any one face showing a sheared surface.

Floaters are often found in an iron-rich mud. This may give a clue to the material that originally surrounded them; in many cases a combination of minerals that contained pyrite, siderite or similar minerals, which were oxidized to a limonite–like mud. Complete crystals loosened from an igneous melt, such as orthoclase crystals and high temperature quartz crystals, are not floaters. This is also true of crystals loosened from pegmatite deposits, such as beryl or tourmaline crystals.

Ground Hog Mine

The Ground Hog Mine is near Vanadium, between Santa Rita and Bayard, New Mexico. It is near the Santa Rita dump. Located in 1900, it did not make a significant contribution until 1928. Cerussite was mined from along the Ground Hog Fault in this period of operation. The Hayward Richard Leasing Company discovered complex sulfide ore in the Crescent ore shoot in 1928 and sold 51 percent interest to the A.S. & R. Company. Production was assured and in the late 1930s and into the 1940s a major zinc deposit was mined. By 1953 most zinc mines were closed down as metal prices control the closings and openings of base metal mines. In 1958, before one of these closings the mine produced 15,000 tons zinc, 1,800 tons lead, 500 tons copper, and 140,000 ounces silver. The mine closed in 1965 and reopened in 1969 to produce 44,667 tons of ore from which 6,125 tons of zinc, 1,673 tons of lead, 155 tons of copper and 66,419 ounces of silver were removed. Mining continued through most of the 1970s. Between 1928 and 1965 about five million ounces of silver were produced as a byproduct of base metal mining.

At least six types of ore deposits are recognized in the Central mining district. Some deposits overlap and grade into each other. The Gound Hog ore deposit is a combination of vein and replacement ore bodies. Argentiferous zinc–lead–copper veins occur in the upper levels of the mine and replacement bodies in limestone are found in the lower levels. The vein deposits are in sills and dikes.

Deposits of primary argentiferous zinc–lead–copper sulfides are found at the junction of intersecting faults, along the reopened walls of dikes, in sheeted ground, and in lenticular masses of breccia. Minor faults in the hanging wall and foot wall zones link with major ore deposits to form an intricate network along the Ground Hog–Ivanhoe Fault. (Fig. 4–7)

Mineralization has been found in the Ground Hog-Ivanhoe Fault Zone for a length of 10,000 feet and has been exposed to a vertical depth of 2,200 feet. Ore shoots are a maximum of 25 feet wide and up to 1,000 feet long and they occurred in bands that dipped 10 degrees northeast and were as much as 350 feet high and 3,500 feet long.

The Ground Hog dike of quartz monzonite porphyry is thought to have intruded along the Ground Hog–Ivanhoe Fault during the dying phase of formation of the ore minerals. A second surge of mineralization that deposited chiefly copper and iron sulfides followed the intrusion of the dike.

Sphalerite veins with lead, copper, silver, and minor gold extend about five miles southwest from the Santa Rita and Hanover–Fierro stocks. Many faults and fractures connect the Ground Hog Fault to both of these stocks and to a northwest zone of fracturing, brecciation, and intrusion that seemingly connects them (Fig. 3–4).

The veins are considered to be Tertiary in age and the hydrothermal fluids arose along the stocks and faults. The complex pattern of the granodiorite beneath Miocene(?) volcanic rocks is thought to represent another intrusive center from which mineralization could have moved upward along the veins.

The Ground Hog is primarily a sphalerite vein deposit with varying amounts of lead, copper, silver, and gold. Galena and chalcopyrite are abundant; the sphalerite is marmatitic, (iron-rich), and silver is associated with the sulfides (Fig. 3–5).

Cerussite found in the upper workings had been leached of silver and secondary enrichment plated out supergene silver in the chalcocite tarnish on chalcopyrite and sphalerite.

Other ore minerals are silver-bearing sulfides, magnetite, hematite and gold. Monheimite, ferroan smithsonite, was reported from the Ground Hog Mine. It is gray to buff in color.

Gangue minerals are: pyrite, quartz, jasper, silicified rock, calcite (usually black and manganiferous), marble, albite, garnet, ilvaite, sericite, chlorite group, biotite, rhodochrosite, rhodonite, and pyrrhotite. Also found are salite, variety of diopside; hedenbergite, manganous-magnesian hedenbergite, and magnesian hedenbergite, of the pyroxene group; johannsenite, which forms a series with diopside and hedenbergite of the pyroxene group; tremolite, ferro-tremolite, actinolite and cummingtonite of the amphibole

Fig. 3–4.   Quartz, sphalerite and chalcopyrite, Groundhog Mine (JM #310).

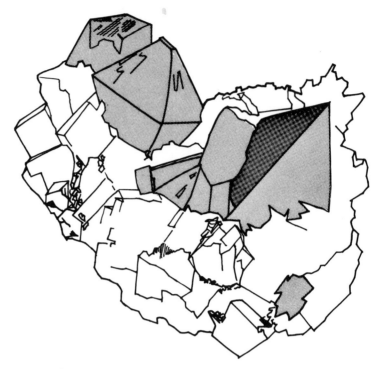

Fig. 3-5.   Disphenoidal chalcopyrite, Groundhog Mine.

group; and epidote, zoisite and clinozoisite of the epidote group. Clay minerals are kaolinite, montmorillonite, and illite. Doubly terminated quartz crystals occurred in slickensided beidellite.

REFERENCES

A-4 Lindgren Volume (Henderson), A-5 Ridge (Anderson), (Hernon), G-10, I-7, J-46, J-54, K-12, L-1, 1948-1974, M-1, M-2, O-7, O-19, O-33, O-38, O-39, R-9, R-12, R-15, R-27, S-64, S-65, S-66, S-67, S-73, S-88, S-91, S-111.

BURRO MOUNTAINS

The Burro Mountains are two small desert ranges about ten miles southwest of Silver City; the Little Burro Mountains are about six miles and the Big Burro Mountains about fifteen miles away, respectively (Fig. 3-6). Mangas Valley, a down-faulted block which exposes only gravel deposits, separates the two ranges. Both are horst blocks and are on the Continental Divide with the Big Burro Mountains rising 2,000 feet above the desert and the Little Burro Mountains only 600 feet. They are in the Great American Rift zone like two small islands.

   Precambrian quartzites and schists were intruded by anorthosite, diabase, and granite of the composite Burro Mountain batholith. At least two episodes

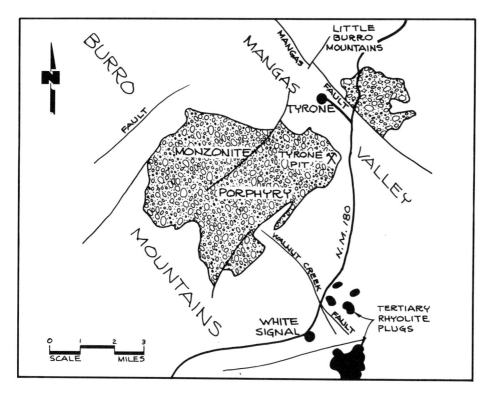

Fig. 3–6.   Location map of Big Burro Mountains, Grant County, New Mexico. Adapted from Bu.M. 83, N. Mex. Bu.M. and M.R., 1964.

of metamorphism occurred before emplacement of the granite of the Burro Mountain batholith and related rocks. The Bullard Peak and Ash Creek series of metamorphic rocks occur as roof pendants and zenoliths (forms of material included in igneous rocks) in the batholith.

Cretaceous rocks were deposited without any record of intervening geologic events on the northern end of the Burro Mountain Range. Before the late Cretaceous and in the late Cretaceous or early Tertiary times, quartz monzonite, as a stock and related dikes, intruded the older rocks. The Tyrone stock was the principal center of these intrusives that cut Cretaceous as well as Precambrian rocks and were probably derived from a pluton which existed under the area.

In the Silver City quandrangle to the north stocks of Laramide age representing at least five stages were eroded prior to eruption of Tertiary lavas.

Tertiary lavas erupted in the Burro Mountain Range after uplift occurred along northwest and northeast faults. These events seem to be similar in both cases.

Gila Conglomerate of upper Pliocene age, and Quaternary gravels overlie parts of the Burro Mountains. Repeated uplift faulted Gila Conglomerate against Precambrian granitic rocks in places. This formation was largely formed from conglomerates from the Burro Mountains; however, it also contains lenses of sandstone, volcanic ash, and irregular masses of travertine from thermal springs. Much of it is also cemented by caliche, an impure calcite compound found in desert areas.

Two large faults, which are roughly parallel occur in the Burro Mountains. The Mangas Fault is marked by a prominent fault scarp on the southwest edge of the Little Burro Mountains along the Mangas Valley and Gila Conglomerate is downfaulted against Precambrian rocks on the scarp. The Mangas Valley also contains Quaternary deposits and movement along the fault in both Tertiary and Quaternary time (rifting), is indicated.

Malone Fault is on the southwest side of the Big Burro Mountains and separates Tertiary volcanic rocks on the northeast from uplifted Precambrian rocks on the southwest. Movement in Tertiary and in Quaternary times is indicated on this fault also. If a hidden fault, probably parallel, exists southwest of the Malone Fault on the southwest side of the Big Burros, a graben structure is indicated. A thick sequence of volcanic rocks, Gila Conglomerate, and unconsolidated Quaternary gravels were deposited since Tertiary time in this area. Renewed movement (rifting) has occurred to indicate this is the correct interpretation.

Pegmatites in the Burro Mountain granite have produced crystals of euxenite, orthorhombic, up to four inches long. Muscovite, microcline, and quartz are associated minerals. The crystals are euhedral and are also found in the soil near the pegmatites.

Smoky quartz was found south of Eules Canyon and a blue variety of quartz was found north of this canyon. Green-fluorescing opal was also found in this area.

In the Ash Creek area serpentine, (var. ricolite), occurs in xenoliths. This material was quarried in 1888 and shipped to Chicago to make interior wainscoting. It has also been used for jewelry and carvings. The name is said to mean "rich stone;" the varietal name was a trademark.

Chrysotile asbestos and other minerals of the xenoliths of Ash Creek are of interest to mineralogists. A black pitchy material containing manganese was considered to be "copperpitch" (the German kupferpecherz), but here was a variety of chrysocolla stained brown or black with manganese oxides.

Big Burro Mountain Fluorspar

In the Big Burro Mountains fluorspar deposits are localized around the Tyrone quartz monzonite stock. This stock is about four miles wide and six miles long and is on the northeast side of the mountains. Fluorspar is also found along the Malone Fault southwest of the Big Burro Mountains. Intrusion of the Tyrone stock prepared favorable host faults and broke up the formations so that mineralization could be deposited.

Fluorspar was mined in the early 1880s for use as a smelter flux. Phelps–Dodge acquired the Burro Chief Mine in 1913 and occasional mining occurred until 1942 when continuous mining was begun at the Shrine Mine and a year later at the Burro Chief Mine. These two mines produced about 100,000 tons of fluorspar between 1943 and 1949. In 1948, Phelps–Dodge started an extensive development program in the Tyrone area and mining on the Burro Chief was stopped a year later. A mill had been in operation on the Burro Chief ore.

In the Big Burro Mountains most of the country rock near the fluorspar deposits is altered to sericite, chlorite and clay minerals.

Azurite, malachite, chrysocolla, halloysite, manganese oxides, pyrite, and quartz occur in the deposits as do smaller amounts of turquoise and chalcopyrite.

Fluorspar may be white, yellow, green, violet, or purple. Possibly three stages of fluorite occur. The green and purple is early and the violet, as octahedrons, is the last stage of deposition. Fluorite occurs as cubes and octahedrons, however, dodecahedrons modified by cube are also found (Fig. 3–7).

Along the Malone Fault the fluorspar deposits are smaller but similar.

Burro Chief Mine

This mine is 1-1/4 miles southwest of Tyrone. It is in Precambrian granite which has been intruded by rhyolite and a wide breccia zone in the granite is cut by quartz monzonite dikes associated with the Tyrone stock. Fluorite fills the breccia and has in turn been brecciated by later movement. The Burro Chief Fault, the main fault of the deposit, has itself displaced Quaternary gravels.

Chemung No. 1 shaft was sunk near this deposit in 1906, to a depth of 532 feet. By 1944, drifts had been driven 230 feet from the 260 foot level to intersect

Fig. 3-7. Fluorite, Burro Mountains (JM#80).

the fluorspar. A block of about 217 feet was thereby opened and stoped. By 1951, a vertical shaft 700 feet deep developed the Burro Chief Mine. Breccia zones 10 to 100 feet wide had been exposed and ore had been stoped from the 260 foot level to the surface. Individual ore shoots 35 feet wide and 400 feet long had been mined. Workings extended 1,000 feet south and 300 feet north of the shaft.

Turquoise Mining in the Big Burro Mountains

Turquoise was mined in the Big Burro Mountains by the Pueblo Indians and the Spanish were thought to have worked the deposits also. J. E. Coleman (Turquoise John) was credited with finding the old workings in 1875 and located the Calliate claim.

The Azure Mine was the most famous producer and probably has been worked more extensively than any other New Mexico turquoise deposit. It is 1-1/2 miles north of Leopold and was opened in 1891. The total output was estimated to be from $2 million to $4 million.

In 1893, the famous "Elizabeth pocket" produced more high grade turquoise than any single pocket to that time. It was a vein filling containing nuggets or concretions embedded in kaolin and as veinlets. This deposit was 40 to 60 feet high, 40 feet wide, and extended 150 feet along the vein.

Turquoise below the second level was associated with malachite and chrysocolla. Down to the fourth level an excess of copper gave some of the material a green color and a decreased hardness. The finest had a hardness of 6. All the best material occurred in the upper 100 feet of the vein.

Vein turquoise filled cracks and was from 1/16 to 3/4 inch thick. Most was from 1/8 to 3/8 inch thick but some was 1-1/2 inch thick. Nodules made the finest gems. The veins contained cavities lined with quartz crystals and some vein turquoise contained small quartz crystals penetrating the turquoise. Olive green masses and nuggets of halloysite also occurred as a matrix mineral.

The cut gems from the "Elizabeth pocket" were marked on the underside with a circle, a guarantee by the eastern company that marketed them that the color would not fade. Some of these gems were a deep translucent blue.

White Signal District

The Whie Signal district includes the southeastern part of the Big Burro Mountains in the vicinity of White Signal. Mining started in the 1870s and has been continued intermittently by small operations. Uranium caused additional activity in the late 1940s and early 1950s.

Precambrian granite of the Burro Mountains batholith containing xenoliths of quartzite, schist, and amphibolite is the principal country rock of the area. Dikes and plugs of various composition intrude the granite and diabase dikes are the most numerous.

Quartz monzonite of the Tyrone stock, rhyolite breccia, and pegmatites, which intrude the granite are also prominent in the district.

Mineralized breccias, fracture zones, and veins are numerous but shallow and small and most of the mining has been confined to the oxidized zones. Production from these various mineral deposits has been small; however, some rich but small surface pockets were mined. Mine workings average less than 100 feet of depth.

Four types of veins or deposits are recognized within the district: Quartz–pyrite; quartz–specularite, some being radioactive; silver or lead–silver; and turquoise deposits.

Mineral products of the White Signal district are impressive in their variation. Fluorspar, uranium, radium, gold, copper, lead, bismuth, turquoise, garnet, and ocher were ore or mineral products of the district.

Minerals of the district are: fluorite (as fluorspar), torbernite, autunite, uraninite (from Blue Jay Mine), bassetite, (monoclinic, the kithilite or keithilite of early reports), apatite, barite, quartz, hyalite (at the Turlock Shaft), magnetite, sphalerite, galena, chlorargyrite, silver, argentite (acanthite); bismuthinite, unidentified iron–uranium-phosphates, gold, malachite, azurite, siderite, chalcocite, pyrope, and euxenite.

Ores of gold, copper, and uranium have been the most important and the most production has come from the quartz–pyrite veins. Minerals in the oxidized zone are limonite (from pyrite), malachite, azurite, gold, torbernite, autunite, bismutite, and iron phosphates. Most of the deposits are radioactive.

The quartz–specularite veins are as much as 75 percent to 90 percent specular hematite. Torbernite, autunite, and uraninite occur in these veins. In the 1920s, uranium and radium minerals were identified from a number of deposits and torbernite was shipped for making "radioactive water" (a cure-all for sure!); radioactive clay was mined for radioactive face powder, and presumably for facial mud packs.

Autunite and torbernite were embedded in plaster plaques to be used in activating drinking and bathing water and for watering plants. About two carloads of this radioactive ore was produced and this activity lasted into the late 1920s. Radium salts for medical uses, including radium, were also made from the autunite and torbernite. Chlorargyrite was the principal mineral of the silver or lead–silver veins and barite and quartz were the principal gangue minerals.

Turquoise was first mined in the district between 1870 and 1900. The Chapman Mine and the Red Hill Mine were the largest producing mines, in terms of quantity.

Fibrous crystals of bronzite (ferroan enstatite) over six inches in length were found at the Apache Trails Mine, about three miles north of White Signal. Limonite pseudomorphs of pyrite were also found at this mine.

Blackhawk Canyon

A small district in Blackhawk Canyon on the east edge of the Big Burro Mountains produced about $1 million in silver between 1881 and 1893. Many minerals containing silver, copper, cobalt, nickel, and uranium have been reported from this small district.

Minerals of Blackhawk Canyon include:

silver (argentite)	bismuthinite
pitchblende (uraninite)	barite
sphalerite	pyrite
quartz	
nickel–skutterudite	skutterudite

Gold Lake Placer

In the Big Burro Mountains, the Gold Lake placer deposit, just below Gold Lake and in a side arroyo north of Gold Lake, was unique in producing placer gold from near quartz–gold veinlet outcrops and for nuggets up to 1/4 inch diameter of bismuth ore. Pyrope garnets, 1/8 to 1/4 inch in diameter, were found and about ten pounds were shipped for jewel bearings for watches to the Elgin Watch Company and to Czechoslovakia.

Tyrone Pit

The Tyrone pit of Phelps–Dodge Corporation is in the northeast tip of the Big Burro Mountains adjacent to the Mangas Valley and separated from the Little Burro Mountains by this valley. The Mangas Fault is on the southwest end of the Little Burro Mountains and forms a scarp on this side of the Mangas Valley.

Copper was discovered in the Big Burro Mountains in 1871 and some prospecting was done through 1875; however, the Apaches gave trouble and prevented mining until they were settled on reservations. In 1885, the first mining was begun in the district.

Phelps–Dodge Corporation came to the district in 1904–5 when they bought the Burro Mountain Copper Company from the Leopold Brothers of Chicago. The holdings were near Leopold and the Sampson Mine was the principal shaft. Ore bodies worked through the Sampson were the East, a large ore body, the East and West Sampson, and the Protection. The St. Luis inclined shaft and the McKinley Shaft were also obtained. They acquired the Tyrone holding in 1918. This deposit had three shafts, nos. 1, 2, and 3. Between nos. 2 and 3 the Niagara Tunnel was driven 7,000 feet into the East ore body at Leopold. It was connected by crosscut to the Niagara Shaft and was used to move ore from the Leopold area to the railroad. At 1,400 feet in the Niagara Tunnel the Bison ore body was found and between the 300 and 400 foot levels in No. 3 shaft a breccia ore body was mined. The Phelps–Dodge Corporation acquired about ten miles of underground workings and about 5,000 acres of mineral land.

In 1914, Phelps–Dodge Corporation was the only operator in the Big Burro Mountains and the town of Tyrone was built. Tyrone was, at its peak in World War I, the most magnificent mining town in the world. It cost Phelps–Dodge

Corporation approximately a million dollars to reproduce a town in Spain. This replica was complete with tree-lined plaza, wrought iron grill work, marble stairs and halls in the office building. Rare tiles were imported from Mexico.

In 1914, ore was mined incidental to exploration work.

The first concentrator was completed at Tyrone in April, and a second section in May of 1916. This was a 700 tpd unit for low-grade copper ore. Peak production from this period of operation came in 1918 when 17 million pounds of copper were produced. Mining was discontinued in 1921 as demand for copper had declined to the place that Tyrone was a million dollar ghost town, soon to be demolished. Modern Tyrone has to be content with functional beauty.

Leaching of dumps was carried on from 1921 to 1929 and from the late 1930s intermittently until about 1950. In 1941, underground leaching was carried on in some of the old stopes. Between 1941 and 1950, 30 million pounds of copper were recovered by this leaching.

Exploration was started in 1949 and carried on through 1969. Six to eight churn drills were active between 1949 and 1958; over 727 holes were sunk on a 200 foot center grid. Footage drilled totaled over 434,000 feet. Raises from the old underground workings helped verify the churn-drill samples. Studies and sampling continued until 1966–7, when a decision to develop the Tyrone open pit was made.

Production of copper was to be 55,000 tpy. Cost of stripping over 50 million tons of overburden, for equipment, mine buildings, a new concentrator, rail haulage in the pit, etc. was estimated to be over $100 million. The operation was to be the third largest of the Phelps–Dodge Corporation, smaller than Morenci and Ajo in Arizona.

Production started in 1969 and 1970 was the first year of full-scale operation. Plans were made to increase production to about 90,000 tpy of copper by 1973.

A copper smelter using a flash smelting process developed in Finland and having a capacity of 100,000 tpy was to be constructed near Animas, in Hidalgo County, New Mexico. Sulfuric acid and elemental sulfur were to be produced as byproducts.

The pit, which was started in 1969, is expected to reach a depth of 1,300 feet and be about 1–3/4 miles N-S and 1–1/4 miles E-W. Copper, minor silver, and gold are the only minerals recovered as molybdenum occurs only in very small quantities.

Tyrone Laccolith and Ore Body.   Until extensive drilling proved it to be a laccolith and not a stock, the quartz–monzonite body at Tyrone was called the Tyrone stock. It intruded Precambrian granite in late Cretaceous or early Tertiary time. This igneous mass is elliptical, about four miles by six miles in size and the northeast part, containing part of the Tyrone ore body, is covered by gravel deposits of the Mangas Valley.

At least three distinct porphyritic dike types cut the granite, earlier dikes, and the laccolith. Two of these dike types are variants of quartz–monzonite and the third type is granodiorite.

Both the quartz–monzonite and the underlying Precambrian granite are mineralized along myriad fractures. A blanket of supergene enrichment makes up the best ore and it may be up to thirty feet thick but varies erratically.

Tyrone ore body occupies a triangular section of the laccolith bounded on the northwest by the Burro Chief Fault, on the south by the Racket-Virginia Fault, and on the northeast by gravel of the Mangas Valley. The deposit is in the Tyrone horst with the Willow Creek Graben to the northwest and the White Signal Graben to the southeast.

In disseminated copper deposits, (porphyry–copper), such as the Santa Rita and Tyrone ore bodies, chalcopyrite is the primary copper sulfide. In the oxidized zone, leaching has carried much of the copper downward to be plated out as chalcocite near or at an old ground water level. This is always the richest ore.

Chalcopyrite, pyrite, molybdenite, and sphalerite are the main primary minerals. Chalcocite, tenorite, chrysocolla, copper carbonates, cuprite, and native copper are the minerals of the oxidized and enrichment zones. Other minerals are turquoise, torbernite, autunite, covellite, bornite, hematite, sericite, quartz, chlorite, epidote, orthoclase, oligoclase, apatite, and magnetite. Copper, iron, zinc, and molybdenum were deposited in Laramide time and fluorite, uranium, lead, gold, and silver were deposited in late Tertiary time according to Kolessar (1970).

The quartz monzonites of the pit area have hexagonal crystals of quartz, up to 1/4 inch long, with well-developed bipyramidal crystal habit and as small crystals in phenocrysts of pink orthoclase. The orthoclase crystals are up to 3 inches long and contain inclusions of quartz, oligoclase, biotite, and accessory minerals. Carlsbad twins and simple crystals occur; small white oligoclase phenocrysts also occur as do apatite and magnetite phenocrysts.

REFERENCES

A–4 Lindgreen Volume (Henderson), A–6, G–10, I–13, I–14, J–54, J–57, J–76, L–1 1967–1973, N–17, 0–12, 0–15, 0–28, 0–41, P–6 Woodward (Gillerman), (Kolessar), R–9, S–44, S–47, S–73, S–82.

APACHE NO. 2 DISTRICT

The Apache No. 2 district is in a small desert range about six miles south of Hachita in Hidalgo County. This area was formerly known as the Anderson district and in the early days produced some rich halide-silver ore.

Paleozoic limestones have been intruded by sill-like bodies of granodiorite porphyry. Ore deposits occur at the contact of the igneous mass and the limestone. Large bodies of marble and tactite are partly replaced by iron, copper, bismuth, and silver minerals. The ore minerals have been oxidized to a depth of at least 500 feet.

Some production of copper–silver ore was made in 1917 to 1919. A shaft on the Apache No. 2 claim was abandoned by the U.S.S. & R. Company in 1938.

The Apache Mine had copper, silver, and bismuth minerals. Only small amounts of chalcopyrite and pyrite were found above 500 feet in depth. Silver halides were found in the early workings. Large quantities of scheelite and wolframite, with oxidized bismuth minerals, occurred in parts of the Apache Mine. It was expected that beryllium would occur in the tactite zones, but tests in 1959 failed to show this to be the case. Malachite and chrysocolla occurred with coarse calcite.

LAKE VALLEY

Lake Valley mining district is in the southwest corner of Sierra County, about 18 miles south of Hillsboro. The district had a short silver bonanza period, from 1878 when C. W. Lufkin first found silver "at grassroots" to the Silver Panic of 1893, and a later period of manganese mining.

Cerargyrite (chlorargyrite) was mined from 1880 to 1885. A smelter built in 1882 and 1883 failed to concentrate the silver to any great degree and was abandoned as useless. All the ore was shipped as high-grade until 1885 when low-grade ores were leached in a silver leaching plant. In 1891, 217,836 ounces of silver were produced.

Since 1893 about 800,000 ounces of silver were produced by small operations up to 1964. During World War I about 8,000 tons of manganese ore were produced and during World War II over 37,000 tons of siliceous manganese ore were shipped to the Government stockpile at Deming, New Mexico. Government support stopped in 1950 and the mine was closed. This ore averaged 20.8 percent manganese. Siliceous ore was shipped from the area for smelter flux from time to time and the dumps were reworked for silver and for manganese.

A 200 tpd mill was built in 1953 to upgrade siliceous manganese ore and ran about seven years.

After the A.T. & S.F.R.R. reached the area in 1884, large amounts of low grade manganese ore for flux was shipped to Pueblo, Colorado, from the Apache Mine. The operator contracted for 500,000 tons but shipments in May and June were interrupted by the rise of the Rio Grande which submerged railroads and washed out tracks and embankments.

The mine shipped from 100 to 150 tons per week about this time and the Sierra Grande Company uncovered new ore deposits in the Sierra Grande, Sierra Bella and Apache Mines, which were worked as a group.

But this is getting ahead of the real story, which is the Bonanza period of Lake Valley.

The Bonanza period hit its highest point in the early 1880s when a shaft was sunk to test the possible extension of an ore body. All of the Bonanza ore was found within 100 feet of the surface, and this shaft hit ore at 24 feet. From this point downward the section was as follows:

Ore averaging 40 oz. silver/ton	5 feet
Ore averaging 60 oz. silver/ton	3 feet
Ore averaging 150 oz. silver/ton	4 feet

Open space lined with calcite crystals	1–1/6 feet
Chlorargyrite, averaging 15,900 ozs. silver/ton	4 feet
Sand carbonates average 500 ozs. silver and 40 percent lead/ton	5 feet
Decomposed limestone heavily stained with iron and manganese Blue (Lake Valley) limestone	25 feet

The ore occurred as irregular pockets and as chambers along bedding planes in Mississippi limestone. The richest ores occurred in jasperoid and narrow pockets and stringers extended considerable distances into the limestone.

The shaft was named the Bridal Chamber because of the sparkling light reflected by "myriads of crystals of cerargyrite and calcite studding the roof of the open space over the chloride streak."

Bridal Chamber ore was one of the richest silver masses found anywhere in the world. A portion about the size of an average dining room produced over a million dollars in silver. A single piece taken from the Bridal Chamber was reportedly worth $80,000.

In 1884 the Director of the Mint's report showed that the Sierra Grande Company had paid within the "last two years" about $1,000,000 in cash dividends to stockholders besides spending "immense sur.is in development and permanent improvement." The company had the best of equipment and three company mines employed 250 men for a year.

The Bridal Chamber, now caved, produced 2–1/2 million ounces of silver and the 30-Stope (about 30 feet deep) produced one million. Altogether the Bonanza period yielded five million ounces of silver. The amount of lead produced is unknown.

The Lake Valley district is in a fault block of Mississippian limestone beds of the Lake Valley formation that dip 15 to 20 degrees to the southeast. Lake Valley Fault bounds this block on the southwest and is considered the channel way for the mineralizing solutions, as most of the Bonanza ore was adjacent to it. The Columbia Fault on the northeast bounds the area of mineralization and prospecting north and east of it disclosed no significant mineralization. The Lake Valley formation is composed of about 200 feet of the Crinoidal limestone member which is overlain in places by ± 100 feet of Tertiary conglomerate and 150 feet of Tertiary rhyolite and andesites. Below the Crinoidal member is 51 feet of blue limestone that was the host rock of the replacing solutions. Below this 40 feet of the Nodular limestone member lies just above upper Devonian Percha shale.

Manganite, pyrolusite, and psilomelane formed the manganese ore at Lake Valley (Fig. 3–8). Pyrolusite, pseudomorph of manganite, occurred as fibrous radiated masses.

Some iron and manganese-bearing calcite or ankerite is found and this is thought by some to be the primary ore and source of the manganese oxides. To some extent the ore may have been secondarily enriched by ground water.

Fig. 3-8.   Manganite, Lake Valley area (JM#942).

The early mineralizing solutions were thought to have been rich in silica and later solutions were rich in calcium carbonate and brought in the silver and lead along with the manganese and iron.

Large bodies of jasperoids, much of it massive red, green, yellow, and white and much of it brecciated and of mixed colors accompanied the ore.

The Bonanza silver ore was chlorargyrite and embolite. It was so massive that in some cases it was sawed from the stopes. Iodargyrite (silver iodide, hexagonal) occurred in small yellow crystals. Descloizite, orthorhombic, and vanadinite (var. endlichite), (Northrop), both occurred in the early-day workings (Mason Shaft). Endlichite was first described by Genth and Rath in 1885 from this type location.

Ramsdellite, orthorhombic, dimorph of pyrolusite, tetragonal, was described in 1943 from Lake Valley, one of the few world locations at which it is found and mallardite, monoclinic, a rose-colored hydrous manganese sulfate also occurs at Lake Valley.

Braunite, tetragonal, and cryptomelane have been reported from this district.

CABALLO MOUNTAINS

Caballo Mountains are a fault-scarp mountain range on the east side of the Rio Grande southeast of Truth or Consequences, in Sierra County, and north of Rincon, in Dona Ana County. They extend for about 30 miles in a north-south direction and are from four to six miles wide. A gentle east slope into the Jornado del Muerto is in contrast to the abrupt western face which borders the Rio Grande. About seven miles from the north end Palomas Pass cuts the mountain into north and south segments.

Cambrian quartzite rests on Precambrian granite and a series of from 12,000 to 14,000 feet of limestone and quartzite forms the main range; some intrusive porphyries and diorite occur. Part of the range is monoclinal. At Palomas Pass and in the north end of the range, copper and lead deposits occur in east-west veins. Small north-trending veins were discovered in 1906 to have values in vandanium. The Dewey, White Swan, and Red Top were the largest mines. Others were the Gladys, Red Top Annex, Billiken, and Owl. A mill was built 1–1/2 miles south and in 1910–1 a plant to make vanadium oxide and lead sulfate was built at Cutter, about 15 miles away.

The veins were small fissures containing breccia cemented with calcite, fluorite, barite, and minor quartz.

The district had a short life which was probably over in about six years.

North of Palomas Gap in the northern section of the Caballos Range, about three miles south of Truth or Consequences, a group of fluorspar mines have been worked from time to time. The White Star, Blue Jacket, Forty-One, and others make up this group. Work was intermittent from 1926 to 1930 and during World War II. Principal minerals of the veins are fluorite, calcite, and quartz. Reticulated veinlets of minute quartz crystals and also late calcite, often in large white rhombohedral crystals, cut the deposits.

Fluorspar prospects also occur scattered throughout the southern Caballos Range (Fig. 3–9).

Manganese deposits occur in the vicinity of Truth or Consequences in connection with the hot springs for which the town was originally named.

Fig. 3–9.   Headframe overlooking Rio Grande Valley in New Mexico. W. H.

Mineralizing solutions rising through pipes and vents formed the deposits. Other manganese prospects occur in the Caballo Range north of Rincon, on the southern end of the range where manganese oxides occur as cementing material of breccia along fault zones.

In the southern part of the Caballo Range sedimentary rocks overlie Precambrian granites. A N-S fault zone on the west side, near the Rio Grande, has had extensive movement. Sediments dip eastward from the range in a partial monoclinal fold, (Fig. 4–1), and erosion on the west side has modified the fault-scarp. This southern part of the range evidently had disturbances not found further north. Manganese mineralization occurs along fissures with psilomelane replacing brecciated quartzitic sandstone. Considerable barite occurs in places. This manganese ore was probably derived from manganiferous calcite. Numerous small mines and pits are found in the area north of Rincon.

Vanadates may occur in the oxidized zones of base metal deposits in areas of arid to semiarid climate according to Fischer (1965). The mines of Palomas Gap had: vanadinite, acicular brown crystals, and hollow crystals up to 1/8 inch in diameter, galena, anglesite, cerussite, descloizite, azurite, pyrite, malachite, mottramite, pyromorphite, wulfenite, calcite, quartz, barite, and fluorspar (white, green, and pink).

Quartz crystals occurred as cavity linings on the Universal Mine property. Some were drusy. The vanadinite "commonly occurs in the form of brown, fragile, hair-like crystals, lining cavities, or bristling from the oxidized surfaces of galena crystals."

CHLORIDE DISTRICT

In 1879, Harry Pye was freighting supplies to the Army Post of Ojo Caliente, 20 miles north of present-day Winston, when darkness caught up with him. Ojo Caliente was one of a string of Army forts along the Black Range to protect the frontier from the Apaches. It was here that Geronimo made his first surrender. Pye camped in a canyon with his drivers that night; it would not have been a good place out on the flats, in fact quite dangerous. Next morning he caught the glint of silver in an outcrop but kept quiet. After his contract with the Army expired, he came back with some trusted friends and found it was indeed silver and lots of it.

Miners came to the new camp of Chloride (silver chloride) and a town sprang up. Pye was getting rich and preoccupied with his new mine and town when the Apaches struck from ambush and that was his fatal mistake. Chloride prospered until after 1896, surviving the Silver Panic of 1893, probably because of the richness of the Bonanza ore that was soon gone.

A specimen marked mottramite, Vindicator mine, Winston, New Mexico was obtained from an old collection. It is presumed to be from Sierra County and the Chloride district. Northrop shows mottramite as occurring in the Hermosa district which seems to overlap the Chloride district to some extent.

IRON MOUNTAIN NO. 2

Iron Mountain No. 2 is the name of a rounded ridge about 600 feet high at the north end of the Sierra Cuchillo, Sierra County. The area is about 7,000 feet N-S and 3,000 feet E-W and is at an altitude of about 8,100 feet. It is about 10 miles north of Winston. Sierra Cuchillo is about 25 miles long in a N-S direction.

On the west side, a steep fault-scarp occurs that exposes the Sierra Cuchillo as a block of Magdalena limestone tipped to dip east. A series of Miocene plugs and dikes, of rhyolite and porphyritic rhyolite and sills and dikes of granite and aplite intrude the limestone and form large irregular bodies of tactite. These tactite bodies occur adjacent to the igneous rock without any apparent regard to composition or size of the intrusive. Fluorite occurs in the ribbon rock, mineral banding, of the tactite zones.

Prospect pits were driven in search of fluorite, lead, zinc, copper and gold, all of which occur in trace to small amounts. These deposits were known for many years but production was not achieved except for a small amount of zinc in about 1930 and possibly a small amount of iron later.

A sample lot of tungsten was shipped to El Paso, Texas for testing. An estimate of 1,500 tons of helvite-bearing ore was made in the early 1940s. Indicated reserves on the north end of the mountain were between 80,000 and 150,000 tons. Sampling during World War II opened the deposits to a degree but metallurgy was disappointing and the deposits have remained idle.

The tactites of Iron Mountain No. 2 have been mined to at least a small extent for magnetite, tungsten and beryllium. Magnetite, garnet, and pyroxene are the chief components of these tactite zones. An unknown brownish mineral was identified as helvite in 1941. It is the largest deposit of this cubic beryllium mineral in the United States. A beryllium-bearing idocrase (vesuvianite) is also found at this location.

Clinozoisite and zoisite have been found at Iron Mountain No. 2. Clinozoisite forms a series with epidote and is dimorphous with zoisite, orthorhombic.

REFERENCES

A-4 Lindgren Volume (Henderson), F-3, G-1, G-9, G-10, G-11, I-24, J-23, J-36, J-54, J-76, L-1, 0-11, 0-18, 0-28, 0-38, 0-40, R-1, R-25, R-26, S-19, S-53, S-54, S-73, S-113, S-144, S-147.

HANSONBURG DISTRICT

The Hansonburg district is in the Oscura Mountains, a low fault-block range that is about 28 miles east of San Antonio, in southeastern Socorro County. U. S. Highway 380 passes through Bingham, a former post office, and from this point a desert road leads southeast about 6.5 miles to the Blanchard Mine.

The MexTex Mine is about 1.5 miles southward along the west-facing fault-scarp of the Oscura Mountains from the Blanchard Mine and the Royal Flush Mine is further north near the end of the range. These three similar mines were the most important mines of the Hansonburg district; however, a copper deposit of the red-bed type occurs between the west face of the mountains and the Jornada del Muerto (Fig. 3–10).

The Oscura Mountains are parallel to the Rio Grande and are east of the Jornada del Muerto and southwest of Chupadera Mesa. They are made up of sediments of the Magdalena group of Pennsylvanian and Permian age that are intruded by Tertiary quartz monzonite and diorite. These rocks are tilted eastward and rest on Precambrian rocks. A north plunging anticline ter-

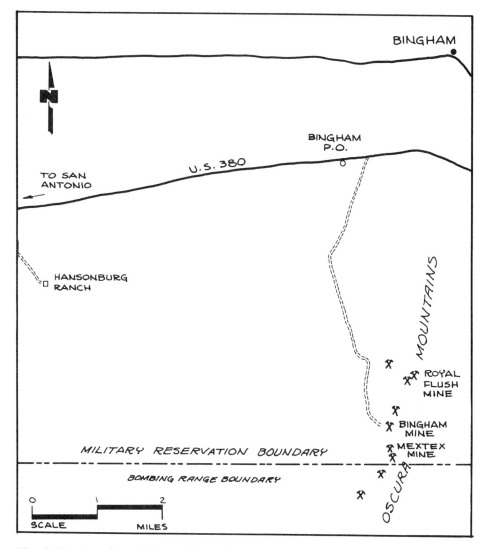

Fig. 3–10. Location of Oscura Mountain mines, Hansonburg mining district, Socorro County, New Mexico. Adapted from U.S.G.S. 15 Min. Series, Bingham Quad., 1948.

minates the range to the north. Step faults along the west side of the Sierra Oscura drop the sediments, mostly limestones, to successively lower levels in the rift.

The Hansonburg district was prospected as early as 1872 and in 1901 a small company worked the copper deposits and shipped a single car of ore. Copper deposits were worked intermittently from about 1895 to 1904 and interest in them from 1910 to 1917 resulted in a small production.

Early mining in the Hansonburg district was on red-bed copper deposits. Chalcocite and tennantite were the principal ore minerals and constituted 95 percent of the ore at the Hansonburg Copper Mine.

In the Blanchard, Royal Flush, and MexTex Mines cerussite, anglesite and galena was the ore sought. Later barite was the mineral sought for use as heavy drilling mud. Most of it came from the MexTex Mine.

Fluorite was similar to the fluorite deposited in the Burro Mountains; however, five stages were recognized.

Stage I	Early stages of fluorite had nearly rounded, pale green crystals with parallel, multiple-stepped cube facets modified by hexoctachedrons.
Stage II	Well formed cubes of pale green.
Stage III	Greenish white cubes.
Stage IV	Limpid blue and blue-green cubes.
Stage V	Lavender purple, may have blue bands.

Minerals are similar for the Blanchard, MexTex, and Royal Flush Mines. The fault zone common to these mines had fluorite in the fault breccia and in caves lined with barite, calcite, quartz, and galena. A second generation of quartz formed zoned and phantom crystals with light smoky or amethystine capping.

Barite crystals over a foot long, from the MexTex Mine, were seen in a private collection as were fluorite cubes up to five inches on an edge and galena cubes coated with anglesite and cerussite, up to two inches on an edge.

Covellite replaced galena in places and it occurred as laths (a long, thin mineral crystal) between galena and anglesite coatings. Barian anglesite occurred as minute, barrell-shaped crystals of brilliant colors, due to light dispersion, in the Royal Flush Mine.

Plattnerite occurred with murdochite in the MexTex Mine. Mottramite and wulfenite, as yellow micro crystals, occurred in the Hansonburg district as did the following minerals: linarite, spangolite, celestite, brochantite, hemimorphite, cyanotrichite, chalcanthite, and antlerite.

Galena, anglesite, cerussite, malachite, azurite, chalcopyrite, enargite, native silver, fluorite, barite, pyrite, calcite, goethite, siderite, limonite, and brown and banded-brown onyx were other minerals of these mines. Specimens of brochantite on fluorite, hemimorphite with aurichalcite and linarite, and spangolite, came from the Hansonburg district.

Blanchardite, a discredited species from the Blanchard Mine, was found by Rosenzweig to be brochantite.

Blanchard Mine

The Hansonburg Mine, McCarthy Lead Mine and Blanchard Mine are all names for the same mine. F. L. Blanchard owned the mine in 1943 and that name is most generally used. This mine is on the west-facing fault scarp at the north end of the Oscura Mountains. There were six patented claims in the group.

Workings extend several hundred feet along the escarpment and include about 800 feet of drifts, crosscuts, and open cuts. The mine was worked as early as 1906. A mill was built in 1916 to treat 50 tpd and make a lead concentrate; some production was recorded for 1917. Periodic work by lessees extended the main underground workings to a total of 1,000 feet by 1932.

Production was small for this mine and for the district. Ore deposits are replacement beds in the Magdalena limestone along faults. Open spaces, including fault breccias and cavities and small caves in the limestone, have been mineralized. Ore along the veins is discontinuous and a well mineralized zone may change abruptly to a silicified shear zone with minor mineralization.

The fissure veins parallel to the fault scarp and associated replacement beds in limestone contained deposits of jasperoid, quartz, barite, and fluorite. Galena and other sulfides are present in lesser and varying amounts. Manto-like deposits were the most important.

Roedder and others (1968), in a study of fluid inclusions, mostly in fluorite, determined that the fluids from which the ore was formed were moderate to strong saline brines, probably high in chloride and except for the last stages, ores were deposited near 200° C. They were saturated at different times with galena, barite, fluorite, and quartz. Well formed and clear crystals do not form under conditions of fast-flowing fluids, and as large crystals occurred in cavities, the mineralizing fluids must not have moved fast. Fluorite was a low temperature mineral that was deposited in fractures and voids left incompletely filled by earlier minerals. These deposits are all similar in occurrence and in mineralogy and are known more for the large variety of secondary minerals than for their economic production.

MexTex Mine

The MexTex and Royal Flush Mines and their minerals were similar to the Blanchard (Fig. 3-11). Some fluorite and some lead was mined from small deposits; however, barite was produced from the MexTex in the 1940s and 1950s for use in making heavy drilling muds. The ore was treated in a mill in San Antonio where water was available. From time to time lead was saved in the mill circuit.

Fig. 3–11. Chlorargyrite with galena altering to cerussite and anglesite, MexTex Mine (PR#56)-T.E.C.

SOCORRO AREA

The Piro Pueblo of Teypana near the present city of Socorro was given its name, which means help or air, by Don Juan de Onate, June 14, 1598, in return for help given to the colonist by the local Indians. A mission was built prior to 1628 by Fray Garcia de Zuniga but was abandoned after 1680 when the Pueblo Rebellion occurred. It was reestablished about 1815. Socorro was a mining center after 1867.

The first silver mined in New Mexico was at Pueblo Springs near Magdalena in 1863. Silver and lead were mined at Magdalena in 1866. The late 1870s and the 1880s were the periods of greatest silver mining activity and between 1879 and 1882 the railroad reached the mines. Large quantities of zinc carbonate had been mined along with the other minerals but had gone over the dump as waste in this early period.

Luis Lopez Manganese District

The Socorro caldera of late Oligocene age, is centered in the Chupadera Mountains, southwest of Socorro. This caldera is about 12 miles in diameter and has a resurgent dome, formation of a dome in the caldera after an eruption, capped by about 2,900 feet of 27 m.y. old tuff. The Luis Lopez manganese district is on the resurgent dome and other manganese mines are around the edges of the Socorro caldera.

During World War II, a government stockpile program made it economically feasible for a small mill to operate in Black Canyon on ores from manganese mines of this area (Fig. 3–12).

The Nancy Tower Mine closed in 1970. It was the largest underground manganese mine in the U.S.A. Ore was milled in the Black Canyon Mill.

Felty psilomelane that resembles pyrolusite occurs on hard black psilomelane. According to Northrop (1959 p. 411), the true nature of this felty mass was determined by x-ray analysis. Mammillary and stalactitic goethite also occurs in this district.

Kelly, Graphic, and Juanita Group

The part of the northern end of the Magdalena Range around Magdalena and the former town of Kelly, is the Magdalena district, Socorro County. This district is only about 1–1/2 miles wide and four miles long. Kelly was near the west center of this strip and the principal mines were within a mile radius.

Kelly had a peak population of 2,700. There were two churches, seven saloons, two dance halls, and two hotels. When the railroad reached the town which is three miles south of Magdalena and before the Apaches were controlled, a string of railroad cars were kept on a siding to be used to rush women and children away in case the camp was attacked. The cars were never used, however, according to Wood (1964).

The Kelly Mine was the most famous. Waldo Tunnel developed the lower part of the Graphic Mine. Both of these mines and the Juanita and South Juanita were all working the same replacement ore beds in Carboniferous

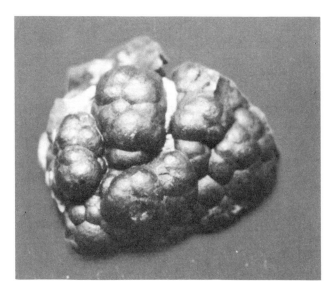

Fig. 3–12. Botryoidal psilomelane, Black Canyon Mine (JM#85).

limestones associated with large granite porphyry intrusions. The mines had various owners over the years.

Ore was discovered in the northern Magdalena Mountains in 1866 by Colonel J. S. Hutchason and the Juanita was located. Three weeks later the Graphic was started. Sand carbonates (cerussite) were smelted in an adobe furnace and the lead bullion hauled by ox teams to Kansas City.

Gustav Billings erected a smelter with "three sixty-ton-stacks" in Socorro in 1881 and bought the Kelly Mine in 1882 to provide ore in addition to the custom ore expected for treatment.

By 1884, the Kelly was able to easily provide the smelter with 170 tpd of ore. At this time, ore to run at capacity for three years was assured by the Kelly Mine alone. Juanita and Graphic Mines were being brought into production from prospects.

Billing's smelter ran until 1893. The Graphic smelter was built at Magdalena in 1896 and ran six years on red-lead ores (minium). Lessees worked the Kelly and Graphic Mines from 1894 to 1902. The mines were worked for lead-silver-zinc in the upper 200–300 feet where large bodies of sphalerite with some galena and chalcopyrite were found. Prior to 1900, the mines at Magdalena had produced gold, silver, and lead.

In 1903, a rich zinc carbonate ore body replacing limestone was discovered. Ore samples were taken to the smelter at Joplin, Missouri, where it was determined that the ore was suitable for zinc pigment for use in manufacturing paint.

Large bodies of zinc carbonate ore were available in the Kelly and Graphic Mines and production was begun. These two mines were major producers of zinc ore from 1903 to June, 1949. Production was high during World War II.

The Kelly was sold to Tri-Bullion Mining and Smelting Company by Mrs. Billings in 1904 and by this time the Kelly and Graphic Mines together had produced $5.8 million. Sherwin-Williams Paint Company purchased the Graphic Mine to use the ore for zinc-lead paint. By 1909, the Kelly was producing sulfide ores on the lower levels and leasors were still producing oxidized ores from the upper levels.

As ores became leaner a number of concentrating plants were built. A dry pneumatic process was tried as was wet concentrating with roasting and magnetic separation.

Work continued intermittently through the years and fluctuated with base metal prices. Production after about 1930 fluctuated, however, the area was credited with 325 million pounds of zinc through 1965. Leasors were working the Kelly as late as 1969.

The ore deposits in this group of claims occur in the Kelly limestone of Mississippian age which overlies Precambrian greenstone schist and is below the Pennsylvanian Magdalena group that, in turn, is made up of the Sandia and Madera formations.

Kelly limestone is sub-crystalline, white and about 125 feet thick. Near the middle a compact five foot layer known as the Silver Pipe serves as a marker bed and is highly mineralized in places. Ore occurs in from three to five horizons in the Kelly limestone as replacement beds.

A less important ore horizon occurs about 165 feet above the Kelly limestone in a limestone contact with white conglomeratic quartzite in the Sandia formation. The Kelly beds, especially the Silver Pipe, were the deposits that made the district famous and ore 40 feet thick was not uncommon.

North of the Graphic Mine, an elliptical body of monzonite about 1/2 mile long terminates the sedimentary rocks. Ore bodies at the contact were exposed in the Waldo Tunnel which was driven to reach the lower Graphic workings. Flexures in the limestone beds occurred at about 1,500 foot intervals and produced three ore shoots which were known for the mines they produced: the Graphic, the Kelly, and the Juanita.

Minerals of the Kelly Mine, most famous of the Magdalena area, were found to at least a minor extent in the other mines of the area. Smithsonite, zinc carbonate, was the most outstanding of Kelly Mine minerals.

In 1884, the Kelly Mine was said to yield all the combinations of lead, including galena, the sulfides, black, white and brown cerussite, native copper, native silver, and green and blue carbonates.

Gangue minerals were: epidote, pyroxene (hedenbergite), tremolite, quartz, calcite, barite, magnetite, and specular hematite.

In the earlier years, smithsonite was produced as oxidized ore but this soon gave way to the primary ore, sphalerite. Small amounts of copper in the smithsonite gave the mineral a green color and this variety is known as herrerite. The color is a translucent apple green, dark green, or blue. In 1907, large quantities were found at various mines in the Magdalena district. A cavity several feet wide and about 25 feet long was found at the Kelly Mine. Green smithsonite lined the cavity in layers up to two inches thick. It coated "drybone" ore in mammillary and odd-shaped masses. Several hundred pounds of excellent material was recovered from this cavity and used to make cabochons.

Smithsonite, in the classic green reniform mass, is illustrated in Bancroft, (p. 108) as one of the world's most beautiful minerals.

Monheimite, the ferroan variety of smithsonite occurred as a pseudomorph of calcite in the Graphic Mine and also as rhombohedrons with curved surfaces. It is gray and has a pearly luster. It also occurs as incrustations.

Turkey-fat ore, the yellow variety of smithsonite, was also found. Cadmium occurred as a carbonate in this material.

Specimens of Kelly Mine smithsonite are on display in museums throughout the world. It was later found in botryoidal crusts up to two feet thick.

Aurichalcite, orthorhombic, occurs in greenish-blue acicular crystals or as incrustations. It is also found as sky blue incrustations.

A cavern a dozen feet in diameter in the Graphic Mine was lined with aurichalcite, which was coated with a layer of calcite up to $1/2$ inch thick. (Keys in Northrop p. 128.) Rice grain crystals, which are elongated curved faces terminated by rhombohedrons, occur on smithsonite and aurichalcite. Azurite occurs as a pseudomorph of cuprite and as floaters in pockets of smithsonite or clay. The color is dark blue to green and nobs and balls made up of flat plates are found. Dump material from the Juanita Mine has been sieved to recover these floaters which have numerous crystal shapes.

Barite from this area is an attractive mineral and is usually pale pink to salmon color. Rosasite, cerussite, hydrozincite, aragonite, and calcite are other minerals found in this area which is a Dana location for numerous minerals including: azurite, malachite, aurichalcite, rosasite, cerussite, hydrozincite, aragonite, calcite (tricolored), and smithsonite.

In the oxidized zone, sand carbonate ore (cerussite) occurred in a zinc carbonate shell with a zone of copper or iron oxides between; cores of relic sulfides occurred. Sphalerite, galena, and chalcopyrite were the principal sulfides.

Rhodochrosite, chalcophanite, allophane, and vanadinite have also been reported.

Dundasite in silky white to light blue acicular crystals was reported from the Juanita Mine.

REFERENCES

A-4 Lindgren Volume (Knope), F-3, G-10, G-11, H-10, J-5, J-46, J-54, K-8, K-9, K-11, K-13, L-1, 0-5, 0-24, 0-25, 0-28, 0-37, 0-40, S-73.

NEW PLACERS DISTRICT

The porphyry belt of the San Pedro Mountains may have been prospected and some mining done as early as the 1580s. Fray Dominguez in 1776, prepared a map of San Pedro showing it at the western foot of the San Pedro Mountains and it is probable that it was a mining community at that time (Fig. 3-13).

Gold was discovered in the Ortiz Mountains, Old Placers district, in 1828. Also discovered were lode deposits of gold in 1833 by a man named Ortiz. Ortiz was said to have taken in an experienced partner named Lopez and later had a corrupt official deport him as a foreigner so he could have the mine for himself. Ultimately, neither one of them profited from the mine.

New Placers, from which the district got its name, was discovered in 1839 and Tuerto, now called Golden, became an important center. In 1845, there were 22 stores; by 1849 the population was 7,000 and there were 35 stores plus gambling halls and saloons. Production of gold from the Old Placers and New Placers districts reached an estimated annual rate of a quarter of a million dollars. As water was scarce, winter was the best time to work the placers and as many as 2,000 men came in winter to work them. Snow was melted with hot rocks and saved in small reservoirs. The gold was washed in homemade wooden bateaus, which were wide, shallow wooden vessels used for panning the placer gravels.

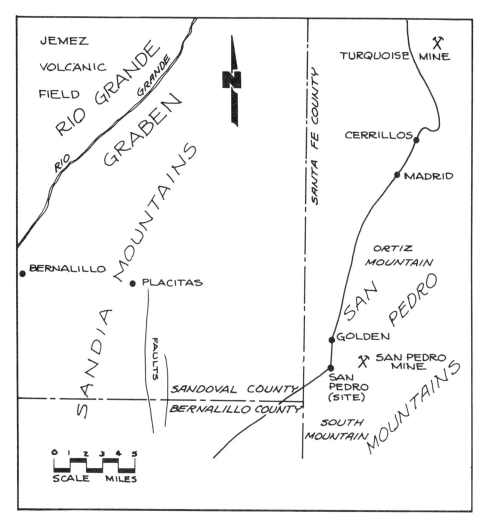

Fig. 3-13.   Location of San Pedro Mine, Santa Fe County, New Mexico. Adapted from U.S.G.S. Bull. 726-E, 1922.

San Pedro Mine

Early travelers tell of the San Pedro Mine being worked in 1846. Ore was carried by mule to San Pedro town to be amalgamated. In 1840, ore had been sent by pack train to Chihuahua for treatment. A. Aguilar and M. Varela of Chihuahua had rediscovered the mine in 1840.

Just before the war with Mexico, J. S. Ramirez obtained a land grant, called Canon del Agua, to about 35,000 acres (or 33,000 acres) from the Mexican government for use as a sheep range—a "pastoral land grant."

After the Mexican War, a patent was finally granted by the U.S. government under terms of the treaty, but not until 1875.

During the Civil War years and after, the area had been deserted. The

Apache threat prevented people from returning until troops were stationed in the territory.

Aguilar and Varela had given a deed to the mine in payment of a debt to a man named Otero who was uncle of a former governor of New Mexico. Later on, a Chihuahua lawyer named Jaquez was found to have an interest in the mine for financing Aguilar and Varela.

A powerful and unscrupulous gang known as the Santa Fe Ring found out about the San Pedro Mine in about 1880. They arranged to have Ramirez get his land grant resurveyed and the boundaries exchanged. The east boundary became the west boundary and therefore included the San Pedro Mine. The San Pedro and Canon del Agua Mining Company was organized in Boston and stock was sold on a grand scale.

Around 1881, one of the Otero family and Judge Jaquez, of Chihuahua, started legal proceedings to regain the mine. The Federal judge would not oppose the Sante Fe Ring and was forced out of office only to be replaced by one of the Ring's own members.

On the death of his father, a younger Otero took matters in his own hands and with a dozen armed men climbed down the shaft into the mine. They hid in the mine and counted 162 men as they came to work. When that number left for lunch, they rushed out of a tunnel behind the miners and captured the mine.

Otero was arrested, when he went back to Las Vegas on business, and was tried. He was not convicted because the Santa Fe Ring's judge was having trouble with the authorities because of corrupt legal practices and the men were allowed to surrender the mine to the court.

In 1884, the 20 stamp mill and smelter were still inactive because of the action brought by the U.S. to set aside patent to 35,000 acres of Public Domain alleged to have been obtained by fraud. Otero won a verdict, which was later upheld by the U.S. Supreme Court. Boundaries to the Canon del Agua Grant were declared incorrect and a resurvey reduced its size. The land that the San Pedro Mine was on was thrown open for location and was promptly claimed by Otero's double-crossing friends in Golden.

In 1887, a gold strike was reported at the San Pedro Mine. The stamp mill and equipment were repaired and 250 men employed. Between 1889 and 1892, several million pounds of copper were produced.

The San Pedro Mine is in the San Pedro Mountains, one of five centers in a belt of intrusive porphyries about 25 miles long by 5 miles wide east of the Rio Grande in Santa Fe County. The mine is on the southwest side of the mountains, about 15 miles south of Madrid and ½ mile southeast of Golden, in the New Placers mining district. It has a long history and the district is one of the oldest in the state. Only Santa Rita has an older recorded history.

The belt of intrusive porphyries form a low-lying mountain link between the Sangre de Criso Mountains to the northeast and the Sandia Mountains to the southwest. From south to north the intrusive centers, commonly known as the "laccolithic mountains," are South Mountain, San Pedro Mountains, Ortiz Mountains, Los Cerrillos, and the Cienega center. Estancia Basin is to the southeast and the Santa Fe embayment is east of the porphyry belt which runs north and south. This area forms part of the west side of the Santa Fe embayment as well as the east side of the Rio Grande Valley. It juts into the Great American Rift on three sides.

Intrusives of the porphyry belt which are monzonites and related rocks cut a thick sequence of sediments from Pennsylvanian to Eocene age. Sedimentary beds on the east side of the Rio Grande Valley generally dip to the east; however, because most of the beds in the intrusive porphyry belt dip northeast to east, this tilting is thought to be associated with faulting in the rift zone. The San Pedro Mountains are part of the San Pedro horst of the Tijeras Fault system.

Dates of the intrusives origin is thought to be between early Oligocene and early Miocene time. Later deformation probably occurred during the major period of uplift of the Sandia Mountains and continuing uplift may have occurred during deposition of the Miocene–Pliocene Santa Fe formation.

Arching of sediments by a laccolith is thought to have been an important structural control of ore in the San Pedro Mine as the deposits are in an anticlinal structure above the intrusive. This laccolith has a roof pendant of about 700 feet of Pennsylvania limestone that is cut by dikes and sills. It forms a mountain mass two miles N-S and four miles E-W, which rises about 1,500 feet above the surrounding country. Alluvial fans radiate from the mountain.

The sedimentary rocks of the San Pedro Mountains have been severely metamorphosed. Marmorized limestone (rocks resembling marble), tactite, marble, and hornfels occur and garnetization occurs along limestone beds for as much as half a mile away from the intrusives. Beds of garnet up to 150 feet thick occur.

On the western side of the mountain, the whole sedimentary series is altered by irregular recrystallization and garnetization which contains chalcopyrite. Calcareous sandstones and shales have been altered to hornfels containing diopside and calcic feldspar. The alteration in places is 500 feet thick above the porphyry.

The mine is in the lower part of the laccolith roof on the southwest slope of the mountains. Three tunnels (the Swan, the Home, and No. 50), a shaft, the Richman, and an old open cut known as the Spanish Cut develop the mine.

The Richman Shaft 300 feet deep was the main entrance to the mine and development extended about 1,500 feet northwest of this shaft along the ore horizon. The workings were inclined 13 degrees uphill and gained an elevation of 250 feet under Montezuma Point. Drifts at 30 foot intervals allowed a modified room and pillar method of mining. About 160 tons per day, which was hand sorted to about 115 tons, was mined from an ore horizon up to 100 feet thick. Garnetized benches occurred with the ore; at one place a garnetized bed 20 feet thick occurred under the ore.

The Lewisohn's of New York acquired the mine in 1889 and operated as the Santa Fe Gold and Copper Company. A 100 ton mill was built in 1891 and an aerial tramway delivered ore from the mine to the mill and smelter. A new smelter was built just below the mine in 1899–1900; however, it ran for only a year when low copper prices caused it to close. It was idle in 1905 but resumed production in 1906 only to close again in 1908. A 200 tpd smelter at Santa Fe was "blown in" in 1907 to work the San Pedro Mine ore.

Small fluctuations in the price of copper made a large difference in operation as smelting costs were high and the ore grade marginal for the time. A matte with 50 percent to 60 percent copper was made during this period of operation.

Hematite and limonite, in a three to five foot thick bed, in limestone associated with an andesite intrusive from the Las Vegas claim, was used as a flux.

In 1916, a private report on the ore deposits of the San Pedro Mine with suggestions to the owners for underground exploration resulted in at least one spectacularly rich ore shoot being developed. The smelter burned in 1918. Copper production from 1923 to 1939 was a million pounds. In 1938, the Lewisohns sold the mine to the Raskob Mining Interest, Incorporated, and it was resold in 1945. Work at the mine was intermittent in the 1950s and 1960s. Leasors shipped manganese ore in 1959 and open pit mining was considered in the early 1960s. Dump ore and stockpiled ore was being milled at the rate of 250 tpd in 1969. Thirteen million pounds of copper were produced between 1900 and 1961. Recent interest in the mine may result in its reopening if this is not the present situation.

The San Pedro Mine is usually cited as a classic contact metamorphic ore deposit in which the preexisting rock is completely replaced by ore. Granodiorite, intruded into limestone beds, has garnetized a limestone bed 200 feet above the contact for 1/2 mile away from the main intrusive mass. The ore zone is 50 feet to 100 feet thick and contains chalcopyrite with pyrrhotite intergrowth. Andradite, specular hematite, green mica, tremolite, quartz, calcite, and rarely wollastonite, vesuvianite, and grossular occur. Ore bodies were from a few inches to 100 feet wide and up to 1,000 feet long, parallel to the bedding planes.

Marble and tactite zones were segregated and the ore occurred in tactite next to the marble but not in it. It seldom occurred over 200 feet from the marble. Cavities were common; some were open and some filled with second-stage mineralization (Fig. 3–14).

There were two stages of mineralization. First stage mineralization was higher temperature in nature than the second stage and deposited specular hematite, pyrrhotite and chalcopyrite in the tactite bodies; calcite, quartz, scheelite, pyrite, and bornite were other minerals of this stage. The second stage filled remaining cavities in the tactite with quartz, pyrite, chalcopyrite, calcite, scheelite, and minor siderite.

In the Spanish Cut workings, coarsely crystalline adularia is found; the (vein) oxidized ore had banded malachite, azurite, and chrysocolla up to 12 inches wide.

In the second stage, chalcopyrite replaced some of the pyrrhotite. Quartz was enclosed by pyrite, chalcopyrite, and calcite. Chalcopyrite encloses pyrite crystals and calcite encloses chalcopyrite. Chalcopyrite crystals up to 3–1/2 inches across have been found. The larger crystals are usually formed around a

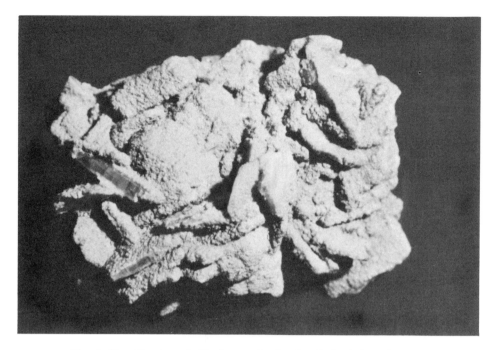

Fig. 3–14.   Quartz and chlorite over barite, San Pedro Mine (JM#912).

pyrite crystal, which is some combination of cube, octahedron, pyritohedron, or diploid. Pyrite cubes to one inch and octahedrons also occur. Among the crystal faces on chalcopyrite are the positive and negative disphenoid and the rare tetragonal scalenohedron. Pyrite as pseudomorphs, up to one inch long, of scalenohedral calcite were found attached to pyrite cubes. Gold in calcite was found.

Specular hematite occurred in cavities as rosettes of thin crystals with deep red internal reflection. Calcite was rhombohedral and scalenohedral (up to six inches long) in form with modifications of both. A cyclic twin composed of six scalenohedrons twinned on a single calcite scalenohedron was found near water level in the mine. Tetrahedrite and molybdenite have been reported; scheelite crystals, to 1/2 inch, occurred as a rare mineral; and siderite rhombohedrons, to 1/2 inch, occurred in vugs as did aggregates of scalenohedral crystals growing vertically from the floor.

Copper mineralization is oxidized to depths of 100 feet. Chrysocolla, malachite, and azurite are common. Cuprite, tenorite, as the powdery variety melaconite, and native copper occur. Chalcanthite coats the old workings in places and chalcocite coats some chalcopyrite but bodies of secondary enriched ore do not occur.

Quartz occurs as the amethystine variety and as Japanese Law twins (Fig. 3–15). Bideaux described a multiple Japanese Law quartz twins from the San Pedro Mine, New Placers district, Santa Fe County, New Mexico. Half inch simple twins are the general rule from this location; however, Northrop cites examples up to 1–1/2 inches in size.

Fig. 3–15.   Japanese Law twinned quartz, San Pedro Mine (JM#337).

On Japanese Law quartz twins, the C-axes are inclined at 84 degrees, 33 minutes. C-axes on the San Pedro Mine multiple twin specimen were 120 degrees apart around the prism section. Bideaux points out that up to six satellites could theoretically occur around one individual parent crystal. Taggart and Grigsby reported a pocket of multiple Japanese quartz twins found at the San Pedro Mine in 1975. One of the parent crystals was twinned by the Dauphine Law and had satellite crystals twinned by the Japanese Law. Some crystals from this pocket were up to 1–3/8 inches long.

Specimens from this area seen in private collections include: nearly clear rhombohedral calcite with some siderite overgrowth enclosing a chalcopyrite crystal group about 1–1/2 inches in diameter; nearly clear rhombohedral calcite over a crystal group of chalcopyrite. Specimen size was about 4 inches (largest dimension).

Lincoln-Lucky Mine

About a 1/2 mile below the San Pedro Mine smelter, a chimney or manto of argentiferous galena about 60 feet in diameter occurred in unaltered limestone. This chimney followed the dip of the strata in a fracture zone. Oxidized ore was cerussite, limonite, and manganese oxides. Primary ore was sphalerite, pyrite, alabandite, and some chalcopyrite in a quartz and calcite gangue.

GRANTS AREA

The Grants uranium area, including the Laguna district, is on the east side of the Colorado Plateau, west of the Rio Grande and south of the San Juan Basin. It is about 50 miles west of Albuquerque and is reached by U. S. Highway 66. Grants and Laguna are central to the area.

The Lucero Uplift, to the southeast, the Puerco fault zone faulted to the east, and to the northeast, the Nacimiento Uplift, separate the area from the inner Rio Grande Rift. Mount Taylor volcanic field parallels the rift zone and separates the Laguna district from the Grants-Ambrosia Lake district. It occupies the Acoma sag and, in part, McCarty's syncline. Mt. Taylor is a late Tertiary volcano that sits on a basalt-capped plateau and is over 11,000 feet high (Fig. 3–16).

Early geologic work in the area was directed to the occurrences of coal; however, uranium minerals were known to occur at least in the 1900s. A discovery of carnotite in limestone near Grants in 1949 started prospecting. Government agencies started work of mapping the area in 1950. By 1951, the first mill was built near Grants to treat limestone ore from the Todilto limestone and Poison Canyon sandstone. An ore buying station was set up at Bluewater by the government and the area was firmly established.

Wildcat drilling in the Ambrosia Lake area in 1955 led to the development of large underground mines. Up to 70 drill rigs were working in the area at one time with drilling tapering off by 1960. In the first 14 years, production of uranium concentrates from the Grants area was valued at over $800 million. In 1964, molybdenum was recovered as a byproduct from Ambrosia Lake ores.

Production from the area continues in the 1980s. In 1970, reserves were estimated at 45 million tons of 0.24 percent uranium oxide. Production was 47 percent of the U. S. total.

The deepest mine in the district and possibly the deepest uranium mine in the world is the Mount Taylor Mine near Grants. Gulf Mineral Resources Company owns and operates the mine which in 1980 was still in the development stage. The lowest level in the mine is the 3200 foot level (also the depth from the collar). Two shafts which were completed in 1979 service the mine. Water in the mine is 126°F and the miners wear ice vests when the temperature exceeds 95°F.

Of a total of over 23 million tons of ore produced to 1968, 22 million tons came from the Jurassic Morrison sandstone and just under a million tons from the Jurassic Todilto limestone. Less than 200,000 tons came from other sandstone formations.

In the Laguna district, the Jackpile deposit, in the Jackpile sandstone of the Brushy Basin member of the Morrison formation, was the largest single deposit. It was approximately 6,000 feet long and 2,000 feet wide; individual layers were about 15 feet thick but were sometimes up to 50 feet in total thickness. Mining was done by open pit methods.

Unusual and interesting occurrences of high grade ore in the Laguna district were in sandstone pipes. A pipe in the Woodrow deposit, about 24 to 34 feet in diameter, produced several thousand tons of the richest ore found in the area and a large pipe occurred in the Jackpile deposit. These sandstone pipes are nearly vertical and range from one inch to 200 feet in diameter and are from a foot to 300 feet high. They may be isolated or occur in groups; some follow Jurassic fold lines.

The origin of sandstone pipes is not clear and several explanations, all

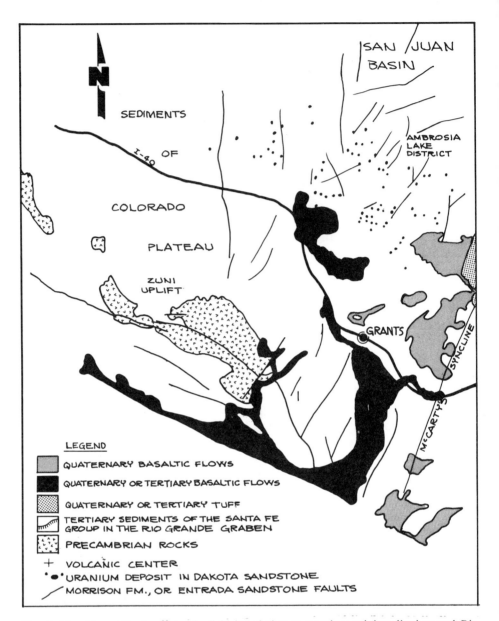

Fig. 3–16. Mount Taylor volcanic field in relation to uranium mining districts and Rio Grande Graben. Adapted from U.S.G.S. P.P. 519.

debatable, have been presented. Foundering of sand into spring vents during compacting and dewatering of the sediments was postulated by Moench and Schlee. New K/Ar dating by Lipman and Mehnert show that the majority of volcanic activity in the Mount Taylor volcanic field occurred between 4.3 to 1.5 m.y.B.P. with the peak activity between 3.0 and 2.5 m.y.B.P. This activity was repeated in the Jemez Mountains area, on the Taos Plateau and in the Raton area during the same period of time. All of this activity is thought to follow northwest-trending old Pce structures or zones of weakness. The Jemez Moun-

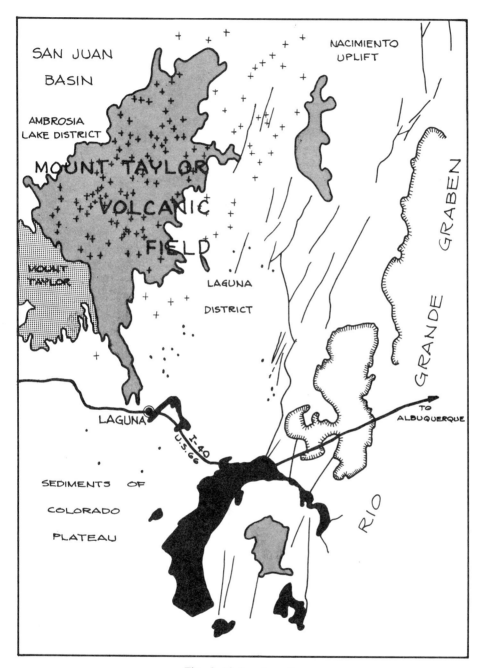

Fig. 3-16 (*continued*)

tains and Taos Plateau are in the rift zone. Mount Taylor volcanic field is on the adjacent Colorado Plateau and the Raton area is on the Sangre de Cristo horst block and adjacent Great Plains.

In the Grants area, the unoxidized ore contains uraninite and coffinite as the principal minerals. They are identifiable only by x-ray methods. Ore carrying as little as 0.04 percent uranium has been milled and most of the host rock contains smaller amounts of uranium. Coffinite that can be identified optically has rarely been reported.

Molybdenum in the form of jordisite occurs, along with ferroselite, in the primary ores of the Grants area. Much of it occurs in medium to coarse-grained sandstone in which pyramidal crystals of autogenic quartz occur as overgrowths. Several tenths of a percent of molbydenum has been detected in some ore. Trace amounts of copper, chromium, cobalt, lead, tantalum, and silver were also detected.

Clays seemed to play an important and not completely determined role in the formation of the mineral deposits. Origin of the mineralization is a lively debated topic. Montmorillonite was the earliest clay mineral in the Morrison formation. In some areas of pre-Dakota erosion surfaces, it and other minerals were displaced by kaolinite. In primary ore, chlorite developed at the expense of montmorillonite.

Vanadium occurs as a vanadium clay in which vanadium is in a mixed-layer, mica-montmorillonite and chlorite. It fills pore spaces in some ore. Pyrite, marcasite, and barite are commonly found in the deposits as is carbonaceous material. Trace minerals in some deposits are galena, wurtzite, cobaltite, and chalcopyrite.

Oxidation of the ores has led to formation of various sulfates, silicates, and phosphates. Chemical analyses have indicated selenium and arsenic are present and semi-quantitative spectrographic analyses have shown trace amounts of titanium, manganese, silver, boron, beryllium, chromium, gallium, molybdenum, nickel, scandium, strontium, tantalum, yttrium, and yerbidium.

Oxidized minerals found above the ground water table are as follows: zippeite, uranopilite, meta-autunite, tyuyamunite, metatyuyamunite, autunite, phosphuranylite, uranophane, and carnotite. Bayleyite and andersonite are found as coatings on the walls and timbers in older workings.

An unusual mineral found in metamorphic zone contacts of the diabase and sandstones or limestones is goldmanite, a vanadium-rich variety of garnet. Grossular also occurs in dodecahedral crystals.

REFERENCES

A-4 Lindgren Volume (Knope), A-5 Ridge (Rischer), (Kelley and others), (Kelley), F-3, G-4, G-6, G-10, G-11, I-4, I-5, I-12, J-54, K-1, K-6, K-15, L-1 1950–1970 and 1973, 0-1, 0-10, 0-12, 0-14 Hawley (Sanford), Q-16, R-12, S-46, S-48, S-73, S-78, S-82, S-90.

NACIMIENTO UPLIFT

The Nacimiento Uplift roughly parallels the inner Rio Grande rift valley for about 50 miles and it is about six to ten miles wide. In general, the uplift marks the eastern edge of the San Juan Basin, a unit of the Colorado Plateau, and it is west of the Jemez caldera area in Rio Arriba and Sandoval Counties. Cuba is at the center of the north-south extent of the uplift and three mining districts, the Cuba, Abiquiu, and Gallina are included.

Precambrian rocks are exposed in the center of the uplift and Paleozoic and Mesozoic age sedimentary rocks are exposed near the margins. Complex faulting along the west side of the uplift has cut out sedimentary rock units.

Copper mineralization occurs in Pennsylvanian and Permian rocks of the Paleozoic era and in Triassic rocks of the Mesozoic era. Volcanic material from the Jemez caldera center cover part of the north end of the uplift.

Nacimiento Mine

At Cuba, the Nacimiento Mine is in the Agua Zarca member of the Triassic age Chinle formation. The mineralization horizon has been referred to as the Poleo Sandstone Lentil.

An open pit mine was worked on this red-bed copper by Earth Resources Company in the 1960s. The pit included the old workings of the Copper Glance Mine. In the January 31, 1970 issue of the *Albuquerque Tribune,* an ore reserve of ten million tons to a depth of 400 feet was reported.

In 1971, Phelps–Dodge Corporation, through their Tyrone Division, began open pit mining on the red-bed copper deposit at Cuba. The ore was principally chalcocite and chalcopyrite mineralization with minor azurite and malachite. The project was to have a six year life at a mining rate of one million tons per year; however, the mine closed January, 1974, due to a decline in copper prices.

Copper mineralization occurs in the red beds in the Nacimiento Uplift area as disseminated grains and cementing material. Replacements of carbonaceous fossil plant material, especially fossil log jams within paleochannels (ancient water courses) have been the most productive. Chalcopyrite, pyrite, bornite, covellite, malachite, azurite, chrysocolla, native copper, and silver occur. Wood replacements can contain up to 38.9 percent copper and 6.42 ounces of silver. A specimen of native silver replacing carbonized wood was seen in a private collection. Trace amounts of lead, zinc, nickel, cobalt, chromium, molybdenum, uranium, and vanadium occur in the deposits at various locations.

Jemez Mountains Sulfur

Sulfur occurs in the Jemez Mountains, Sandoval County, as a result of relatively recent volcanic action. It is found around vents and fumaroles associated with hot springs. Four and a half miles north of Jemez Springs a Carboniferous limestone bed has been subjected to sulfurous vapors and the top 2 to 3.5 feet is the host for sulfur deposited from the vapor. Free sulfur content is from 15 percent to 39 percent and sulfur combined as sulfate is 6 percent to 8.5 percent.

The deposit is about 400 feet long and 60 to 75 feet wide and it is exposed along the west bank of the Jemez River. Silver was deposited in small pockets in the upper two to three feet of the deposit.

A thermal spring along the Jemez River, at a point 1.7 miles north of Jemez Springs, is depositing calcareous tufa and massive travertine that is radioactive. This material has formed a dam, known as Soda Dam, across the Jemez River. The excess of barium in the 10° to 70° F water is thought to have caused precipitation of uranium in the form of a black powder in the tufa.

At Sulfur Springs, about 14 miles north of Jemez Springs, a deposit of sulfur was mined from underground in 1902–1904 and about 100 tons were produced. A circular area about 600 feet in diameter was explored. Vapors escaping from vents in rhyolites deposited acicular or stout yellow crystals in the vents and on the walls of the underground workings.

A small hotel specializing in vapor baths formerly operated in the area. At least one mud pot was active as late as the early 1960s. Sulfur mixed with sulfates was being deposited around the vent. This area is within the Baca Location No. 1 Grant.

The Jemez Mountains were the site of the first steam well tests in New Mexico. A well drilled in 1960 about a mile north of Sulfur Springs hit steam and potash brine. A second well drilled at Sulfur Springs hit the same. These wells were 2,600 and 3,700 feet deep and steam at 500°F was discharged. Both were capped.

The Valles and adjacent Toledo calderas are in the larger Jemez caldera, one of the largest in the world. All are centered in the Jemez Mountains. They are thought to have developed where two intersecting faults, associated with the Rio Grande rift provided a conduit for magma from a relatively shallow magma chamber. Warm springs ring the calderas.

In 1968, 140,180 acres in the Jemez Mountains were withdrawn from open land for filing mineral claims by the Bureau of Land Management as having potential geothermal value.

Northrop records the occurrence of skeletal sulfur crystals up to two inches long and 1/2 inch in diameter as being found in 1955.

HARDING PEGMATITE

The Harding Pegmatite is in the Picuris Range, a group of small hills between the Sangre de Cristo Range and the Rio Grande. They jut westward into the Rio Grande Valley and six miles northeast of Dixon, on New Mexico Route 75, there is a mine road that leads three quarters of a mile to the mine workings (Fig. 3–17).

North central New Mexico was searched in the early 1900s for mica to be used in stove door windows and undoubtedly the outcrop was examined. Joe Peyer is credited with the discovery of the pegmatite in 1910; however, it was 1919 before the mine was leased to Minerals Mining and Milling Company. This company explored the deposit for lepidolite by the use of shot coredrill-

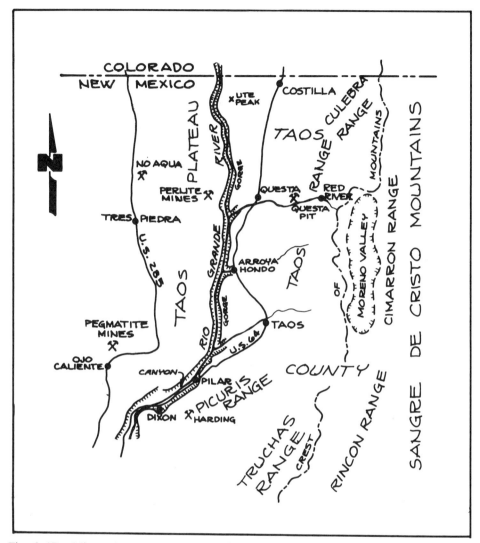

Fig. 3–17. Mines of Taos County, New Mexico. Adapted from N. Mex. Bu. M. and M. R. Bull. 71, 1960.

ing. This was a method, new at that time, in which steel shot was fed into a race in the drill bit to cut a circle around a core which was then removed for inspecting the rock drilled.

Lepidolite, the lithium mica, was mined for use in making opaque white glass, which was used chiefly in making jar cap liners and lighting fixtures. Two shipments in 1924 caused problems in the glass making process and use of lepidolite from this deposit was discontinued. It is thought microlite was the cause of the trouble.

Embudo Mining and Milling Company completed a mill at Embudo in 1927 and began mining and upgrading the ore. Pacific Minerals worked the deposit from 1928 to 1930 and then returned it to Embudo Mining and Milling Company. The largest part of the lepidolite and logs (large crystals) of spodumene had been worked out by this time; however, approximately 12,000 tons of ore averaging 3.5 percent dilithium oxide had been produced.

The mine was inactive between 1930 and 1942 when Arthur Montgomery acquired the property and started producing microlite. By February of 1946, about 17,200 pounds of microlite concentrate, containing 65 percent to 71 percent tantalum pentoxide had been produced. In this same period, a few hundred pounds of placer tantalite, containing 43 percent tantalum pentoxide and 36 percent columbian pentoxide; a 40 ton lot of hand cobbed spodumene, and 27.5 tons of white beryl, 24 tons mined and hand sorted and 3.5 tons picked from the dump, had been produced. The spodumene and white beryl came from zones at the top of the pegmatite, which was complexly zoned (Fig. 3–18).

By the middle of 1947, production of microlite was recorded as over 20,000 pounds averaging 70 percent tantalum pentoxide. This was the only mine in the world, up to that time, with a substantial production of microlite. Drilling on the south side of the quarry established that reserves still exist in that area. A mine with reserves of microlite is indeed a rarity.

Between 1945 and 1947, a ten ton mill was in operation at Rinconda on the Rio Grande to produce microlite concentrate. No work was done in 1948–9, but in 1950–1, the New Mexico Mining and Contracting Company mined 806

Fig. 3–18. Spodumene, Harding Pegmatite Mine (JM#224).

PLATE 1

New Mexico Minerals

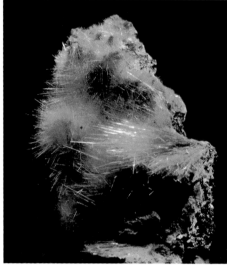

½ inch CHALCOPYRITE sphenoids with QUARTZ and CALCITE, GROUNDHOG MINE

BROCHANTITE, BLANCHARD MINE C.E.W.

CYANOTRICHITE, BLANCHARD MINE C.E.W.

CHALCEDONY and QUARTZ, GROUNDHOG MINE

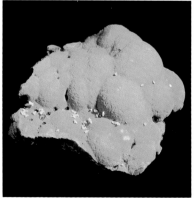

FLUORITE, BLANCHARD MINE

Wheatgrain SMITHSONITE on AURICHALCITE, KELLY MINE

PLATE 2

SMITHSONITE, KELLY MINE

FLUORITE, MEXTEX MINE T.E.C.

LEPIDOLITE, HARDING PEGMATITE MINE

ROSASITE on CALCITE, JUANITA MINE

TYUYAMUNITE, McKINLEY COUNTY

MURDOCHITE on phantom AMETHYST and BARITE, MEXTEX MINE

PLATE 3

BERYL in matrix, OJO CALIENTE
AREA

BROCHANTITE, ORGAN MOUNTAINS

FERRIMOLYBDITE, QUESTA PIT

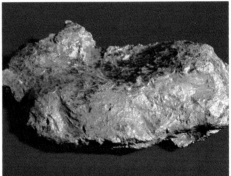

MOLYBDENITE, QUESTA PIT T.E.C.

MOTTRAMITE, SIERRA COUNTY

AZURITE, TENORITE, and
MALACHITE, TYRONE PIT

PLATE 4

Colorado Minerals

GOLD in QUARTZ, AMERICAN MINE

RHODOCHROSITE, AMERICAN TUNNEL

RHODOCHROSITE pinacoids on QUARTZ, AMERICAN TUNNEL

RHODOCHROSITE, CALCITE and SELENITE, AMERICAN TUNNEL

SPHALERITE, BIG FOUR MINE

ALSTONITE, BITTER ROOT MINE

PLATE 5

GALENA, BLACK CLOUD MINE

DOLOMITE and PYRITE on blue
QUARTZ, BLACK CLOUD MINE

AMETHYST pseudomorph after
BARITE, BULLDOG MOUNTAIN

MOLYBDENITE, CALIFORNIA MINE

Fibrous EPIDOTE and bladed HEMATITE,
CALUMET IRON MINE

EPIDOTE, CALUMET IRON MINE

PLATE 6

SCAPOLITE, AMETHYST, and
EPIDOTE, CALUMET IRON MINE

ANKERITE and CALCITE on blue
QUARTZ, CAMP BIRD MINE T.E.C.

CALCITE pagoda, CAMP BIRD MINE

MANGANOCALCITE, CAMP BIRD MINE

FLUORITE and brown carbonate on blue
QUARTZ, CAMP BIRD MINE

QUARTZ, CHALCOPYRITE and
SPHALERITE, CAMP BIRD MINE

PLATE 7

RHODOCHROSITE, CHAMPION MINE

FLUORITE floater, CLIMAX
MOLYBDENUM MINE

DOLOMITE on RHODOCHROSITE on
QUARTZ, CLIMAX MOLYBDENUM MINE

CINNABAR, COCHETOPA CREEK
AREA

MANGANOSIDERITE, EAGLE MINE at
GILMAN T.E.C.

MALACHITE and CHALCOCITE
on CHALCOPYRITE, EAGLE
MINE at GILMAN

PLATE 8

GALENA on MARMATITE, EAGLE MINE
at GILMAN

PYRRHOTITE, PYRITE and
OLIGONITE in MARBLE, EAGLE
MINE at GILMAN

Wire SILVER and EMBOLITE,
EMPERIUS MINE

CHRYSOPRASE (Creede jade),
AMETHYST, GALENA, ANGLESITE
and SILVER, EMPERIUS MINE

AMETHYST on CHALCOPYRITE,
EMPERIUS MINE

OLIGONITE, JULIA FISK MINE

PLATE 9

Yellow QUARTZ, MOUNT ANTERO

Capped AMETHYST, MOUNT ANTERO

Banded FLUORITE, NORTHGATE–CRYSTAL AREA

Boxwork FLUORITE, NORTHGATE–CRYSTAL AREA

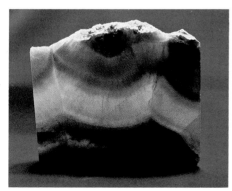

Banded FLUORITE, NORTHGATE–CRYSTAL AREA

QUARTZ on FLUORITE, RANSOME MINE

PLATE 10

BARITE, SHERMAN TUNNEL T.E.C.

RHODOCHROSITE, QUARTZ, PYRITE,
FLUORITE, CHALCOPYRITE, GALENA,
TETRAHEDRITE, SPHALERITE,
HUBNERITE, APATITE, CHLORITE and
and DICKITE, SWEET HOME MINE

RHODOCHROSITE, GALENA and
CHALCOPYRITE, SWEET HOME MINE

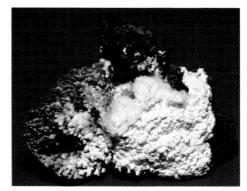

PSILOMELANE, ARAGONITE and
SELENITE, SANGRE DE CRISTO
MOUNTAINS

SMITHSONITE variety MONHEIMITE,
ANKERITE on DOLOMITE and
ROSASITE on BARITE, SHERMAN
TUNNEL

Blue and golden COVELLITE,
SUMMITVILLE MINES

PLATE 11

Red and yellow HUBNERITE, YUKON MINE

MANGAN--CALCITE, IDARADO MINE

Bent QUARTZ, IDARADO MINE

TENNANTITE–TETRAHEDRITE over CHALCOPYRITE, IDARADO MINE

PYRITE, IDARADO MINE

QUARTZ cast-pseudomorph of cubic FLUORITE, IDARADO MINE

PLATE 12

MANGANOCALCITE, IDARADO MINE

Feathered CALCITE, IDARADO MINE

CALCITE, IDARADO MINE

CALCITE sphere on QUARTZ, IDARADO MINE

QUARTZ, SPHALERITE, and TENNANTITE–TETRAHEDRITE over CHALCOPYRITE, IDARADO MINE

Irridescent PYRITE on CALCITE and QUARTZ, IDARADO MINE

tons of lepidolite and 249 tons of spodumene ore averaging 4 percent dilithium oxide.

A. Montgomery and his partner mined beryl from 1950 to 1959 and produced 848 tons of 10 percent beryllium oxide which was sold to the National Stockpile. Between 1950 and 1955, the quarry face was solid beryl for days at a time and production was as high as a ton per day. Production during this time was 20 percent of the nation's production.

A plan to mill the pegmatite to produce microlite, spodumene, and beryl was made in 1957 by Cordillera Mining Company, however, after 1959, mining was mostly cleanup operations. A small amount of beryl was produced in 1969.

The mine has been turned over to the University of New Mexico by Arthur Montgomery to "preserve the state's natural assets," and for the benefit of future generations. A representative group of minerals from the mine were donated to the University's Geology Museum by Arthur Montgomery.

The Harding pegmatite, one of the world's outstanding mineral deposits, is a complexly zoned, flat-lying dike between Precambrian schists, granite rocks and quartzites in what is known as the Vadito formation. Quartz-muscovite schist, on the northern end and amphibolites, on the southern end, form the wall rocks.

By K/Ar and Rb/Sr dating, four muscovite samples from the mine gave an age of 1260 m.y.B.P. and lepidolite gave an age of 1350 m.y.B.P. Another muscovite from a similar deposit in the Picuris Range gave an age of 1335 m.y.B.P.

Pegmatites of a similar nature in north-central New Mexico were thought to have been emplaced at a depth of about seven miles in a fluid rich in fluorine and chlorine in a silicate melt. Fluid inclusions in quartz and beryl indicate the solution was halide-rich. A granite mass common to the general area was the probable source.

In the Harding pegmatite, the principal minerals were ores of lithium and tantalum. Spodumene occurred as logs up to 6 feet by 1 foot by 1 foot. Lepidolite, columbite–tantalite, and beryl were produced in quantities.

Accessory minerals were quartz, microcline, muscovite, albite, almandine, apatite (dark greenish-blue), allanite, amphibole, andalusite, bertrandite, (alteration on beryl), clevelandite, biotite, chloritoid, chrysocolla, cordierite, epidote, eucryptite (alternation crust/spodumene), illite (hydromuscovite of early reports), kaolinite, montmorillonite, pyrophyllite, and thorite (mainly in smoky quartz with colors reddish brown to black).

Topaz, schorl, zircon, bismite, cassiterite, gahnite, ilmenite, limonite, magnetite, pyrolusite, rutile, titanite, tenorite, azurite, beyerite, bismutite, malachite, amblygonite, lithiophilite, monazite, wavellite (not confirmed), bismuthinite, chalcocite, chalcopyrite, loellingite, pyrite (rare), bismuth, fluorite, calcite (var. Iceland spar), and hatchettolite–betafite, cubic, (pyrochlore group) occurred. White, pink and yellow-tinted beryl occurred in quartz-albite-perthite-muscovite zones that were from six inches to eight feet thick adjacent to either the hanging wall or foot wall. A single mass of beryl weighing over 100 tons was mined. A globular form of lepidolite has been reported from the island of Elba and from Mt. Mica, Paris, Maine. This form also occurs at the Harding Pegmatite Mine.

Iceberg Mine

The Iceberg Mine is about 300 feet southwest of the large quarry on the Harding pegmatite. It was located in 1931 and optical calcite mining was started in 1939. Unfortunately, the surface was blasted and some optical calcite ruined; however, about 850 pounds were mined and shipped mainly to Bausch and Lomb Optical Company. The largest usable piece mined weighed 5 pounds, 8 ounces.

Arthur Montgomery relocated the mine as the Iceberg Spar claim and it is part of the Harding property. The Iceland spar occurred in a pipe-like body 30 feet long and about 9 feet wide at the center. Walls of the pipe, which were amphibolite schist and quartzite of the Vadito formation, were brecciated and altered around the calcite. There were three types of calcite; white, clear containing the optical grade, and banded pink calcite. A single crystal was estimated to weigh from 30 to 40 tons; however, twinning ruined much of the deposit for optical purposes.

Kelly believed that an escape of gases from depth formed the breccia pipe which was then filled with calcite by hydrothermal action.

About two miles north of the Harding pegmatite, a calcite deposit similar to that at the Iceberg Mine occurs in a bean-like pod. One partly developed crystal was 18 feet long.

Small though they are, these two deposits probably would be classed as carbonatites today. Our knowledge of this type of deposit has increased dramatically since Heinrich's classic work on carbonatites, published in 1966.

OJO CALIENTE PEGMATITE DISTRICT

Deposits of mica in pegmatites in north-central New Mexico were worked in the 17th century before the Pueblo Revolt. Large books were split and trimmed for window panes for use in buildings in Santa Fe, Espanola and other north-central New Mexico towns. This mica was thought to have come from the Cribbensville deposits near Petaca, in Rio Arriba County.

The old mica mining center of Cribbensville dates from about 1870 when mica for stove doors was produced on a commercial scale. A popular brand of stoves gave the place its name. Plate mica was the only material sought and it was transported by pack animals to Pueblo, Colorado.

Scrap mica was produced from other deposits in 1900 as demand for stove mica dwindled. Demand for electrical mica renewed interest in sheet mica by 1912. Mining of pegmatites was sporadic and periods of activity were followed by long inactive periods. When the demand for special minerals was present, such as beryl during and after World War II, activity was renewed.

From 1930 to 1940, scrap mica was selectively mined at the Joseph Mine, in the Ojo Caliente area, and in 1948 bulk-screening was tried. Los Compadres Mining Company concentrated ground mica at a plant in Ojo Caliente.

A group of eight pegmatite mines and prospects about two miles north of Ojo Caliente mark the southern end of the extensive Petaca pegmatite area. Workings consist of cuts, small adits, and trenches; however, the deposits are representative of a large number of pegmatites found in the Precambrian rocks of north-central New Mexico.

Pegmatites in the district start about one and a half miles north of the hot springs, which are well known for having calcium fluoride in the water. The pegmatite area is in the Rio Grande Valley and an amygdaloidal basalt (a basalt with the gas cavities filled with secondary minerals) and sediments of the Santa Fe formation occur in a down-faulted area between the deposits and the Caliente River. Foliated dark green to black amphibole schist and greenish to buff quartz-mica schist are the principal rocks containing the pegmatites. Inter-layers of vitreous quartzite, buff to gray quartz-staurolite schist, quartz-andalusite schist, and minor kyanite-bearing schist occur. Further north, a complex of older metamorphic rocks occur and much of the area is underlain by a fine-grained gneissic granite.

Minerals of the Ojo Caliente pegmatites other than quartz, mica, and feldspars are: salmon to wine-red colored spessartine, fluorite, pale green to lemon yellow in large masses without crystal faces, up to 15 inches in diameter, beryl, blue-green to yellow (two small white beryl crystals with pale pink cores were found), large microcline crystals, columbite-tantalite, (Fig. 3–19), monazite, samarskite, bismutite, staurolite, kyanite, and andalusite. Sulfide minerals were reported but not identified.

The thermal springs at Ojo Caliente are depositing fluorite, barite and calcite.

Fig. 3–19.   Columbite/tantalite, Petaca area (JM#87).

Joseph Deposit

The Joseph deposit is probably the largest pegmatite of the group and is a large plus-shaped mass about 250 feet long and 80 feet wide. It was opened in about 1905 by an adit that disclosed a fault zone between the Precambrian pegmatite and Tertiary andesite and basalt. The pegmatite is composed of red microcline, white to red albite, quartz and mica. Accessory minerals were garnet, fluorite, minor beryl, columbite, samarskite, and bismutite. Books of mica as large as 24 inches by 36 inches were mined. The average book was about 6 inches. Large crumpled books four to six feet in diameter were found with ruling, wedging, crumpling and intergrowth. Feldspar was shipped in 1969-70 from the Joseph Mine.

Star Deposit

The Star deposit is a much smaller pegmatite. Garnet, staurolite (Fig. 3-20) and fluorite were said to be abundant. Columbite, samarskite, monazite, and beryl were accessory minerals.

Other Deposits

Winston Mines Company, a long time operator of various mines in this area, announced in 1964 they had discovered a deposit of 76,000 tons of bertrandite, averaging 0.57 percent beryllium oxide. Metallurgy had not been developed for the deposit, however.

Questa Pit

Questa Open Pit Molybdenum Mine is in the Taos Range of the Sangre de Cristo Mountains. The Taos plains, part of the southern end of the San Luis Valley, are to the west, adjoining this area. The mine is in Sulfur Gulch about 6.5 miles northeast of Questa. Sulfur Gulch is a tributary of the Red River which flows into the Rio Grande about 12 miles below Questa.

A large area of outcrop in Sulfur Gulch was thought to be colored yellow by sulfur by the early prospectors; however, impure ferrimolybdite was the pigment responsible for the color. The early development of this deposit was by adits driven from Sulfur Gulch and later exploration of the ore body was also done from deeper tunnels in this gulch. Late in World War I, a demand for molybdenum developed, for alloying with steel, and the mine was first worked at this time. In 1918, a company acquired seven claims and located claims to assemble about 300 acres in the Sulfur Gulch outcrop area.

Molybdenum Corporation of America (Molycorp) became the operating company in 1921 and is the present owner. A small gold mill on Red River was used to mill the molybedenum ore at first and in 1923 a 40 tpd flotation mill was built. Between 1921 and 1937, the underground workings produced 10.6

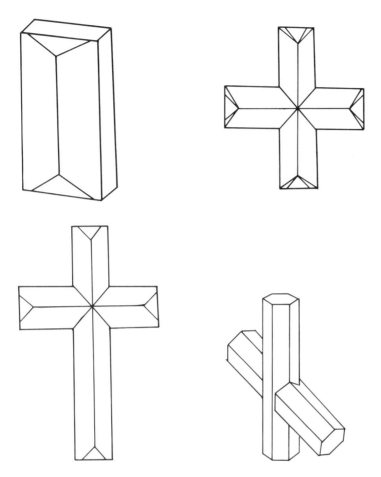

Fig. 3-20   Staurolite crystals; Single, Manx Cross Twin, and St. Andrews Cross Twin.

million pounds of molybdenite from almost 20 miles of tunnels, raises and drifts. Ore was mined from high-grade veins through a vertical range of about 500 feet. Underground work continued until 1957 and the production increased to 20 million pounds of molybdenite.

This phase of mining had been on small but rich streaks of ore that occurred along the contact of the red ground and the green ground. The red was a granite intrusive and the green was an epidotized and otherwise altered sedimentary—metamorphic—igneous rock complex into which the granite intruded.

Molybdite occurred with quartz and other matrix minerals along shear fractures up to ten feet maximum width and several hundred feet long.

As early as 1953, underground workings were extended into target exploration areas when it became apparent that there was a lot of MoS_2 in the deposit, but high-grade was becoming too costly to find. Long hole drilling was done from these drifts to sample the deposit and favorable results were obtained. Exploration was expanded; mining ceased in 1957, and full effort was devoted to the exploration program. By 1963, costs of this program were running $100,000 per month. Underground exploration was expanded to determine if the ore extended to the surface in upper Sulfur Gulch.

A $32.5 million program to develop an open pit mine and to build a mill was started and a contract was let in 1964 for a mill that would produce ten million pounds of MoS_2 a year by the year 1966. The mill was finished by 1966 and after an expenditure of $40 million, production in the open pit was 10,000 tpd to the mill and 20,000 to 30,000 tpd to the low-grade ore and waste dumps. Increased reserves found in 1969 brought the total of 0.185 percent molybdenum sulfide ore up to 126.8 million tons and production was increased to 17,000 tpd. This reserve was expected to last beyond 1973. In two and a half years, after 1966, 21 million pounds of molybdenum sulfide were produced. It was estimated that stripping of 40 to 75 million tons per year would be required to extend ore reserves for mining after 1972. Up to 1969, diamond drilling was being done to extend the ore reserves and new finds were extending the life of the pit. The main ore body was estimated to still contain 333 million pounds of molybdenum sulfide and a new area six miles southwest of the Questa pit was capable of producing an additional 106 million pounds of molybdenum sulfide. It is interesting to note that much of the ore mined underground averages 5 percent molybdenum sulfide or 100 pounds of molybdenum sulfide per ton. The 1980s will see extensive developments.

Molybdenum deposits at Questa are in an eastward trending graben known as the Red River volcanic trench that extends from the Taos plain and the main Rio Grande rift zone about 12 miles into the Sangre de Cristo uplift and it is apparently terminated by a thrust zone in the Moreno Valley. The Moreno Valley formed along the deflection line of the Sangre de Cristo Mountains contemporaneous with rifting in the Rio Grande Valley. Mineralization occurs in the upper zone of one of three porphyritic–granitic intrusions along the Red River volcanic trench. These intrusives have been termed granite (by the early miners), granite porphyry, porphyritic granite, and probably more correctly, aplite–porphyry bodies. They have been dated radiometrically at 22 to 23 m.y.B.P. These Miocene intrusives are thought to have originated from a cupola of a deep-seated granite batholith. They formed a breccia pipe as they intruded a mid-Tertiary volcanic section, Pennsylvanian-Permian sediments, and Precambrian metamorphic and igneous rocks, all of which were brecciated and were broken into disorder. Tertiary rhyolites and latites cap the deposit in places where not eroded. Hydrothermal alteration is intense in the area.

A molbydenum-mineralized breccia pipe complex of possible Miocene age in the eastern edge of the West Elk Mountains, (near Crested Butte), Colorado, was described by Sharp in 1978. The West Elk Mountains are on the west side of the Sawatch Mountains and are a part of them. This deposit has features similar to those of the Questa, New Mexico, deposit and also the Climax, and Henderson deposits of Colorado. The breccia pipe developed over the top of a forcibly intruded rhyolite porphyry stock. Amax Company is developing this deposit as their Mount Emmons Project.

The Mount Emmons Mine in Red Lady Basin west of Crested Butte, in the Elk Mountains volcanic field, has the potential of becoming the third largest molybdenum mine in the world. The ore body is 1000 feet below the surface. Early exploration was through the old Keystone Mine lead–zinc workings.

In the Questa mineral deposit, mineralization was first introduced in a series of veinlets and stringers. After this, veins, inches to ten feet wide and several hundred feet long, were formed. In some cases these veins were reopened and rhodochrosite, fluorite, calcite, galena, sphalerite, and chalcopyrite were deposited. The fractures and veins were caused by subsidence along the Red River volcanic trench and surges of mineralization were related to periods of subsidence.

Minerals found in the Questa molybdenum deposit are: akaganeite containing molybdenum (trimorphic with goethite), biotite, calcite, chalcopyrite, chlorite, ferrimolybdite, fluorite, galena, graphite, limonite, sphalerite, ilsemannite, malachite, molybdenite, pyrite, quartz, rhodochrosite, sericite, topaz, adularia, dolomite, potassium feldspar, kaolinite, illite, jarosite, and powellite. Also reported were: apatite, hubnerite, and rhodonite. In oxidized zones in very minor amounts occur: chalcocite, covellite, cerussite, anglesite, copper carbonates, base metal oxides, gypsum, carbonates, secondary silica, manganese oxides; pyrite crystal floaters were found in clay-filled pockets.

No Agua Perlite

Just below the Colorado–New Mexico state line, west of the Rio Grande in the Servilleta volcanic field (4.1 m.y.B.P.), a cluster of four domes of rhyolite form the No Agua Perlite deposits. Centers of these domes are flow-laminated and devitrified, but the margins are glassy and contain obsidian blebs (Apache tears). This material forms the perlite deposits.

Perlite is an acid volcanic rock having a vitreous luster and containing from 2 percent to 5 percent included water.

These deposits were first worked in 1948 and a processing plant was in operation by September, 1951. They have been in continuous production since.

The No Agua Perlite domes have been dated at 3.8 m.y.B.P. and a large volcanic shield southeast of them, Cerro del Aire, which is composed of olivine andesite, has been dated at 3.4 m.y.B.P. These vents are in the Great American Rift zone and indicate the activity occurring in this time interval.

REFERENCES

A–4 Lindgren Volume (Vanderwilt), (Hess), (p. 177), A–5 Ridge (Carpenter), B–4, E–14, G–10, I–6, I–8, I–9, I–10, I–19, I–20, I–23, J–6, J–26, J–54, K–12, K–19, K–21, L–1 1969–1970; 1971–1974, M–3, O–3, O–4, O–6, O–10, O–16, O–19, O–20, O–27, O–31, O–32, O–35, O–36, P–1 Johnson (Kelley), P–2 Rosenzweig (Kelley), P–0 Siemers (Woodward), (Long), (Jiracek), (Judo), P–9 Siemers (Woodward), (Talbott), (LaPoint), (Chenoweth), (Jahns), Q–1, Q–34, Q–39, R–4, R–18, R–21, R–23, R–24, S–26, S–45, S–50, S–82, S–104, S–109.

CHAPTER 4
COLORADO MINES AND MINERALS

HISTORY OF THE SAN LUIS VALLEY
AND THE SAN JUAN MOUNTAINS

The history of the San Luis Valley is tied to that of the San Juan Mountains because this valley gave the early prospectors a known, if not altogether safe, place from which to venture into the unknown mountains.

In 1641, Governor Luis de Rosas led an expedition from Santa Fe into the San Luis Valley and captured 80 Ute Indians who were forced into slavery in Santa Fe. It is possible that colonists came into the area from San Gabriel, predecessor of Santa Fe, in the early 1600s. This cannot be documented; however, by 1680, the Indians of the Rio Grande Valley revolted and drove the Spanish south out of Santa Fe. This retreat over the Jornada del Muerto (Journey of Death) area is well documented.

Arrastras, primitive, massive grinding mills, usually cut from a single large boulder, were used by the Spanish to recover gold. Several have been found in the San Luis Valley near gold deposits; one was found at Summitville. These mills were thought to predate the Indian revolt as the early land grants were given by the Spanish crown to promote development of mineral wealth.

The first Spanish fort in the valley was built on Cerro San Antonio in 1768 to defend Ojo Caliente from the Ute Indians. American trappers were in the valley in the early 1800s and Ft. Garland was established in 1858 to protect settlers. In 1861 the San Luis Valley was transferred to the Territory of Colorado and by 1867 Otto Mears introduced wheat farming on his ranch near Sagauche and several wheat raising communities developed.

J. L. Wighman and his party discovered gold near Summitville in 1871 and a large group of people flooded the district. Most left disappointed but a few claims were staked in 1872. A new wave of prospectors in 1873 found some of the best mines.

In July, 1860, Charles Baker and a party of men went into the upper Animas River country and found a small amount of gold. They laid out townships and proposed toll roads near present-day Silverton. Baker then returned to Denver and organized a party of three hundred men, women, and children who left for the ''Baker's Park'' area in December, 1860. This ended in a tragic loss of life.

Baker was to reenter the area again after the Civil War in 1867 only to be killed, possibly by his companions.

Placer gold was found in Arrastra Gulch in 1870 and the Little Giant claim, the first successful gold claim in the Silverton area, was found in 1871. Ore averaged $150 per ton and 27 tons were milled in an arrastra. By 1872, the Little Giant had a 1,000 foot wire rope aerial tramway and in 1873 produced $12,000 in gold.

The Brunot Agreement with the Ute Indians in 1873 threw the area open to prospecting and in the spring and summer of 1874, over 2,000 men swarmed over the San Juan Mountains. One of the main routes into the Silverton area was from Del Norte up the Rio Grande, over Stony Pass and down Cunningham Gulch. Claims had been staked before the treaty was signed, but now the mines could be worked without being in trespass or without fear of Indian reprisals.

Orient Iron Mine

Orient Iron Mine is on the west side of the Sangre de Cristo Mountains at an elevation of about 9,000 feet. Five miles south of Villa Grove on U. S. Highway 285, just before it junctions Colorado 17, a dirt road goes east in a straight line across the San Luis Valley and ends at the site of former Orient, a company town operated by Colorado Fuel and Iron Company of Pueblo, Colorado. The mine workings are directly uphill from the old foundations at the foot of the mountains. Largest commercial production of iron ore in Colorado from any one mine, about two million tons, came from this mine which was discovered in 1880. Ore was produced from 1881 through 1933. It was reported as still shipping a few thousand tons annually in 1914.

The San Luis Valley has been down faulted several thousand feet and the Sangre de Cristo Mountains have furnished fill to a depth of at least 1,000 feet, in the vicinity of the mine. Facet cut on spurs of alluvial fans suggest recent uplift in the area.

The ore is described as limonite derived from near-surface oxidation of replacement bodies of iron-bearing carbonate in Leadville limestone. This limestone has been equated to the Leadville dolomite, which consists of a dolomite member and the Gilman sandstone member, of Mississippian age, and the Dyer dolomite member, of Devonian age, in the Leadville area, the type locality. The manganese–iron ores of Leadville and of the Red Cliff-Gilman areas have a similar origin and are also found in this limestone formation. Small intrusive sills of monzonite porphyry are found near the deposit and a large body intrudes the Sangre de Cristo formation three miles east, at the crest of the range.

This interpretation of the ore formation process has been suggested: Siderite, in lenses and pipes, was formed by ascending hydrothermal solutions. Oxidation of the primary ore was due to descending meteoric waters. The remarkable depth of the oxidation was due to channelways along faults, probably border faults along the rift zone.

Deposits of iron ore are known to extend at least 200 feet below present ground water levels. Solution cavities in the Leadville limestone and in the Chaffee formation extend for hundreds of feet and are 60 to 70 feet high. Walls of these water courses are sometimes covered with radiating crystals of aragonite and sometimes small stalactites of calcite and aragonite. The workable iron deposits are confined to the Leadville limestone but veinlets of brown iron-bearing carbonate occur in all the rock formations present, from the Precambrian to the Sangre de Cristo formation. Ore bodies are elongated pipes parallel to the bedding planes and one ore body was 210 feet long and 80 feet wide. Ore has been developed over a vertical range of 1,000 feet and one ore horizon was worked for a vertical distance of 550 feet and is known to extend another 200 feet. The ore is hard, cavernous limonite, slaggy limonite, soft yellow ochre, massive red ore, and sometimes flakes of specular hematite. Ore is separated from the unreplaced limestone by a border of brown lime, which is made up of coarsely crystalline brown carbonate and ocher.

At the Orient Iron Mine, ascending hydrothermal solutions deposited siderite, barite, chalcopyrite, and gold, the last three in small amounts. The siderite was relatively free of manganese as analyses showing over 1.43 percent manganese were rare. Mangano-siderite of the Eagle Mine at Gilman contained up to 17 percent manganese.

Oxidized ore was called limonite. Goethite is 62.9 percent iron and iron ore in the upper workings contained 63.7 percent iron so the ore was interpreted as composed of goethite with small amounts of admixed hematite.

In open cavities in the upper workings, limonite pseudomorphs of rhombohedral siderite, with curved faces, were found. Ankerite was also found as rhombohedrons.

Barite occurs as radiating crystals; chalcopyrite is present and in oxidized zones, malachite occurs in minor amounts. The iron ore contains from 0.01 to 0.04 ounces of gold per ton and manganese occurs with unoxidized ankerite as rhodochrosite. White calcite forms small veinlets in the limestone but is thought not to have any connections with the ore.

BONANZA DISTRICT

The Bonanza mining district is in the northern part of the San Luis Valley, on the west side of the valley in the southern tip of the Sawatch Range and in the Kerber Creek drainage. Bonanza is in the middle part of this mining district and Villa Grove is east of it. Mines are clustered around the Bonanza caldera, northern-most of the San Juan calderas and the area is considered part of the San Juan volcanic field. To the southwest, the LaGarita Hills form a connecting link with the main San Juan volcanic field. A relationship with the Thirty-Nine Mile volcanic field, which lies to the east over the Sangre de Cristo Range, has been postulated.

Geologic history of the Bonanza district is closely tied to the tectonic events of the Great American Rift. A brief review is inserted to correlate the setting of the mineralization that was later emplaced entirely within units of the Bonanza volcanics.

During the Laramide orogeny, which began in late Cretaceous time and extended into late Eocene time the Sawatch anticline (Fig. 4–1) developed and the Bonanza district is on its southeast end.

Paleozoic strata in the northern part of the Sangre de Cristo Range, and on north in the continuing Mosquito Range, outline the eastward extent of this anticline. Drainage was to the east and southeast into South Park.

A section of the Paleozoic strata in the Kerber Creek area of the Bonanza district, modified from Knepper and Marrs is as follows:

Cambrian	Sawatch quartzite	0–20 feet
(On erosional surface of the Pce)		
Ordovician	Manitou fm. (Manitou dolomite, Canadian)	90–225 feet
Harding Sandstone	(Champlanian)	60–116 feet Tomichi of former usage
Silurian	Fremont limestone (Cincinnatian) Absent	
Devonian	Chaffee fm. Lower member, parting quartzite	10–26 feet
	Upper member, Dyer domolite	87–123 feet Ouray of former usage
Mississippian	Leadville limestone	210–336 feet
Pennsylvanian and Permian	Belden shale Minturn fm.	

These Paleozoic rocks are found in the Monarch district to the north; in the Sangre de Cristo Range to the east; in the Alma-Fairplay district on the east slope of the Mosquito Range to the northeast; (Fig. 4–2) and in the Leadville district, and northward. They also occur in varying thicknesses as inliers within the Sawatch Range where not eroded.

A series of northwest-trending anticlines and synclines developed in this strata south and east of the Sawatch anticline and, in Oligocene time, several

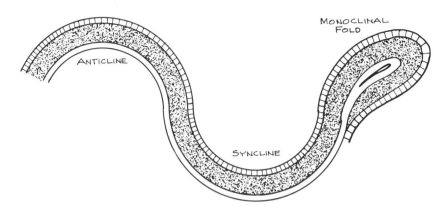

Fig. 4-1. Simplified illustration of rock folding.

volcanic centers developed near Bonanza. The Rawley formation with two major flows, one dated at 34.2 m.y.B.P., and the younger one at 33.4 m.y.B.P. were deposited. These early basic to intermediate lava flows were covered by the Bonanza Tuff (27.8 m.y.B.P.) and with younger latites and andesites. The Bonanza Tuff had a wide distribution in the San Juan volcanic field but much of it was eroded. When the Bonanza area collapsed a caldera was formed with internal domes and multiple intrusions. Present day remnants of this volcanic activity are the Bonanza Mountains, a part of and southern most end of the Sawatch Range.

Before late Miocene time, sediments of the Dry Union formation were

Fig. 4-2. Horseshoe Amphitheater showing formations dipping under South Park off of the Mosquito Range in Colorado. Alpine glaciation caused the horseshoe-shaped cirque. W.H.

deposited in a Tertiary fault-bounded trough between the Upper Arkansas and San Luis Valleys. In Miocene and Pliocene time, movement along bordering faults of the rift zone raised the Sangre de Cristo Range to its present position.

Faults on the west side of the Tertiary trough strike southward to join a series of faults associated with the collapse of the Bonanza caldera. Faulting has been reoccurring along these older faults and a series of transverse faults, including the Salida–Maysville fault, have raised the area around Poncha Mountain a minimum of 2,500 feet. Poncha Mountain is west of the Sangre de Cristo Mountains in the rift zone. Numerous small intersecting faults occurred with the collapse of the caldera. These became the mineralized veins and ore shoots of the Bonanza mining district. All but a few were small.

Homesteading started on Kerber Creek near Villa Grove in 1865. When the railroad was extended from Mears Junction on the Marshal Pass route, over Poncha Pass to Villa Grove in 1880, that community was well established.

The first mining claims were staked in the Bonanza area in the 1870s but the veins were narrow and did not extend any length nor were they persistent. Tom Cooke, while looking for some of his horses, found rich float, loose rock from a vein, in 1880 in Copper Gulch. A small amount of pyrite was found near the surface on the White Iron claim but it was soon abandoned. On July 9, 1880 the Bonanza claim was staked on ore that was said to be worth $200 per ton. It occurred on the surface and continued downward. The rush was on and Bonanza was incorporated November 1, 1880. Numerous small communities developed in the area as the flood of people who were going to the Gunnison country were diverted to this new mining camp. Parkville, Claytonia, Kerber, and Sedgwick were communities that flourished for a brief period only to fade into history. Thousands of people came only to move on disappointed. Most of the larger mines were discovered by 1882. The most productive ones were the Rawley, Eagle, Paragon, Michigan, and Antero.

Bonanza Mine

The Bonanza was one of the first mines opened in the district and was responsible for the early boom. It was mined through an incline shaft with six levels reaching 400 feet below the surface. Considerable drifting was done on each level. The mine was said to have produced about $300,000 by 1890 and was worked possibly for another 15 years by leasees on a smaller scale.

Ore of the Bonanza Mine was galena, sphalerite, chalcopyrite, and tetrahedrite in a gangue of pyrite, quartz, barite, and fluorite. Silver was the mineral of principal value and gold values were minor. Copper mineralization was mostly absent above the 300 foot level.

Empress Josephine Mine

The Empress Josephine Mine produced about the same amount of mineral as the Bonanza Mine and was active until 1915. The shaft was 500 feet deep. At the 350-foot level acid water was such a problem that wooden rails had to be used. Activity since 1915 has been intermittent.

In the Empress Josephine Mine, oxidized ore was found to a depth of 80 feet and sulfide ore below that depth. Cerussite, gold, and silver occurred together. This mine was famous for its telluride minerals; however, the ore was extremely spotty and did not develop into sizable ore shoots.

Empressite, a silver telluride, was the name of a mineral found in the mine in 1914 by Professor R. D. George, of the University of Colorado. Other telluride minerals were: native tellurium, rickardite, sylvanite, hessite, and petzite. Samples of ore from the mine in 1907 gave assays of 5 to 14 ounces of gold per ton and as high as 6,465 ounces of silver per ton.

Rawley Mine

The Rawley Mine was discovered in 1880 and was producing by 1883. Much of the work done up to the early 1900s was development, but the 1891 production was given as $5,981 in silver and lead by the Director of the Mint's Report of 1892. Production was small because most of the ore was mill grade. A smelter built in the district in the early 1880s was idle by 1884 because it could not treat the ores successfully. Two 50 tpd mills operating by 1900 and one 100 tpd mill that was constructed in 1903 were largely unsuccessful, probably due to lack of a source of water.

In 1911, the operating company decided to drive a drainage tunnel from Squirrel Gulch under the old workings in Rawley Gulch. This tunnel was to cut the Rawley vein at a depth of 1,200 feet or 600 feet below the deepest workings above it.

Six levels with 4,000 feet of drifting, three adits, and a winze from the third level to the sixth level developed the Rawley vein in Rawley Gulch. Pumping was a problem from the lower levels.

Work on the drainage tunnel was started May 7, 1911, and the Rawley vein was cut October 23, 1912, at a point 6,212 feet from the portal. In driving the drainage tunnel, the steam plant that furnished power for the compressor consumed 2,000 cords of wood. Six animals were used to the point of exhaustion to haul the muck to the dump in this period of activity.

At a point 3,910 feet from the portal, a fault zone was cut and a water inflow of 1,000 gpm with accompanying disintegrated rock made work impossible until a drift was driven to intersect the fault at another point and thus relieve the flow to the working face. When the Rawley vein was cut it took 38 days to drain the workings 600 feet above.

The operating company found the value of ore at the drainage tunnel level to be almost twice as much as the ore in the upper workings. They considered they had about $5 million worth of ore blocked out and could net about a fifth of that amount if conditions were right.

Work done on the Rawley vein between 1905 and 1910 had been mainly on developing ore and a large body of mill ore had been blocked out. After the drainage tunnel was driven, no other work was done until 1916 and 1917 when small shipments of ore were made. A 300 tpd mill was planned but not completed until 1923.

An aerial tramway 7–1/4 miles long was constructed in 1921 from the mill to Shirley on the Rio Grande Railroad, Marshall Pass Branch, above Mears Junction. Today, part of an old ore-loading platform is all that is left of Shirley.

After a great deal of money was spent on developing the mine and much ore was produced, the mine closed in 1930. During World War II and up to the early 1960s, the mine was worked by leasees and small shipments were made, according to the *Minerals Yearbooks* for that period of time. Production to 1946 was about $9 million.

Quartz, barite, pyrite, sphalerite, galena, bornite, chalcopyrite, tennantite, stromeyerite, and covellite were the minerals found in the Rawley Mine. Barite was white. Rhombic brown siderite and pink or reddish rhombic rhodochrosite also occurred. Chalcopyrite occurred in vugs as a plus and minus sphenoid. Bornite occurred as octahedrons or dododecahedrons. Quartz pseudomorphs of barite were found in the Rawley and in the Great Mogul or First Chance Mine.

Eagle Mine

The Eagle Mine was discovered in 1880, but little work was done until 1898 when a 200 foot shaft was sunk. In earlier work, a pocket of silver ore which netted $1 per pound was found at the 40 foot depth, but nothing was found to 90 feet where the water level occurred. At the 200 foot level, rich sulfide ore was hand sorted and shipments ran 130 ounces silver and 0.3 ounces gold per ton. Production up to 1906 was approximately a quarter of a million dollars. The mine worked until 1907 and was then closed until 1917. At that time some work was done up through 1922, when it again closed because the ore was of too low grade. A shaft, 650 feet deep with about 4,000 feet of drifts, developed the mine. This mine is in the so-called manganese belt, an area of manganese mineralization that surrounds the main silver–lead–copper–zinc ore deposits of the Bonanza district.

In the Eagle Mine, quartz, rhodochrosite, and green fluorite occurred with proustite, pyrargyrite, native silver, and polybasite. The fluorite appears to be octahedral but is a composite of cubes and dodecahedrons.

Rhodochrosite occurred in warped, light pink to light red rhombohedrons up to 3/4 inch in size. Quartz crystals occurred on rhodochrosite crystals in some vugs. Pyrargyrite crystals also occurred on rhodochrosite, manganocalcite, and sulfide minerals. Late rhodochrosite replaced quartz and formed a pinkish rock which resembled intergrowths of quartz, rhodonite, and rhodochrosite found in the district in other mines. Wire silver occurred with galena, sphalerite, and rhodochrosite. Pyrargyrite blebs occurred in rhodochrosite. Near the edges of ore shoots, the rhodochrosite occurred as a soft mixture with nontronite, of the montmorillonite group, according to one author. Burbank was able to confirm the presence of kaolinite only.

A specimen of the rhodochrosite-fluorite ore from the Eagle Mine was shown at the World's Fair, St. Louis, Missouri in 1904.

The Express Mine

The Express Mine is situated at the edge of a large neck of volcanic breccia. Ore is similar to that of the Eagle Mine. A 224 foot shaft develops the property.

A vein of quartz, fluorite, and rhodochrosite four feet thick is said to be exposed in the shaft of the Express Mine. This mineral is soft and bleached and may be the outer edge of the ore shoot.

Pershing Mine

The Pershing is the third mine in the manganese belt. It was mined for manganese oxides during both World Wars. Pyrolusite and psilomelane are the principal minerals. Some of it may be pseudomorphic after manganite.

The mine is developed by two short tunnels 116 feet apart vertically. Over 600,000 pounds of ore containing from 39.7 to 44 percent manganese were shipped in 1926-7. Ore was shipped to the Strategic Mineral Stockpile during and after World War II and up to the end of the government purchasing program.

Manganese oxides were mined from the upper part of this mine. Primary ore, which was probably rhodochrosite, was not reached during the World War II period of mining activity. Crystalline pyrolusite with quartz crystals and manganite occur in the ore.

Minerals Of the Bonanza mining district:

Adularia	Covellite	Psilomelane
Altaite	Dolomite	Pyrargyrite
Alunite	Embolite	Pyrite
Anatase	Empressite	Pyrolusite
Anglesite	Enargite	Quartz
Apatite	Epidote	Rhodochrosite
Argentite	Fluorite	Rhodonite
Azurite	Galena	Rickardite
Barite	Gold	Rutile
Bornite	Hematite	Sericite
Bromargyrite	Hessite	Siderite
Calcite	Jarosite	Silver
Cerargyrite	Kaolin	Sphalerite
Cerussite	Limonite	Stromeyerite
Chalcedony	Malachite	Sylvanite
Chalcocite	Manganite	Tellurite
Chalcopyrite	Mangano Siderite	Tennantite
Chlorite	Pearceite	Tetrahedrite
Chrysocolla	Petzite	Wad
Copper	Proustite	Zunyite

A bulk sample of several hundred feet of zunyite-bearing altered volcanic rock from the north side of Greenback Gulch was tested and found to contain only 0.001 percent beryllium oxide.

Villa Grove Turquoise Mine

The Villa Grove Turquoise Mine is on the northeast edge of the Bonanza mining district. This locality has produced a distinctive turquoise for many years; however, operations are erratic and not continuous.

COCHETOPA CREEK CINNABAR PROSPECT

The Cochetopa Creek cinnabar prospect is in Cochetopa Creek Valley near the Flying M Ranch. State Route 114, from U.S. 50 to Sawatch, gives access to the general area which is in Sawatch County about 20 miles south of the junction of Route 114 and U.S. 50.

Vanderwilt speaks of the prospect as a recent discovery and that considerable trenching was done during World War II to try to find the deposit in place. A 72 foot shaft was said to have cut cinnabar, in place, at a depth of 60 feet. Although other occurrences of cinnabar are known or have been reported in Colorado, (Cripple Creek and in the LaPlata Mountains) this deposit seems to be the only one in Colorado in which cinnabar was the principal mineral.

Much of the ore was found in boulders of silicified sandstone from the Dakota sandstone formation. It was highly brecciated and pyrite occurred. The Dakota sandstone occurs below volcanic rocks.

This area is near or in the Cochetopa Park caldera, one of the calderas of the San Juan volcanic field. Ash-flows from this caldera center covered large areas in the north-central part of the San Juan volcanic field; however, the local accumulations were not as great as they were away from the caldera. This caldera, one of the smaller ones, was unique in that it collapsed after the major eruptions and it did not form a complete ring, but had a trap door bounded by a horseshoe-shaped fault on the southwest side.

LA GARITA

After the Civil War, soldiers of the First Regiment of Colorado Volunteers settled in the Saguache Creek drainage of the San Luis Valley. Hispanic settlers were already in the Carnero Creek and La Garita Creek areas to the south. Ute Indians roamed the San Luis Valley and although relations were peaceful at first, the influx of people soon changed their attitude and Indian raids on the settlers began. This situation was resolved by a treaty with the Utes and their removal to a reservation.

The Hispanic people began their settlements about ten years after the Treaty of Guadalupe Hildalgo and small groups settled around La Garita. Many of them were unaware of the new laws and lost their water and land rights to the new settlers by not registering them as required. Hills around La Garita had been used as lookout points by the Indians and the name, The Lookout, seemed to fit the place. La Garita had a small telephone company by 1917 and some 230 miles of telephone lines. The school was closed in 1955 and the church in 1968. There were still fifteen to twenty families using the post office in 1972.

A small brecciated area about two miles west of La Garita, was found to contain free gold in tight veins. This area, on Carnero Creek, was reported by the Director of the Mint as the Carvero Mining Camp in 1881. The name was probably misspelled with a ''v'' instead of an ''n''; however, this area became the Crystal Hill mining district. Gold–silver ore was produced from the La Garita area from time to time through the 1920s. Total production was less than $100,000. This area is usually combined with another small mining area between Lime Creek and Beidell Creek. (Fig. 4–3).

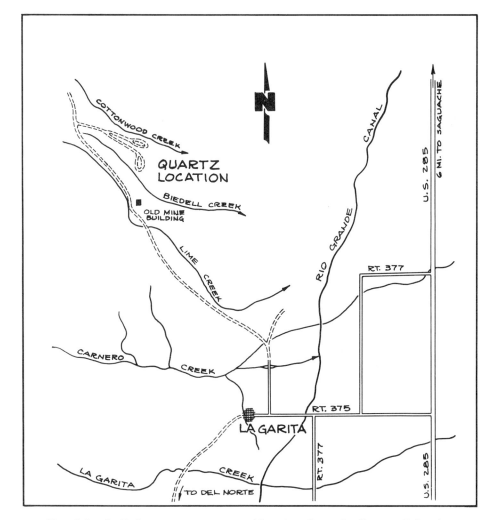

Fig. 4–3. LaGarita quartz area—general location, Saguache County, Colorado.

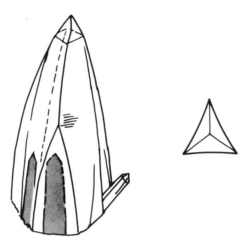

Fig. 4-4. Trigonal termination of quartz showing phantom growth. △ = Typical view down C-axis of trigonal termination.

In 1865, Mark Beidell bought some land on La Garita Creek. Later, a small creek north of Lime Creek was named for this pioneer rancher and mining man who had holdings in the Bonanza and Silverton mining districts. A small mining camp, Beidell (Biedell) was later established on the divide between Lime Creek and Beidell Creek, about eight miles northwest of La Garita. The mineral, beidellite was found in the Buckhorn and Esperanzo Mines and named for Beidell, the type locality. A find of good ore was made in 1881 and the name of this location became Crystal, which was at the site of early Beidell.

Confusion in spelling names seemed to go with the area and changing the name to Crystal was the easy solution. The occurrence of many quartz crystals was a Bonanza for mineral collectors.

The bid to fame of the La Garita area lies not in its mineral production, but in a lowly clay material of the montmorillonite group, beidellite, that has its type locality in this area.

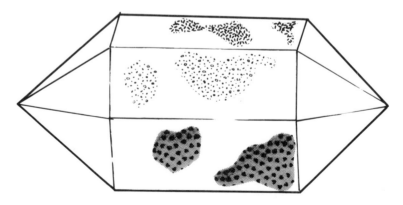

Fig. 4-5. Phantom solutions pits in quartz (often amethyst), LaGarita.

Beidellite was abundant on the dumps of the Buckhorn and Esperanzo Mines and found in several other old gold–silver mines. Larsen and Wherry in 1916 first described the mineral as leverrierite but later changed it to beidellite. The type locality was Beidell. Grim and Rowland found that beidellite, from type locality Wagon Wheel Gap was a mixture. Ross and Hendricks redefined the species and it is valid today. Dana describes the mineral as occurring in thin crystal plates, white, reddish, or brownish gray in color, with a waxy to vitreous luster. It occurred as a clay gouge of minute crystal plate at Beidell and the mineral occurred in Ouray and San Miguel Counties in the Virginius, Terrible, and other mines south of the Stony Mountain stock. It was thought to be formed by hydrothermal alteration of fault gouge.

Quartz from this area has been collected for many years. Most of it occurs with trigonal terminations, with three faces depressed. Some specimens are amethyst. Other specimens found exhibit phantoms, as solution pits, and bubbles. (Figs. 4–4 and 4–5).

REFERENCES

A–4 Lindgren Volume-(McLaughlin), A–5 Ridge (Tweto), (Sec. 27), (Tweto), (Sec. 32), C–9, C–12, C–14, C–16, D–1, (Burbank), (Traver), F–3, G–1, G–5, G–7, G–8, H–13, J–18, J–34, J–38, J–39, J–45, J–46, J–56, L–1, 1946–1970, N–12, P–7 James, (Buchanan), (Bruns), (Bauer), (Knepper), R–7, R–11, S–11, S–29, S–40, S–52, S–62, S–68, S–97, S–102, S–116, S–134, S–136, S–148.

SAN JUAN MOUNTAINS

The San Juan Mountains fill the southwest corner of Colorado, south of the Gunnison River. They are a large volcanic pile and related volcanic field occupying the area west of the San Luis Valley and east of the Colorado Plateau. Although their complex geologic history has been studied for almost a hundred years, it is only now starting to unfold. Modern technology is supplying the magic ingredient.

MINES NEAR SAWPIT

In the red beds of the Colorado Plateau exposed by the San Miguel River near Sawpit, San Miguel County, small but interesting ore bodies were mined in the past. This area is just west of Telluride and the San Juan volcanic field. Economic value of these deposits was not significant. Sawpit is about two miles up the river from Placerville, an early day placer mining and later a vanadium mining center. An impure limestone bed in the Entrada formation, the same formation in which bedded deposits of vanadium occurred, called the slick rim by the miners, was replaced to form an ore deposit. These deposits were 100 to 200 feet long, 25 feet wide, and 3 to 5 feet high. They were parallel to each other along a series of E-W fissures. East of the area, a laccolithic mass of diorite occurs and pyroxene-andesite dikes cut the local area. Sandstone dikes similar to the ones found near Ouray (described ahead in that section) occur. Red sedimentary beds have been bleached yellow to gray-white by hydrothermal alteration near the deposits.

Hydrocarbons occur with the ore minerals. Gold values were four times the silver values and were up to an ounce per ton. Lead ran as high as 18 percent. Pyrite, galena, and cerussite were ore minerals. Limonite in the oxidized ore carried the gold.

In his study of the hydrocarbon-bearing veins of the Placerville area, Wilmarth found the sequence of mineral deposition to be calcite, barite, and pyrite, hydrocarbons and then base metal sulfides. Sulfide minerals were deposited in the following order: pyrite, chalcopyrite, bornite, tetrahedrite, galena, and sphalerite.

The hydrocarbons were found to be more like those found in oil and not like those found in coal. Some were radioactive and some were not. Coffinite and metallo-organic compounds were thought to be the source of silver, cobalt, chromium, copper, molybdenum, nickel, lead, vanadium, and yttrium as trace-metal constituents of the hydrocarbons. Calcites contained greater quantities of the trace elements lead, cobalt, nickel, scandium, vanadium, and rare-earth metals than the barite. Small hydrocarbon masses were found in the Smuggler Mine at Telluride. This material collected in the mill circuit but was said not to be a problem in concentrating the ore.

MT. SNEFFELS-TELLURIDE DISTRICT

Mt. Sneffels–Telluride district is in the upper part of Canyon Creek drainage of Mt. Sneffels, Ouray County, and the adjacent upper part of San Miguel County. The district extends to Telluride and has been the most productive area of the western part of the San Juan Mountains.

An extensive fracture system extending from the ring-fracture zone of the Silverton caldera northwest to the Mt. Sneffels–Stony Mountain stock has been filled with intrusive dikes that outline the fracturing. Later reopening along these dikes allowed deposition of ore minerals to form the strong and continuous veins of the area (Fig. 4–6).

Several stages of mineralization have been recognized in the veins and the gold-quartz stage of the Camp Bird Mine was probably the last; it has been dated at 10.5 ± 0.3 m.y.B.P. Below the San Juan volcanic units replacement beds occur in the Telluride Conglomerate adjacent to the veins. Mineralization of these replacement deposits is thought to be contemporaneous; however, replacement ore from the Argentine vein, of Idarado Mining Co., was dated at 17.0 ± 0.6 m.y.B.P. The youngest mineralization on the Camp Bird vein is therefore almost seven million years younger than the last mineralization on the Argentine vein.

Minerals of the Mt. Sneffels–Telluride district as listed in 1896-7 by Purington included: galena, freibergite in the Japan, Smuggler, and Virginius

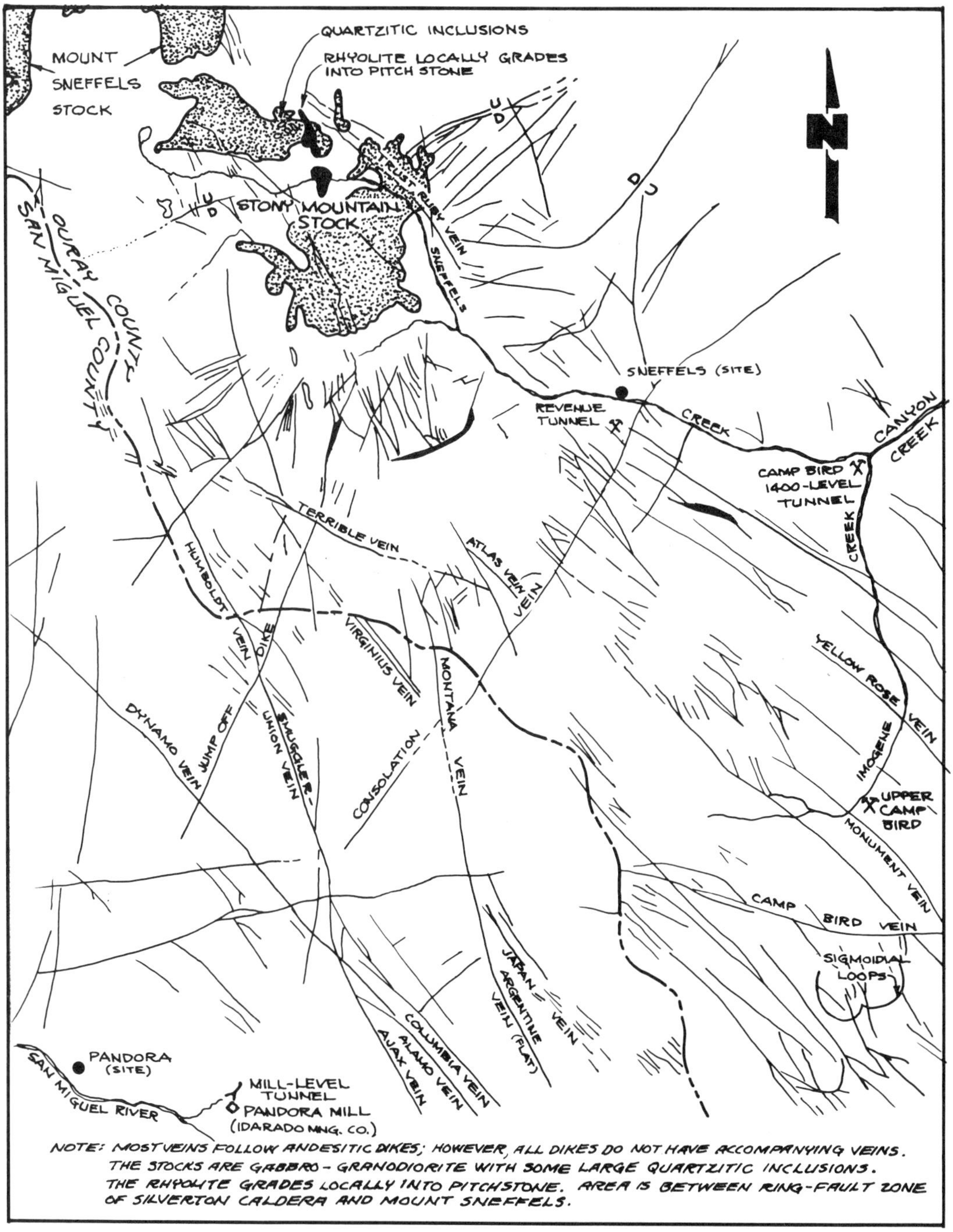

Fig. 4–6. Relation of dikes and veins to the Mount Sneffels and Stony Mountain stocks, Telluride and Mount Sneffels mining districts, Ouray and San Miguel Cos., Colorado. Adapted from U.S.G.S. Ironton Quad., 1964 and Telluride Quad., 1966 (Burbank and Luedke).

Mines; polybasite, proustite, and pyrargyrite in the Smuggler Mine; and stephanite in the Humboldt and Smuggler Mines.

Zinc-blende or sphalerite was not considered an ore mineral at that time. The Big Elephant vein in Savage Basin, the Tomboy, Japan, Smuggler, Yankee Boy, Ruby Trust, sometimes called the Trust Ruby Mine, and Virginius Mines all carried zinc blende. Chalcopyrite was not considered an ore mineral at that time either. It was found in the Tomboy and Virginius Mines.

Amphibole occurred in the Japan Mine, barite in the Smuggler Mine, fluorite in the Ruby Trust Mine, chloride of copper in the Smuggler Mine; zoisite in the Yankee Boy Mine; rhodochrosite in the Japan, Smuggler, Cimarron, Ruby Trust, and Virginius Mines, and calcite in the Japan, Smuggler, Yankee Boy, Ruby Trust, and Virginius Mines.

Mispickel, the old name for arsenopyrite, occurred in the Yankee Boy Mine, chalcanthite, magnetite, sericite, siderite, and pyrite were other minerals found in the mines working at that time.

Beautiful quartz crystals occurred in the Smuggler vein. Quartz was black and blue as well as clear or milky. The black and blue quartz had minute crystals of pyrite included. Fragments of vein quartz were enclosed in later quartz in the Virginius Mine. Inclusions in quartz included gas and liquid and they were found in the Tomboy, Ruby Trust, and Virginius Mines. Streaks of fluorite up to two feet wide were found in the Tomboy Mine.

Idarado

Idarado Mining Company was organized in the late 1930s to mine a group of famous mines through the Treasury Tunnel, formerly the Hammond Tunnel. There were a large number of mining claims involved but the most famous mines were the Black Bear, Barstow, and Imogene.

Treasury Tunnel, on U.S. Highway 550 north of Red Mountain Pass and on the east side of LaPlata Mountain, had been driven in the early 1900s to the Handicap vein and extended by crosscut tunnel to the St. Paul vein. It had a length of 5,500 feet at the time Idarado acquired it. Later, the Barstow was connected to the Treasury Tunnel by a cross cut and raises as the old workings were above the Treasury Tunnel level.

In San Miguel County on the west side of Telluride Peak, the Black Bear Mine is in Ingram Basin at 12,325 feet elevation. This mine was discovered and worked by a group of Finnish miners from the iron mines of the Lake Superior area. But by 1912, it was sold at a sheriff's sale. It was intermittently worked until 1926 when a snowslide killed two men and destroyed the mine buildings. Two years later, it was again sold at a sheriff's sale. An aerial tramway and a packtrail provided the only access. Idarado acquired the mine in 1939.

The Barstow–St. Paul vein and the Handicap–Tomboy vein are two of several nearly parallel veins that extend radially from the ring fault zone of the Silverton caldera northwest toward the Sneffels–Stony Mountain granodiorite stock. They are the strongest veins of the local area. The Barstow–St. Paul vein passes through Upper Imogene Basin in the Cabin Creek drainage; however, the Handicap-Tomboy vein passes through Savage Basin in San Miguel County. Barstow-St. Paul vein splits and one part junctions one split of the Camp Bird vein just north of Chicago Peak and both vein systems seem to disintegrate at this point. The Pandora vein is considered by some people to be the continuation of the Camp Bird vein.

Under a series of World War II programs to provide metals for the war, Metals Reserve Company leased the Idarado Property and appointed Sunshine Mining Company, one of the three owners, as operator. The Treasury Tunnel was to be extended to the Black Bear (lead–zinc) vein, a distance of 3,000 feet. This would make the Treasury Tunnel 11,725 feet long and it was also planned to drive 3,225 feet along the Black Bear to develop the ore shoot exposed in the old workings above. A 1,100 foot raise would also be driven to connect the old workings with the Treasury Tunnel.

Newmont Mining Company and Mine and Smelter Supply Company were the other partners in Idarado and Newmont had an option to purchase Idarado when Metals Reserve Company felt production of the needed metals was assured. Newmont exercised this option in March, 1944, and became sole owner of Idarado.

By October, 1943, the Treasury Tunnel reached the Black Bear vein, a flat vein, at a distance of 8,700 feet from the portal. The ore was there—four to eight feet of solid galena-sphalerite ore. Long John Austin, famous tunnel foreman, who later drove part of the Leadville drainage tunnel, set a few new records as he had in driving other such tunnels (Fig. 4–7).

When the Black Bear vein was reached, the tunnel was turned to follow it for about 3,000 feet. A raise to the old Black Bear workings was started at a point 450 feet from the east end of this drift. Treasury Tunnel was designated the 12th level and the 1,000 foot raise cut the old workings at the 6th level. A block of mill grade ore 2,000 feet long by 1,000 feet high by 7 feet wide was exposed for mining. This vein was worked for a length of 4,000 feet.

The flat Black Bear vein splits off the southeast end of the Argentine vein and strikes more E-W.

Red Mountain Mill, at the mouth of the Treasury Tunnel, shipped the first load of concentrates in March, 1945. By April, 1946, mill capacity was increased from 300 to 800 tpd.

A 1,000 foot winze was started from the Treasury Tunnel to explore the Telluride Conglomerate and red beds below the San Juan formation. Replacement ore was later found and mined at this horizon. Crosscuts were driven to the Argentine, Columbia, Ida, and Ajax veins, which, with the Smuggler-Union, Liberty Bell, Flora, Ansborough, Japan, Montana, Pandora, Tomboy, and many other mining claims had been acquired from Telluride Mining Company in May, 1953. The Pandora Mill, 1,800 tons per day capacity, at Telluride, was part of the acquisition. These mining properties were all old and famous.

Mines and veins which were worked by the Idarado Mining Co., Inc. were collectively known as the Idarado Mine. Some retained their earlier, and often

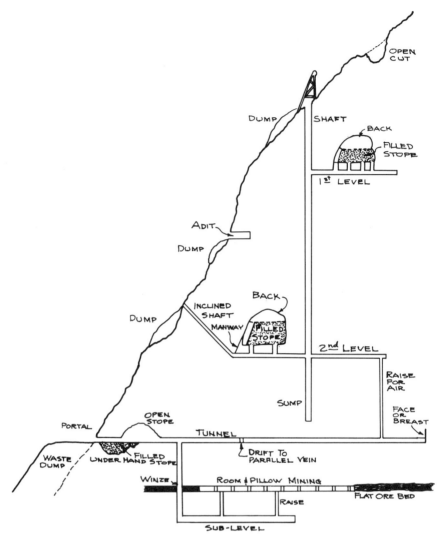

Fig. 4-7. Terminology of underground workings.

famous, identities while others simply poured out their ore reserves to swell the mill feed.

Hillebran recognized four stages of mineral deposition in the Idarado Mine. These stages are:

1. Formation of base metal sulfides and most of the pyrite; epiodote as a product of wallrock alternation, rhodonite (see discussion on rhodonite under American Tunnel section, ahead), chlorite, sericite, and most of the clay minerals.

2. Quartz with brecciation and veining of earlier sulfides, adularia, flourite, rhodochrosite, and rhodonite.

3. Base metal sulfides in interstices of quartz crystals, calcite, late quartz, and gold (overlaps with stage 4).

4. Gold in quartz (white, "bony", greenish, and amethystine), fine-grained chalcopyrite, and sphalerite.

He also found that zoning occurs along the veins as follows: gold decreased at depth to the south end of the vein system; lead decreased in depth to the north; silver and copper increased with depth to the south; zinc and base metals decreased with depth to the north.

Nash recognized four gross stages with multiple reopening of the veins and shearing to varying degrees. They were:

1. An early sulfide stage with abundant sphalerite and galena, small amount of quartz, and lesser amounts of chalocopyrite and pyrite.

2. Quartz and gangue minerals encrusted the first stage, much crushing and shearing occurred with amounts of sphalerite, galena, and pyrite. Hematite and anhydrite formed in the Basin vein.

3. Late sulfides with sulfide grains occurred intergrown or interstitial to well-formed quartz crystals (Fig. 4–8). Gold, this stage cut and coated stages one and two.

4. Gold, quartz, fluorite, and tan carbonates fill cavities in structures not well aligned with earlier vein trends.

In the replacement deposits in the Telluride Conglomerate below the volanic formations, Nash noted a first stage in which calc-silicate alteration changed limestone clasts, original carbonate, and hematite to pink or green epiodote, secondary carbonates, rhodonite, chlorite, and more rarely garnet and diopside. Pyrite was probably the only sulfide of this stage.

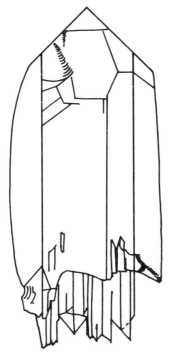

Fig. 4–8.   Quartz crystal showing root structure due to Dauphine twinning, Idarado Mine.

Lipman found the composite veins extending northwest from the Silverton caldera ring fault zone toward the Sneffels intrusives (Idarado and Camp Bird) to have three stages of mineralization:

1. Early near-barren quartz and pyrite.
2. Base metal sulfide stage with highest grade ore, and
3. A local gold-quartz stage (10.5 ± 0.5 m.y.B.P. for ore high in the Camp Bird vein and 10.2 ± 0.3 m.y.B.P. for replacement ore beds of the Orphan Mine. Replacement ore in the Argentine vein, Idarado Mine, had an age of 17.0 ± 0.6 m.y.B.P.). Casadevall and Ohmoto give dates of 13.1 to 17.0 m.y.B.P. for Idarado Mine ore.

Greenockite and cosalite occur in ores of this area. Dana gives bismutite as a mineral found in this district. Benjaminite (a mixture of berryite and other sulfosalts) was reported in early literature but this discredited bismuth species was found to be a mixture.

Quartz cast pseudomorphs have occurred in the minerals of the San Juan Mountains. Many of these casts have come from the Idarado Mine and have been brought from the mine in sheets as large as three feet square (Fig. 4–9).

The quartz coatings are usually composed of myriads of small crystal points and are a brilliant white, saccharoidal by some descriptions, but some are heavily iron stained. Cubic casts after fluorite are up to an inch in size and casts of octahederal fluorite are somewhat larger. Although fluorite is the most common mineral of which casts are found, calcite, barite, and anhydrite casts also occur (Fig. 4–10).

In the middle 1960s, a large vug lined with calcite crystals coated with pyrite

Fig. 4–9. Quartz cast of calcite, Idarado Mine (JM#232–2).

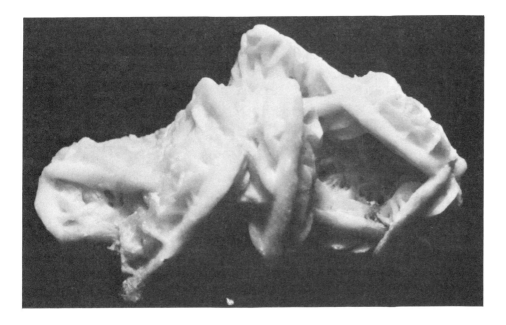

Fig. 4–10. Calcite pseudomorph after barite, Idarado Mine (JM#246–1).

was opened. This vug furnished specimens to many museums and collectors but was second in importance to the manganocalcite vug opened in 1971-2. Pink manganocalcite, now a rare classic from this vug is probably as fine as any ever recovered in mining. It fluoresces a brilliant red.

Idarado Mining Co., after the mine closed, cooperated with the Denver Museum of Natural History to mine and reproduce at the museum an example of one of the vugs for which this mine was so famous. When completed, it will be on display at the museum as a companion to the Cave of the Swords Grotto.

Quartz crystals of the Argentine vein frequently had fluid inclusions in them. Scepters from this vein were seen in private collections.

Black Bear Mine

Minerals of the earlier workings of the Black Bear were sphalerite, galena, pyrite, chalcopyrite, and silver. The silver was in argentiferous gray copper (tetrahedrite-tennantite) and galena. Gangue minerals were quartz with minor rhodochrosite, rhodonite, and calcite.

Tomboy Mine

Original discovery of the vein on which the Tomboy Mine was developed was on the Belmont claim discovered in 1880. The Tomboy Mine was located in 1886 but not much work was done until 1894-5 when $0.6 million was produced. In 1886, this was raised to $0.8 million and by 1897 production was running at the rate of $1.8 million per year. The vein was 4 to 7 feet wide with some widths up to 12 feet reported.

The two largest mines in the Telluride district at that time were the Liberty Bell, which produced $16 million, and the Tomboy in Savage Basin. The Tomboy was sold in 1897 for $2 million to the Rothchilds of London and it operated until 1928.

The Tomboy Mine was famous for its gold which occurred in saccharoidal or granular quartz with manganese oxides. Calcite, fluorite, siderite, galena, sphalerite, and rhodochrosite occurred in minor amounts.

It was said that total length of underground workings in the Sneffels–Telluride district was 350 miles.

Smuggler Vein

John Fallon discovered the Sheridan Mine in Marshall Basin in 1875. He did not work it but leased it until 1883 when he sold it for $40,000 to an English–Scottish group of bankers living in Shanghai. They also acquired the Mendota, Union and the Smuggler veins, all on the same vein system. It was in 1876 that J. B. Ingram found that the Sheridan and the Union claims overlapped the legal limits by 500 feet. He staked the area in between these two claims and called it the Smuggler Mine. The English Syndicate, as they were called, bought the Pandora Mill in 1888. A 6,700 foot aerial tramway was built to send 300 to 400 tpd to the mill from Marshall Basin. By 1898, the Smuggler-Union Vein was being mined for a length of two miles and the Humboldt and Seventy-Six claims had been added to the group. Ore from the Humboldt had to be packed down the mountain to the head of the aerial tramway. That same year Father Gibbons reported in his famous sketch book that the Sheridan and the Humboldt Mines were working in February. Not all of the high mines were worked in the winter due to snowslides and severe weather conditions.

By 1900, underground workings on the Smuggler-Union vein totaled 35 miles in length. The Smuggler vein was offset to the east in the middle of the Seventy-Six claim and it was also offset by the Pandora vein. Some of the ore first mined on the Smuggler ran 800 ozs. silver and 18 ozs. gold per ton. Average value of the ore was "slightly over 1/2 oz. gold and 12 ozs. silver per ton." The ore was hand sorted with higher grade going directly to the smelter and the rest to the mill. Production up to 1898 was $12 million from the Smuggler vein.

In 1884, the Sheridan produced 400 tons of ore worth $225 per ton and 1,000 tons of ore averaging from $50 to $55 per ton. Concentrates produced in the mill at Pandora ran $400 to $450 per ton.

The Smuggler–Union Mine closed in 1928 after 52 years of continuous operation. It had been stoped for a horizontal distance of about 10,000 feet and a vertical distance of about 6,000 feet. The 696-winze in the Smuggler-Union Mine below the Pennsylvania Tunnel level explored the Telluride Conglomerate which was found to be 370 feet thick and resting on the Morrison formation.

Tomboy Gold Mines, an English company, mined the Montana–Argentine vein from 1912-27 and produced $26 million. That part of the Montana–Argentine vein between the Ophir Tunnel level and the Revenue Tunnel was mined between 1900 and 1910 through the Revenue Tunnel, which is in Canyon Creek drainage, Ouray County. Stopes between the 1700 and Revenue Tunnel levels and some high stopes were mined by Telluride Mines, Inc. in the 1940s. Montana vein was developed on the Pennsylvania Tunnel level for over 4,000 feet and on some upper levels it was stoped for over 6,000 feet; Argentine vein has been mined for over 15,000 feet in length and 3,700 feet in depth. The Japan vein, a cross vein, produced $0.60 million east of the Montana–Argentine vein; this mine had a large production of silver–gold base-metal ore in the early days of the Telluride district. Idarado had over 5,000 acres of patented mining claims, 80 miles of interconnecting tunnels, drifts, and crosscuts, and about 20 miles of drifts. About seven miles of crosscut tunnels are open, mostly on the Montana–Argentine, Black Bear, and Ajax sections of the Ajax–Smuggler–Union vein.

The Mill Level Tunnel, with portal at the Pandora Mill, intersects the Argentine vein 7,150 feet from the portal and by way of interconnecting raises and drifts it was possible to go from the Pandora Mill to the Red Mountain portal of the Treasury Tunnel, a distance of about six miles.

Idarado started work on the Smuggler–Union Vein in 1955, and in 1957 most of the work was being done on the Montana–Argentine and Black Bear veins. After 1956, when the Red Mountain Mill was dismantled, all ore was milled at the Pandora Mill. Production of the group was said to be $6.6 million in 1958.

By 1961, Idarado was mining on 7,200 feet of strike length and 2,000 feet of dip along the Argentine vein and 5,000 feet of strike and 1,500 feet of dip on the Black Bear vein. Work started on the Cross vein in 1966.

In 1972, the Montana–Argentine vein had been developed for a length of 15,000 feet and for a depth of 3,700 feet. Ore was being mined from more than 15 veins and from replacement deposits in the Telluride Conglomerate.

In the fall of 1978, after over 40 years of continuous operation, the Idarado Mining Company closed their San Juan operations. Base metal prices were said to be the cause of this action.

Open vugs with interlocking quartz crystals were common in the Smuggler Mine. Calcite, siderite, ankerite, barite, and rhodochrosite were other gangue minerals. When rhodochrosite was present in quantity enough to color the vein, the ore was deficient in gold and silver. Gold in quartz replaced earlier sulfide ore. Pyrargyrite, tetrahedrite, proustite, polybasite, pearceite, possibly stephanite, and arsenical silver minerals were said to have occurred in the ore. Galena, sphalerite, gold, chalcopyrite and pyrite were the principal minerals. Freibergite–tetrahedrite series minerals were present and were probably some of the unidentified arsenical silver minerals. Hydrocarbon material occurred in the ore and was found in the mill circuit as floating globs, however, it did not seem to cause any real problems. Hydrocarbons also occurred in the mines at Sawpit and Placerville just a few miles down the San Miguel River from Telluride.

Japan Vein

Galena, sphalerite, gold, argentite, and wire silver in a gangue of quartz with rhodochrosite and fluorite occurred in the Japan vein.

Barstow Mine

The Barstow Mine is in the ring fault zone of the Silverton caldera on the Red Mountain side of LaPlata Mountain. It was worked by one company from 1895 to 1913 and produced $0.7 million. Leasees worked the mine until it was consolidated with the Idarado holdings in the early 1930s. It has almost two miles of underground workings, most of which are not accessible due to soft, caveprone ground. It is connected to the Treasury Tunnel by a crosscut tunnel and raises and was worked through this tunnel during World War II.

Gold and silver were the most important minerals produced; however, 17,000 tons of fluorspar were produced at one time. This material ran 85–90 percent calcium fluoride and it was closer to fluorite than to the common fluorspar usually mined in Colorado. This fluorite came from an intersecting vein and not the main one. It was the largest body of fluorspar found in any of the San Juan Mines.

A cymoidal (sigmoidal) loop in the vein was evidently responsible for the ore bodies and the largest two were at opposite ends of the loop. This loop widened and increased with depth; the largest ore body being up to 800 feet long. White quartz in the mine contained slivers of wall rock as inclusions. A dark colored quartz with fine-grained sulfides carried free gold.

Meldrum Tunnel

Every early mining area had its share of people with big dreams. Some dreamers made their dream a reality, most did not. One such dream was the Meldrum Tunnel that was started in the late 1890s and projected to be a railroad tunnel 4-½ miles long. It was to go from the Red Mountain district to Pandora, a mile above Telluride.

The east portal is above Ironton Park and below the Treasury Tunnel of Idarado Mining Co. The east heading was extended 1,500 feet and the west heading 2,500 feet. Cross section of the tunnel was 12 feet by 12 feet. Projected cost was between $4 million and $5 million.

The mines in the Red Mountain district and the Telluride mines were at their zenith and it looked like a good investment. Then the company went bankrupt and one more dream faded. In 1952, Idarado Mining Co. lengthened the 2,500 foot west section of the Meldrum Tunnel to connect with the Black Bear and Ajax workings. It is part of the 2,000 level workings.

Revenue Group

The Virginius, Cumberland, Atlas, and Terrible veins were consolidated as a group and the Revenue Tunnel was driven to serve as a drainage and transportation tunnel for the group. The tunnel was completed in 1899 and with the various mines had 30 miles of underground workings by 1900. A depth of 3,000 feet was obtained on some of the veins.

The Cumberland–Atlas vein crosses the Revenue Tunnel 4,000 feet from the portal and the Virginius is 7,500 feet from the portal. At this point, the Revenue Tunnel is about 2,000 feet below the surface. A winze 750 feet was sunk at this point and some mining was done; however, most of the ore came from above the tunnel level. Drifts to the Sidney and Terrible developed these veins. The Terrible drift was 200 feet beyond the intersection of the Terrible and Ansborough veins. A drift to the Montana vein was about 500 feet above the Pennsylvania Tunnel. On the Pennsylvania level, the Montana was stoped for over 4,000 feet and on some upper levels for 6,000 feet.

Production from the original Revenue Group exceeded $11.6 million. The tunnel, which is in Upper Canyon Creek at the site of the ghost town of Sneffels, is in the Mt. Sneffels mining district. Most of the veins developed are in San Miguel County.

Minerals of the district are the same, both vein and replacement ore, as found in the Telluride district.

The Montana vein produced some hubnerite ore during World War II from the northern part of the vein. It was sacked but never shipped.

Virginius Mine

The Virginius Mine is in the Upper Canyon Creek drainage and was one of the earliest mines worked in the Mt. Sneffels district. As early as 1881, a report by the Director of the Mint gave a production of $75,000. In the early 1890s the Revenue Tunnel was driven 7,500 feet to cut the vein at a depth of 2,000 feet below the old workings. By 1887, the vein had been worked for a length of 3,000 feet and a vertical distance of 2,000 feet. By 1896, all the ore was coming from the lower level (Revenue Tunnel). Haulage and lighting in the mine were by electric power. Production by 1896 was $4 million.

The Denver Times, in 1898, reported that 500 to 600 men were working in the Virginius and Revenue Mines. The value of ore had fallen off and was lower in silver but higher in gold; however, in 1885, all the ore produced for the year averaged $400 per ton. The mine had been working for twenty years and had 12 to 15 miles of underground workings at that time.

The Virginius produced chiefly silver in silver–tennantite ore with base metal mineralization in a quartz–carbonate gangue.

Beidellite was one of the gangue minerals in the Virginius Mine. Beidell, for whom the mineral was named, from the type locality in the Beidell Creek mines of Sagauche County, was said to have had an interest in this famous mine.

Camp Bird Mine

William Weston and George Barber staked the Una and Gertrude claims and five others in Imogene Basin in 1877. As these claims were at an elevation of 11,500 feet and the ore ran only $12 to $20 per ton in gold, they did only assessment work. The smelters would not pay for less than an ounce of gold per ton ($20); therefore, it would not pay to work. It cost $35 per ton and $45 per ton, respectively, to transport the ore and to smelt it; ore had to run at least $100 per ton to pay.

The Reed brothers drove a crosscut tunnel that intersected the Una vein 150 feet below the outcrop but it was barren of ore where they cut it. They retained the Una claim. Weston and Barber continued to work their other claims until in 1881 they sold the group to a lawyer of Quincy, Illinois, for the sum of $50,000. The new owner embarked on a stock selling scheme and ordered a big mill for the mines. The company was wrecked by such tactics. The last work done on the Gertrude was a contract to drive 50 feet on the vein but money ran out and the other work was closed for the winter. The contractor quit after 38 feet had been driven. Later it was found that the last 10 feet of this contract had passed through gold-bearing quartz.

In 1896, Tom F. Walsh, who was operating a smelter in Silverton, principally on lead–silver ore from the Guston volcanic pipe on Red Mountain, visited the area in search of siliceous ore which carried some gold. The silica was needed to flux the lead–silver ore of the Guston and if that flux ore contained some gold this would help pay the cost of obtaining it.

A. W. Richardson, one of the first prospectors in Imogene Basin, was asked by Walsh to obtain dump samples for assay for him. Ore from the Gertrude dump was rich in gold and a check of the mine showed gold–quartz ore in the last ten feet of that 38 foot drift.

In the intervening years the old Weston and Barber group had been sold for taxes but H. W. Reed still owned the Una claim that Walsh bought for $10,000. He bought up all the other claims in the area and had Richardson stake the Camp Bird claim east of the Gertrude, after the ore was found in place on the Gertrude (Fig. 4–11).

The Director of the Mint's report for 1898 best describes what next happened:

The property of Thomas F. Walsh which less than 18 months ago was a prospect has developed into a Bonanza property. Values are entirely in gold. Two levels of 2,500 feet each are being worked in Imogene Basin and a third level has been started. Erection of a 80 tpd mill at Potosi, 6 miles from Ouray, at the confluence of Imogene and Sneffels Creeks, in 49 days was a

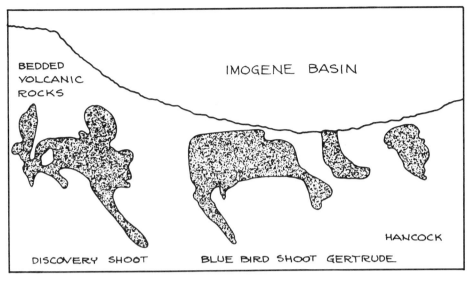

Fig. 4-11. Early Bonanza ore shoots of the upper part of the Camp Bird vein. Sketch is a projection into plane of the vein. The 1400-foot Level Tunnel, on Canyon Creek, is about that distance below the upper workings in Imogene Basin. Adapted from Lindgren (1933) from an earlier section by J. E. Spurr.

marvel of speed as was the erection of a 2 mile long aerial tramway from mine to mill. Electric power from Ames power station, 17 miles away at Ophir, was being used throughout mine and mill.

By 1900, the Director of the Mint reported the mill capacity had been increased to 300 tons per day and 260 men were working.

Walsh sold the Camp Bird in 1913 to Camp Bird, Ltd., an English company for $5,250,000 and as a major stockholder he received part of the nearly $6 million paid in dividends. By 1916, most of the high grade gold ore which occurred in the upper 500 feet of the vein had been mined. The Una crosscut; the Gertrude crosscut; and the Camp Bird upper workings tunnels had been used to exploit the Blue Bird gold ore shoot. Ore above the third level averaged 1.4 ounces gold and 2 ounces silver per ton. Below the third level gold decreased so that, at the sixth level, it was averaging 0.13 ounces gold per ton, 4.5 ounces silver, 2.2 percent lead and 2.4 percent zinc, pyrite and chalcopyrite ore occurred below the gold quartz ore. The gold ore was free milling and was treated in a stamp mill. Free milling ore was ore in which the gold was released from the gangue when it was crushed.

There were four ore shoots mined in the Camp Bird vein. The Hematite shoot was the most easterly and was named for the hematite in the ore. Blue Bird shoot was the gold quartz shoot of early Bonanza days. To the west was the Big Discovery shoot and the smaller Hancock shoot. The Big Discovery was still being mined as late as 1950.

Drilling under the Hematite stope in 1945 had disclosed mineralization of the Telluride Conglomerate horizon; however, another management followed this up 24 years later.

A subsidiary company was organized to drive the 1400 foot level tunnel to intersect the vein below the Imogene Basin workings, about 2,000 feet below the outcrop. The portal was at the mill. This tunnel was driven 11,078 feet to intersect the vein and then drifted 3,000 feet eastward and 2,000 feet westward along the vein. Little ore was encountered, however, by 1950 the Camp Bird had produced $34 million. In 1925, King Lease, Inc. leased the mine and worked the basemetal ores for the next 37 years. By 1952, there were seven miles of underground workings and in 1956 the mill was being revamped. The Revenue Tunnel dump was run through the mill and a four year period of development work was started. A 600 ton per day mill was built at the site of the 1906 mill in 1960, but mine and mill were closed March, 1963.

Federal Resources acquired the mine, mill, and the Revenue Tunnel in October and spent the next two years doing development work. The old Hidden Treasure Mine, one of the mines worked in Imogene Basin in the early days, was leased from Edward and John McLean, grandsons of Thomas Walsh. Work was started full scale in 1965 and 1966. In 1968, seven diamond drill holes into the 8,572 vein intercepted the Telluride Conglomerate 700 feet below the 1,400 foot level tunnel and silver–lead–zinc replacement ore up to 50 feet thick was cut in four holes. Further drilling in early 1969 disclosed a replacement body, along the Orphan vein and between the Orphan and 8572 veins, 145 feet wide by at least 500 feet long and from three to 63 feet in depth.

A winze was sunk on the 1400 foot level, 8,572 feet from the portal, to the ore body at a depth of 700 feet. This became the 2100 level. The Camp Bird vein is cut in the 1400 foot level tunnel at 11,500 feet from the portal and the Pierson vein at 5,500 feet. The winze followed the Walsh crosscut vein (8572 vein) and it was found this vein intersected the Orphan vein 75 feet above the 1400 foot level tunnel.

Some work was done on the Pierson vein and the west Camp Bird in 1975, however, the replacement beds were thought to be worked out and the mine closed in the fall of 1977, about 100 years after Weston and Barber located their seven claims.

Spurr pointed out that gold in the Camp Bird vein came up through a thick volcanic sequence to be deposited under a specific andesite sheet.

The Camp Bird vein produced $27 million from the upper 3,000 feet between 1903 and 1916. Four ore shoots, the Discovery, Blue Bird, and the small Gertrude and Hancock shoots, were worked. Gold was the principal mineral with silver, lead, and copper of less value. Gold was fine grained and occurred with galena, sphalerite, pyrite, and finely distributed tellurides, in a gangue of quartz, sometimes encrusted with rhodochrosite, calcite, and fluorite.

The Camp Bird vein was a compound system of mineralized fault zones and may have had three main mineralizing stages in the southeast end of the vein. On the 1,400 level hematite formed the principal mineral of the Hematite stope. Base metal sulfides veined and in some cases replaced the hematite. Gold-bearing quartz was the last stage of mineralization. This ore is the earliest ore that has been radiometrically dated in the San Juan Mountains— 10 m.y.B.P.

The gold zone extended from the old third level in Imogene basin, upward for about 500 feet. Hematite also occurred in some of the old upper workings.

Between the sixth and 1,400 levels, the ore averaged 0.13 ounces gold, 4.5 ounces silver, 2.2 percent lead and 2.4 percent zinc per ton.

Below the oxidized zone iron, lead, copper and zinc sulfides were the ore minerals with some hematite. Calcite, in large crystals, was frequently found and barite and fluorite occurred on the 1,400 level.

After work was confined to the winze below the 1,400 level, many fine specimens of chalcopyrite, sphalerite, galena and calcite came from the Orphan vein and the Walsh cross-vein as well as vugs in the base metal replacement beds in the Telluride Conglomerate where vugs were frequently found.

In the Telluride Conglomerate epidote occurred as dark greenish-black to brownish-green encrustations. Yellow-green, transparent, minute crystals of a manganese-rich variety also occurred. Sometimes both minerals were found together. Dana gives the varietal names of thallite, delphinite, iosanite to yellowish green crystals of epiodote. The name thallite has been used for this mineral. (Fig. 4-12).

Pink and red varieties of epidote have been reported from the replacement deposits. Hurlbut says a solid solution extends from clinozoisite to epiodote and zoisite is the orthorhombic polymorph of clinozoisite. Fleischer gives the epidote group a general formula. There are undoubtedly several members of the epidote group represented in the replacement ore.

In the upper workings, matildite, hexagonal; hessite, monoclinic; and rhodonite have been reported.

Fig. 4-12.   Calcite, thallite, and quartz, Camp Bird Mine (JM#18).

In the southeastern part of the Camp Bird vein native gold and specularite both occurred as inclusions in quartz crystals.

Thuringite, (ferrian var. of chamosite of the chlorite group), occurs in the replacement ore. Pebbles in the Telluride Conglomerate are often completely replaced.

A blue quartz occurred in the Camp Bird, Virginius and some other mines in the Mt. Sneffels area. This blue quartz was well documented in earlier reports of the district.

Scepter quartz and twins after the Japanese Law, in micro to thumbnail size, have been recovered from the mine. One cluster containing three scepters has been found (Figs. 4–13 and 4–14).

Hancock Mine

The Hancock Mine was east of the old Camp Bird workings in Imogene Basin. It was said to have produced about 80 tons of ore in 1884 and Ransome (1901) described the lode as similar to that in the Hidden Treasure Mine, also in Imogene Basin. Later the Hancock stope, one of the four principal stopes of the Camp Bird Mine, developed an important body of ore above the 1400 foot level tunnel.

Leasees have worked the upper part of the vein in Imogene Basin since 1974 on a limited scale.

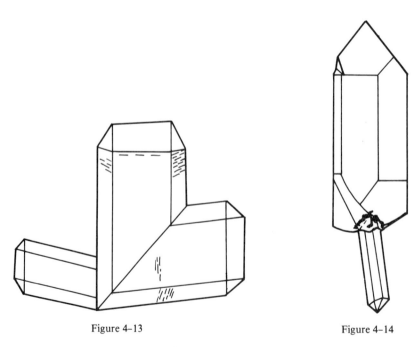

Figure 4–13   Figure 4–14

Fig. 4–13.   Japan Law twinning of quartz, symmetrical on the right, asymmetrical on the left, Camp Bird Mine.

Fig. 4–14.   Offset quartz scepter, Camp Bird Mine.

Hidden Treasure Mine

The Hidden Treasure Mine in Imogene Basin, close to the Blue Bird ore shoot of the Camp Bird vein, was opened in 1875. Like the nearby Camp Bird vein the mineralization was in the highly fractured area between the ring-fault zone of the Silverton caldera and the Mt. Sneffels–Stony Mountain stock. Early production unlike the gold–quartz ore of the Camp Bird was from gold–copper–base metal ore, mostly galena–sphalerite–tetrahedrite–chalcopyrite ore. The property was said to have been operated in 1920 and again in 1926.

Wheel of Fortune and Bimetallist Mines

The Wheel of Fortune and Bimetallist Mines are on a vein that follows an igneous dike which cuts northeast across the general trend of others in the area at the head of Canyon Creek drainage. In 1877, rich ore was produced from small pockets in the Wheel of Fortune Mine. Prior to 1880, a shipment was sent to the Black Hawk, Colorado, smelter that contained 10 ounces gold and 800 ounces silver per ton. In 1882, the mine shipped 62 tons of ore, containing 176 ounces silver plus gold, valued at $800 per ton.

Clastic dikes occurred in this mine (See the Ouray section).

The Bimetallist vein was also pockety and one near-surface pocket produced between $40,000 to 50,000 from ore averaging 10 ounces gold and 10 ounces silver per ton.

Mineralization was unlike other veins of the area. It was said to have silver–copper–sulfantimonic–arsenite ore. The values were in freibergite, stephanite (orthorhombic) and ruby silvers (or pyrargyrite and proustite, both trigonal).

REFERENCES

A–4 Lindgren Volume, A–5 Ridge (Burbank), C–6, D–1, D–3, E–3, E–4, E–5, F–3, F–5, F–6, G–1 G–3, G–5, G–6, G–9, H–8, H–9, H–11, I–2, I–5, I–9, I–22, J–9, J–26, J–31, J–39, J–40, J–46, J–53, J–58, J–64, J–73, J–74, J–75, L–1, 1948, 1951, 1952, 1954, 1955, 1956, 1958–1964, 1966, 1968, 1970, 1971, 1973, N–7, N–9, N–10, N–12, N–13, N–16, O–Hawley (Tweto), (Map), P–3, Baldwin (Kelley), (General), (Bejnar), (Kelley), (Veins), (Hillebrand), P–5 Shomaker, (Chapin), Q–15, Q–18, R–3, R–5, R–14, S–3, S–5, S–13, S–20, S–22, S–24, S–52, S–58, S–71, S–75, S–84, S–96, S–98, S–114, S–116, S–117, S–122, S–145.

RED MOUNTAIN DISTRICT

The most unusual ore deposits of the San Juan volcanic field occur in the ring fault zone along the west and northwest side of the Silverton caldera. These are the chimney or breccia pipe deposits of the Red Mountain district, which occur in a zone of altered and fractured rock, that extend from Anvil Mountain in the Silverton district, over Red Mountain Pass and past Red Mountain No. 1. This part of the ring fault zone is about seven miles long and from 3,000 to 7,000 feet wide. A basin about three miles wide and 500 feet in depth, extending north from Red Mountain Pass toward Ironton, is the center of the most productive areas. Burbank called this structure the Red Mountain Sag. (Fig. 4–15.)

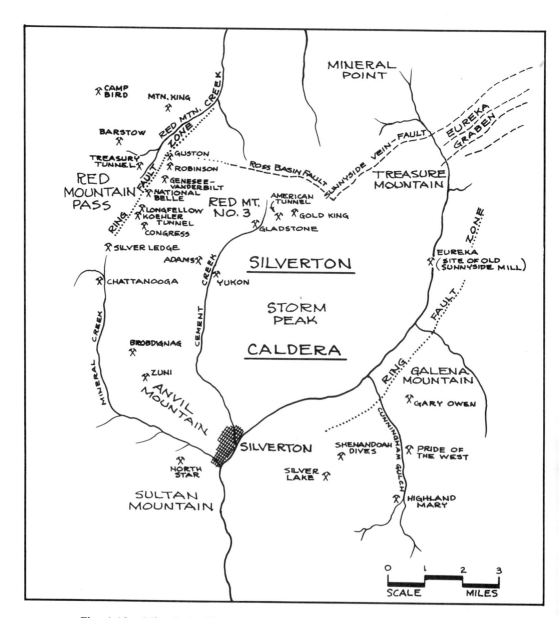

Fig. 4–15.   Mines in the Silverton caldera area, Colorado. Adapted from Colo. Sci. Soc. Proc. Vol. 13, No. 5, 1933.

Alteration in the Red Mountain Sag extends to a known depth of about a mile and has changed the rock in part or all to sericite, quartz, clay minerals, hydrated ferric oxide, alunite, diaspore, and pyrite.

These volcanic pipes are cylindrical, near vertical openings that were filled with breccia followed by intrusions of quartz latite porphyry and rhyolite. Breccia continued to form with the intrusions and in some pipes it grades into unbroken country rock. Envelopes of vertically sheeted rock encircle the better defined pipes. Size of the pipes varies from relatively small up to 300 to 2,000 feet wide.

Burbank, working in the district for many years, has proposed the most widely accepted sequence of pipe formation. In abbreviated form, this was as follows:

1. Magmatic emanations passed up through a favorable jointed and fissured rock and caused chemical or volume changes along major axis.

2. Distintegration of rock spread outward along curved surfaces. Crackled rock was incorporated in breccia, sometimes with rounded corners, in a matrix of clastic material.

3. Flow-structure texture and changes in mineralogy indicate breccia in final stages was saturated with vapor and reacted by plastic flow. As a state of complete flow was reached, the breccia mass spread into the surrounding rock in the form of a ring or as a cylindrical core.

4. Rhyolite and porphyry intruded and partly displaced breccia cores. Brecciated country rock was assimilated in rising fluids or in the molten intrusive. Pipes that reached the surface probably erupted as tuff, latite, or rhyolite flows.

Ore bodies were lenticular, pod-shaped, spindle-shaped, or combinations of these shapes. Some deposits of ore occurred within the pipes, such as those of the Yankee Girl, Guston-Robinson, and National Belle Mines. Deposits that formed outside or at margins of the pipe are present in the Hudson, St. Lawrence, Congress, and San Antonio Mines.

Formation of the ore was thought to be in a fumarole or hot springs environment at depths of 2,000 to 3,000 feet. The Red Mountain Sag developed and the rocks were later altered. Ore bodies were formed by filling solution cavities and by replacement of silicified or argillized rocks and were as much as 150 feet vertical and 15 to 30 feet in diameter. Hydrothermal leaching formed open caves and cavities.

The Red Mountain district was most active between 1882 and 1900 with the Guston, Yankee Girl, National Belle, and Genessee some of the more active mines. Deposits were small but rich in silver–lead and silver–copper ores. Production from the district could have been as much as $10 million. Some estimates are much higher.

Interest in the district has continued up to the present and it is a favorite one with small operators who hope to find a rich but overlooked pipe.

The breccia pipes, or chimneys, of the Red Mountain district occurred in the ring fault zone of the Silverton caldera and contained mineralization unlike that of any other district of the San Juan Mountain. Intensely altered rocks of the district contain disapore, alunite, zunyite, beidellite, sericite, dickite, pyrophyllite, and massive fine-grained quartz (Fig. 4–16).

Distribution of clay minerals in some of the chimney ore deposits suggest a zoning pattern from the center of the ore bodies, which have undergone acid-sulfate alteration, outward to the propylitically altered country rock.

Minerals of the Red Mountain district were: pyrite, chalcopyrite, enargite, sphalerite (orange or red), proustite, pyrargyrite, stromeyerite, (orthorhombic), galena, bournonite, (orthorhombic), covellite, chalcocite, bornite, ten-

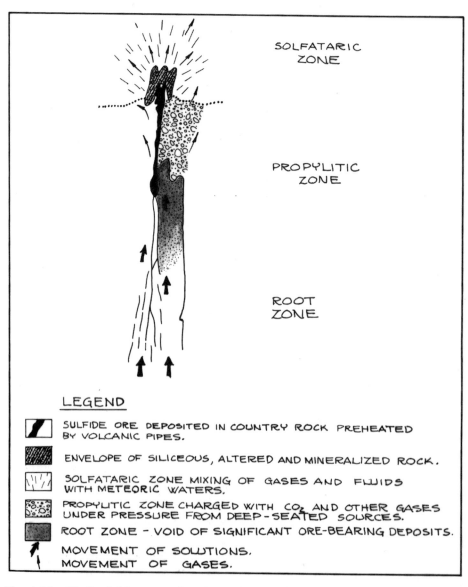

Fig. 4–16. Idealized chimney ore deposit of solfatarically altered ring-fault zone of Silverton caldera. Adapted from Burbank and Luedke (1961) and Luedke and Hosterman (1971).

nantite, colusite, (cubic), and gold. The colusite occurred as tiny specks in enargite–tennantite–galena ore. Spectroscopic analysis gave trace amounts of tin and larger amounts of gallium and indium. Bulk samples of sulfides from several deposits gave 0.01 percent tin and as much as 1 percent indium.

Gangue minerals of the pipes were kaolinite, zunyite, white barite, calcite, fluorite, and sericite. The upper zones were oxidized and supergene enriched to form Bonanza ores.

Ransome said the best ore, carrying free gold, occurred in irregular lenses parallel with the plane of the lode and were sometimes 30 or 40 feet in diameter. It was usually associated with rosin-colored sphalerite and small amounts of lilac fluorite.

In the primary sulfide zone argentiferous galena graded into silver-rich copper ore. The chimney deposits bottomed at relatively shallow depths in massive and barren pyrite.

In general, enargite increased as chalcopyrite decreased with depth. Fine-grained character and presence of enargite, chalcocite, bornite, and covellite distinguished the ore from vein ores of nearby mines. A paragenetic sequence, as shown by mine dumps, is as follows: early fine-grained quartz, intergrown with clay and pyrite, fine-grained galena overlapped by sphalerite, enargite, and other copper minerals, and last to form, barite, calcite, and fluorite.

Burbank realized in his earlier work that iron, copper, or arsenic would be useful as geochemical indicator elements. Selective testing in 1964 confirmed that residual arsenic in surface rocks that have been attacked by acid-sulfate solutions can be used as a geological indicator to locate pipes.

Caves were common in these deposits and many were lined with fine crystals.

Yankee Girl Mine

The Yankee Girl Mine was discovered in 1881 and worked until 1896. Mining was carried to a depth of 1,050 feet and five chimneys were mined, the Yankee Girl probably the most important one. In the upper levels it was 20 to 30 feet in diameter but decreased to 8 to 10 feet on the fifth level. On the sixth level, 432 feet below the outcrop, the chimney was 32 feet long and 10 feet wide and elliptical in plan. A small neck of ore connected with the Orphan Girl chimney 150 feet south.

Estimates of total production ranged from $3 million to $12 million, the lower figure probably being closer. The Director of the Mint's report for 1884 quoted a local paper as saying the mine produced $600,000 last year, but adds this was doubtless exaggerated.

Ore was transported by pack animals over Red Mountain Pass and shipped by railroad from Silverton, Colorado.

At the Yankee Girl Mine, the upper 75 to 125 feet of the chimneys carried galena–pyrite ore that ran 77 ounces silver and 36 percent lead per ton. Below this, copper ores high in silver consisting of stromeyerite, chalcocite, "in which about half of the copper is replaced by silver," chalcopyrite, tennantite, bournonite, and bornite occurred in a rare gangue, quartz. This ore ran 240 ounces silver and 29 percent copper per ton. Silver decreased with depth but bornite increased. Some rich ore was shipped and several carloads carrying 1,500 to 3,000 ounces of silver and 30 to 33 percent copper were shipped. The level from the No. 2 shaft was said to be in "bismuth–silver" ore. A 6 ton lot of stromeyerite ore contained over 5,300 ounces of silver per ton.

Polybasite occurred in six-sided, stocky, tabular prisms with triangular striations and beveled edges.

Guston-Robinson Mine

The Guston–Robinson Mine was second in size to the Yankee Girl. It was opened in 1882, but not developed until 1888 and was closed in 1897. Some ore ran 15,000 ounces silver per ton and carried 3 ounces gold per ton, the richest gold ore reported from the district. Production was estimated in excess of $2.5 million. Ore within a single pipe, 1,200 feet N-S, occurred without gangue. Ore 20 to 30 feet wide was common and some stopes were 200 feet long and 200 feet high.

In this mine, combination zoning in the ore was pronounced. Lead–silver ore extended to 288 feet in depth, stromeyerite–chalcopyrite–pyrite ores, containing 0.1 to 3 ounces gold, 25 to 700 ounces silver, and 9 to 15 percent copper, was next. The mine bottomed in pyrite with some silver and gold. On the tenth level, bornite ore with high silver content was found. Chalcopyrite carried high gold values and barite containing free gold occurred in small quantities below the ninth level. The Robinson Mine reportedly bottomed in pyrite at 600 to 700 feet.

A small lot of stromeyerite ore from the Guston contained 15,000 ounces silver per ton.

National Belle Mine

This mine was worked from 1883 until 1897 and probably produced between $1 million and $2 million. A knob of altered rock stands 200 feet above the outcrop and ore was found in caves in jasperoid in the central part of the outcrop. Oxide lead ores formed most of early production. Burbank considered the ore to be leached hydrothermally.

Caves in the National Belle Mine were lined with jasperoid. Inside of this lining there were quartz crystals, cerussite with galena cores, clay minerals, alunite, barite, and malachite over enargite. Enargite in radiating prismatic crystals with malachite and quartz overgrowth was in unattached masses in some of these caves.

Genessee-Vanderbilt Mine

The Genessee was started in 1882 but not developed until combined with the Vanderbilt. Most production occurred from 1891 to 1896. This mine at first was not very profitable although it produced nearly a million dollars in ore. Two shafts were working the same deposit and when this was learned they merged into a single operation. The Joker Tunnel connects the two workings. The ore was galena, pyrite and small amounts of complex silver-bearing minerals. At 700 feet in depth the deposit changed to barren pyrite.

In the Genessee–Vanderbilt Mine Ransome reported covellite and silver-rich bornite. Stalactites of pyrite were observed in the 7–1/2 (level) ore body, which was discovered by diamond drilling in 1913. This ore body was in a near-vertical chimney 10 to 20 feet in width.

Lark Mine

An early-day producer, the Lark Mine, was reopened in 1942. It is in Prospect Gulch in the Cement Creek drainage, on the southeast flank of Red Mountain No. 3. Early miners removed the silver-bearing oxidized ore from this chimney deposit but did not mine the primary ore because of zinc and the low grade of the ore. It is not in the Red Mountain Sag area but is similar to these deposits.

Koehler-Breccia Pipe

The Koehler breccia pipe is on the south side of Red Mountain Pass in the Mineral Creek drainage. It is about twelve miles south of Ouray. The Salem and Carbon Lake shafts develop the upper part of the pipe and the Koehler Tunnel, started in 1908, develops the San Antonio. The Congress and the St. Paul workings are also in this large compound breccia pipe. Some of the mines were first worked in 1878 for silver, however, enargite is the principal ore and it is associated with pyrite, sphalerite, and galena (Fig. 4–17).

The ore bodies are elliptical in outline and usually occur at the junction of two fracture zones. Their longest dimension is vertical. High grade silver ore occurs near the center of some pipes. Pipes average 10 to 60 feet wide and 30 to 150 feet in length.

Later production was made in the periods 1907 to 1910 and in 1942 to 1948, when some enargite–pyrite–covellite ore was mined.

The Koehler breccia pipe was one of the largest in the Red Mountain district. Enargite was the principal mineral. Long bladed crystals radiating from a common center were found. Botryoidal encrustation of scorodite, orthorhombic, were found on enargite from the Charter Oak Mine. Pyrrhotite was found associated with enargite in Koehler ore.

Longfellow Mine

The Longfellow Mine is on the San Juan County side of Red Mountain Pass and just east of U.S. Highway 550. Unlike most of the other chimney and breccia pipe deposits of this area this mine was not developed until the late 1940s. The others were mostly mined for silver up to the Silver Panic of 1893, or worked since then only in time of high metal prices, especially for copper.

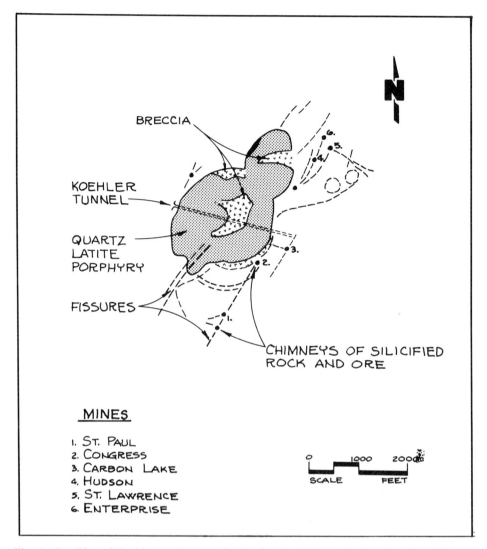

Fig. 4–17.   Plan of Koehler compound volcanic pipe, Red Mountain Pass, San Juan County, Colorado. Adapted from Colo. Sci. Proc. Vol. 14, No. 5, 1941.

North and south ore bodies were explored by shaft, several short tunnels, and bulldozer cuts.

   Mineralization in these vertical pipes is mostly massive sulfides, quartz and clay gangue. Distribution of clay minerals in some of the chimney ore deposits suggest a zoning pattern. From the center of the ore bodies, which have undergone acid-sulfate alteration, outward to the propylically altered country rock the zones are:

1. High-alumina montmorillonite
2. High-alumina montmorillonite and pyrophyllite
3. High-alumina montmorillonite, pyrophyllite and dickite
4. Dickite and illite
5. Illite and chlorite

Enargite from the Longfellow Mine is shown on p. 46 of *The Encyclopedia of Minerals* by Roberts, Rapp, and Weber.

Mountain King Mine

The Mountain King Mine develops a vein in the highly faulted part of the ring-fault belt of the Silverton caldera. It is in the Red Mountain district northeast of the Treasury Tunnel, in the Red Mountain Sag and it is traceable on the surface for 6,000 feet. It passes below Ironton Park and looses its identity.

There are several thousand feet of workings but they are not accessible as the walls of the vein are heavily altered and were hard to keep from caving. The mine was last worked in 1948. Mineralization consisted of galena and sphalerite with values in silver and gold. Rhodochrosite and barite were two gangue minerals.

Ironton Park

In 1944, one of possibly the last discoveries of valuable ore at the surface was made at the Lost Day and Columbine claims above the old mining camp of Ironton, in Ironton Park, Ouray County, Colorado. Ore was bulldozed from the outcrop and shipped directly to the smelter.

REFERENCES

A-2, A-4 Lindgren Volume, A-5 Ridge (Burbank), C-2, C-3, C-4, C-5, D-1, (Burbank), (Traver), E-3, E-5, F-3, G-5, H-8, H-9, I-11, J-40, J-41, L-1, 1942–1948, N-11, P-3, Baldwin, (Kottlowski), (Kelley), (Baars), (Hillebran), R-14, S-5, S-13, S-14, S-16, S-21, S-42, S-52, S-75, S-84, S-85, S-86, S-99.

CEMENT CREEK TUNGSTEN AREA

North of Silverton, in the San Juan County part of the Red Mountain district, an elliptical area extending six miles up Cement Creek and about two miles on either side of the creek has produced tungsten from hubnerite ore. The area is in the Silverton caldera near faults, such as the Eureka Graben system.

Although mines in the Eureka Graben system have minor hubnerite mineralization, it is not tungsten ore. Twenty four mines or prospects in the Cement Creek tungsten area have reported production of some ore and 17 others have reported tungsten mineralization. Total production from the area has been small but it extends back to 1899 when tungsten prices were up to $5.00 per unit.

Hubnerite was identified from samples sent to Freiberg, Germany, in the early 1880s; this material came from the Adams Tunnel Mine.

A mill on Dry Gulch produced 5-1/2 tons of tungsten concentrates containing 69.5 percent tungsten trioxide in 1900 and a small production occurred in the district between 1901 and 1908.

During both wars, when metal prices were government subsidized or otherwise favorable, some production was made. Some production is recorded for 1951 and hubnerite was shipped from the Ohio Mine in 1952. The Yukon Mine produced some tungsten in the late 1970s.

The original discovery of this area was reported to have resulted when a large boulder loosened by a snowslide rolled down the side of Cement Creek and split so as to reveal a vein of tungsten-bearing ore which was said to be worth $8,000 per ton. Miners from as far away as Mancos rushed to the area by snowshoes and claim staking along Cement Creek was started at a frenzied pace, in spite of the deep snow.

In the Cement Creek tungsten area hubnerite and minor wolframite, molybdenite and adularia occur in quartz veins. Rhodochrosite, rhodonite, and minor pyrite, galena, and fluorite are accessory minerals. The tungsten minerals and molybdenite also occur in small amounts in veins of the Sunnyside vein system to the north of this area.

Adams Mine

Adams Tunnel is usually applied to this mine which is developed by two short adits. It is about nine miles away from Silverton on the east side of Cement Creek.

The Adams Mine produced tungsten in 1955 and, in addition, 800 pounds of rhodonite was sold for use in making jewelry.

Exceptional specimens of hubnerite have been recovered from this mine (Fig. 4–18).

Fig. 4–18. Hubnerite in albite, Adams Tunnel (JM#922).

Yukon Tunnel (Uncle Sam)

A long crosscut tunnel four miles above Silverton on the east side of Cement Creek is known as the Yukon. In 1936 a mill was built and a small amount of tungsten concentrates were produced.

The Uncle Sam vein was cut by the Yukon Tunnel and this vein was said to crop out about 5,000 feet to the northwest. An ore shoot about 100 feet long and 6 to 18 inches wide contained hubnerite, scheelite, galena, sphalerite, and pyrite. Excellent hubnerite specimens occurred in this ore shoot. The mine was being rehabilitated in 1971 and diamond drilling was done under contract for the operator, Domain Metals. Work continued in 1978; some red and yellow hubnerite with green fluorite and quartz was mined in 1979. The mine was closed in late 1979 or early 1980.

REFERENCES

A-4, L-1, 1953, 1955, R-3.

OURAY (UNCOMPAHGRE) DISTRICT

An area extending from the vicinity of Ouray about five miles north and about three miles east of the Uncompahgre Valley has mines clustered around an eruptive center; the principal intrusive is the Ouray stock. One laccolithic center of igneous activity gives direct evidence of age between late Cretaceous and early Eocene.

At the beginning of this period of early volcanic activity, this region was covered by at least 4,000 feet of upper Cretaceous formations, chiefly shales. Later, they were overlapped by late Cretaceous or early Eocene formations so as to indicate a domal uplift (Laramide orogeny) of the region. These later formations contained volcanic debris indicating volcanism had already started in the San Juans. The uplift was accompanied by intrusion of stocks and laccoliths of monzonite porphyry, after which the first period of ore deposition took place and one of the oldest ore deposits in the San Juan Mountains was formed.

Erosion, including a period of glaciation, carved this great dome into the ancestral San Juan Mountains, but they were eventually eroded to form an Eocene peneplane. Only the more resistant monzonite porphyry masses remained as hills. The upper Cretaceous and, locally, all of the Morrison formation were removed.

Some of the mineral deposits were destroyed and others exposed to weathering. In later Eocene time, the Telluride Conglomerate was deposited on the peneplane, mostly around the resistant hills of monzonite porphyry; however, it has been found overlying one laccolithic center.

This Eocene-age peneplane is not to be confused with the San Juan peneplane postulated by Atwood and Mather and later questioned by Steven.

This peneplane was said to have been cut from a high volcanic plateau in the interval between deposition of the Fisher volcanics, 26.4 m.y.B.P. and the Hinsdale series 22.4 m.y.B.P.

Mineral veins of the early period of deposition did not cut the Eocene surface; however, some were reopened in later Tertiary disturbances and barren quartz, barite or calcite mineralization was deposited. Some veins were opened to continue up into the thick volcanic sequence that overlies the Telluride Conglomerate.

Clastic dikes are an unusual feature found in the mines of this area. At least eight or nine are known; some follow porphyry dikes; some follow fissures; and some are mineralized. Burbank considers the clastic dikes and the mineralization to have been formed at a shallow depth, a mile or less, below the surface. Ore bodies filling caves influenced this decision.

Width of the clastic dikes vary from a few inches to ten feet. Their texture varies from a fault breccia with angular fragments to rounded fragments cemented so as to resemble a conglomerate. These dikes are considered to be formed by clastic material torn from the walls and injected upward, diagonally or laterally, by expanding gases and vapors related to the igneous and mineralizing activity.

Shale fragments are aligned parallel to the walls and they are not a fault or friction breccia. Some dikes were closely associated with eruptions of igneous rocks and some were not. Some were formed between early and late stages of vein deposits of ore and are believed to have been formed by sudden expansion of mineralizing solutions during reopening of the vein fissures.

Some mineralized fissures were filled with igneous dikes, major amounts of premineral injected clastic material, and finally, by vein minerals and minor intramineral clastic material.

In the Ouray district, a zonal relationship of the vein deposits is recognized to the Ouray stock. Veins associated with the stock and central intrusives include barren pyrite or pyrite–copper veins containing gold. Chalcopyrite and bornite are the primary copper minerals. Further north from the stock are pyrite–gold replacement ores of the American Nettie Mine. These deposits are replacements of the Dakota formation and have tellurides of gold, sphalerite, galena, tetrahedrite, and gold-bearing pyrite. Near the north flank of the Ouray stock, contact metamorphic deposits contain magnetite, hematite, garnet, lime silicates and low grade pyrite (Fig. 4–19).

American Nettie Mine

The American Nettie Mine is about a mile and a half north of Ouray on the east wall of the Uncompahgre Canyon. Wooden brackets were used to attach the mine buildings to the wall of the canyon. An aerial tramway formerly delivered ore to bins along the Rio Grande Railroad in the valley below the mine. This aerial tramway was 4,100 feet long, had a span across the valley of 1,800 feet, and was 900 feet above the valley at one place (Fig. 4–20).

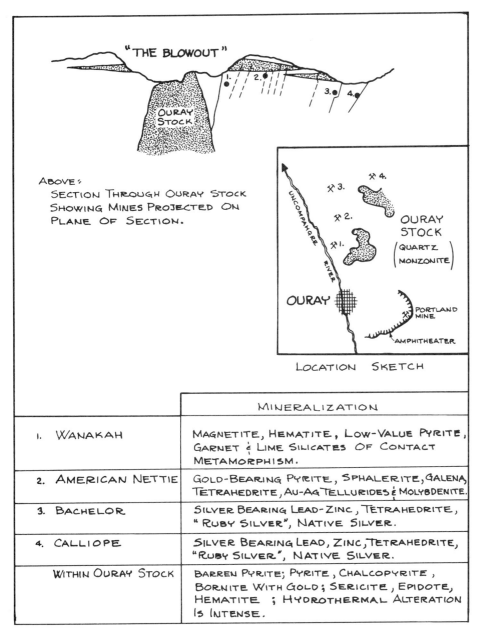

"THE BLOWOUT"

OURAY STOCK

ABOVE:
SECTION THROUGH OURAY STOCK
SHOWING MINES PROJECTED ON
PLANE OF SECTION.

UNCOMPAHGRE RIVER

OURAY
STOCK
(QUARTZ
MONZONITE)

OURAY

PORTLAND
MINE

AMPHITHEATER

LOCATION   SKETCH

	MINERALIZATION
1. WANAKAH	MAGNETITE, HEMATITE, LOW-VALUE PYRITE, GARNET & LIME SILICATES OF CONTACT METAMORPHISM.
2. AMERICAN NETTIE	GOLD-BEARING PYRITE, SPHALERITE, GALENA, TETRAHEDRITE, Au-Ag TELLURIDES & MOLYBDENITE.
3. BACHELOR	SILVER BEARING LEAD-ZINC, TETRAHEDRITE, "RUBY SILVER", NATIVE SILVER.
4. CALLIOPE	SILVER BEARING LEAD, ZINC, TETRAHEDRITE, "RUBY SILVER", NATIVE SILVER.
WITHIN OURAY STOCK	BARREN PYRITE; PYRITE, CHALCOPYRITE, BORNITE WITH GOLD; SERICITE, EPIDOTE, HEMATITE ; HYDROTHERMAL ALTERATION IS INTENSE.

Fig. 4-19.   Relation of mineralization to Ouray stock, Ouray mining district, Ouray County, Colorado. Adapted from Colo. Sci. Proc. Vol. 12, No. 6, 1930.

Between 1889 and 1905, the mine produced about $1.4 million from ore that averaged 6 ounces gold/ton. Some ore ran as high as 120 ounces silver/ton but silver was of secondary importance. When the mine was visited in 1907, however, the ore was only averaging $60/ton, which would indicate that gold was below 3 ounces/ton, and cost of producing it was $35 per ton.

Bonanza gold ore was first found in pockets that outcropped in the Dakota sandstone that had been metasomatically replaced to quartzite. This outcrop-

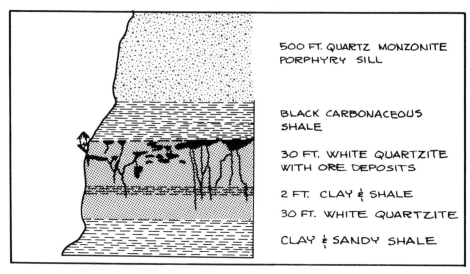

500 FT. QUARTZ MONZONITE PORPHYRY SILL

BLACK CARBONACEOUS SHALE

30 FT. WHITE QUARTZITE WITH ORE DEPOSITS

2 FT. CLAY & SHALE

30 FT. WHITE QUARTZITE

CLAY & SANDY SHALE

Fig. 4–20.   East-West section of American Nettie Mine, Ouray mining district, Ouray County Colorado, showing ore bodies. Adapted from U.S.G.S. Folio 153, 1907.

ping was below thick beds of black shale, which, in turn, were below a 500 foot thick igneous sill.

The ore formed as replacement deposits in the quartzite at the base of the black shale. Free gold as wires, nuggets, and fines occurred in the Bonanza ore with limonite. Some ore contained up to 30 ounces gold / ton.

The Jonathan dike, a clastic dike, was followed by an inclined tunnel which started at the outcrop on the cliff overlooking the Uncompahgre Valley.

Burbank believed the Jonathan dike to be the last cross-barrier between the apparent source of the mineralizing solutions and the axis of the Uncompahgre Uplift, which is thought to be the zone through which the solutions finally escaped. Release of pressures on the solutions caused boiling or vaporization of the original solutions and affected considerable changes of the channel walls. Mineralization occurred in the Jonathan dike in some places and cut across it in other places. Open vugs occurred in the quartzite and extended as much as 30 feet away from the mineralization. These vugs were lined with quartz crystals which evidently derived, at least in part, from the quartzite.

At the Wanakah Mine, which was about 800 feet stratigraphically below the American Nettie in the "Pony Express" beds and in the Morrison formation, the mineralization was somewhat similar; however, magnetite and low-grade pyrite occurred. The ore was much less productive of gold and contact metamorphic minerals such as garnet and lime silicates were in the gangue minerals. Tellurides were evidently lacking.

The *Minerals Yearbook* for 1959 showed work being done on the American Nettie Mine.

Carbonates of copper and of lead occurred in the Bonanza ore of the American Nettie Mine with free gold. Primary ore contained tellurides of gold and silver especially hessite, argentiferous tetrahedrite (freibergite), sphalerite, galena, and minor molybdenite occurred in a gangue of quartz, sericite, chlorite, and barite. Gypsum formed fibrous bands.

Bachelor Mine

About two miles north of Ouray a road leaves U.S. Highway 550 and goes about a mile and a half east to the Syracuse Tunnel of the Bachelor Mine in the Dexter Creek drainage. The Khedive adit, Bachelor shaft, Wedge shaft and extensive underground workings developed this group of claims which up to 1905 had produced nearly $2 million worth of Bonanza–type silver ore.

The mine was discovered in 1892, and in a few years all of the rich silver ore had been mined. In 1898, the Wedge was working 70 to 80 men and shipping a carload of ore per day; it was said to be "making a fortune" for the owners. After the rich ore was mined, some ore had been valued up to $800 per ton, treating the mill-grade ore gave unsatisfactory results. Treating lower grade mill ores was undertaken in both World War I and II and at times of higher metal prices. The mine also worked during the period 1960-4.

Mineralization was of late Cretaceous or Eocene age, and except, possibly, for the ores at Rico and LaPlata Mountains, the oldest in the San Juan Mountains. It was related to the Ouray stock of quartz monzonite and occurred in "rolls" or flexures in the Morrison formation, in the Pony Express beds of the underlying Wanaka formation, and in the overlying Dakota sandstone along the Bachelor clastic dike.

The Bachelor clastic dike, which is similar to others in the area, was called a "Sandstone Dike" by the miners. This dike caused a great deal of speculation as to its origin. It was made up mostly of sandstone grains and fragments, other rock fragments, and black shale chips that tended to align themselves with the wall of the dike. Injection of this dike was the result of a violent escape of volcanic gases and vapors, according the Burbank. Accompanying solutions became temporarily trapped under an impervious cover of sedimentary rocks. This clastic dike was mineralized in some places and ore channels and dike channels are related. The ore becomes higher in zinc and iron and lower in silver content toward the east suggesting that the clastic injections also came from that direction.

Some of the early ore mined from the Bachelor Mine contained up to 15,000 ounces of silver/ton. Pyrargyrite, freibergite, and unidentified bismuth–silver ores in streaks up to three feet wide formed this early Bonanza ore. Galena, sphalerite, chalcopyrite, tetrahedrite, pearceite, "copper pitch ore," native silver, and argentite were in the complex ore. A "pinkish-white carbonate which presumably carries considerable manganese" (manganocalcite) and a gray quartz, said to be of secondary origin, occurred in the ore. This gray quartz brings to mind the blue quartz of the Camp Bird and other veins in upper Canyon Creek.

Portland Mine

The Portland Mine is about a mile east of Ouray in the Amphitheater, a cirque-like structure the walls of which rise some 4,600 feet above Ouray. About 3,200 feet of San Juan Tuff is exposed. Weak beds of Molas shale in a paleovalley with possibly 1,000 feet of relief caused landslides that formed this geologic oddity. The north wall rests on an erosional surface of quartz monzonite, possibly associated with the Ouray stock, and the south wall rests on Precambrian quartzite. San Juan Tuff is exposed in the center of the Amphitheater (Fig. 4–19).

History of the Portland Mine is little known; however, the report of the Director of the Mint for 1884 stated drifts were run from 60 to 150 feet in the mine.

Cross and others have described the vein as a silver-bearing vein with a gangue of white quartz and rhodochrosite and having some carbonate between rhodochrosite and calcite. In many of the veins, ore minerals of galena, gray copper, and a gangue of quartz occurred in small bunches that pinched out in short distances. Stephanite was reported to occur but this was not confirmed.

Burbank found the Portland vein to have mineralized the Telluride Conglomerate and Ouray limestone adjacent to it; however, no large ore bodies were developed.

In 1940, Burbank revisited the mine and described the Portland Mine as developing a complex base-metal and precious-metal ore in the fissures that cut the San Juan Tuff and the underlying Paleozoic limestone.

There was lateral replacement of the basal layers of tuff, which locally contained thin beds of calcareous limestone and the underlying brecciated limestone.

The principal ore shoot was about 400 feet long and had a small vertical range. A drift 400 feet long was driven past this shoot to the south but no other ore was discovered. Paleozoic rocks were expected to wedge out to the south and give way to Pce quartzite. The Ouray Fault is about 2,500 feet south of the Amphitheater.

A shaft sunk 100 feet into limestone was not as productive as workings above the tunnel. Ore minerals were reported as pyrite, sphalerite, galena, and chalcopyrite in a gangue of silicified limestone, quartz, barite, rhodochrosite, and manganiferous carbonate.

This ore was cut by a later generation of comb quartz, pyrite, and kaolin that was possibly gold-bearing. A still later barren stage of mineralization contained abundant drusy quartz with coarse calcite. In the oxidized portion of the vein manganese oxides coated much of the vein material. This type of ore probably represented most of the mine production. Secondary enrichment in localized areas was probably caused by surface water from the Amphitheatre rim following cracks to the vein area, much of which must have been wasted away by erosion. Pockets were said to have contained ore assaying from 1/3 to 1 ounce gold per ton and 20 to 90 ounces of silver. Small shipments from the mine contained from 0.02 to 0.20 ounces gold and up to 16 ounces silver with 3.5 percent lead and some copper.

This mine may have the distinction of being the only mine in the San Juan Mountains that was worked for quartz. In the early 1970s, the mine was worked for quartz crystals as mineral specimens and considerable white to partly clear quartz was produced at this time. One large cathedral crystal group was reported to have been 15 inches high and was said to have sold for $1,200. "Cathedral" type groups, a central crystal or group surrounded by smaller attached crystals in parallel growth, were mined. These groups were especially attractive. (Fig. 4–21.) Damage to the crystals was minimal as they were carefully mined. The exposed crystals were worked out but some specimen hunting has continued.

Floaters with double terminations, quartz pseudomorphs of calcite, in which rhombohedral edges gave the crystals chisel-like terminations, and "reverse scepters" in which the rhombohedral terminals stepped down and continued as tiny prism sections, terminated in turn by rhombohedral faces, were produced in limited quantities. Some green sphalerite crystals and quartz pseudomorphs, casts of barite, were produced as specimens also.

Other veins in the area are the Denver and the Oak Street (named from a street on the west side of Ouray). Mineralization in these veins was said to consist mainly of quartz; however, they were said to have produced some gold.

In 1950, a 2,000 foot tunnel was being extended to cut the intersection of the Oak Street and Denver veins. Production is not known but was probably small from these veins.

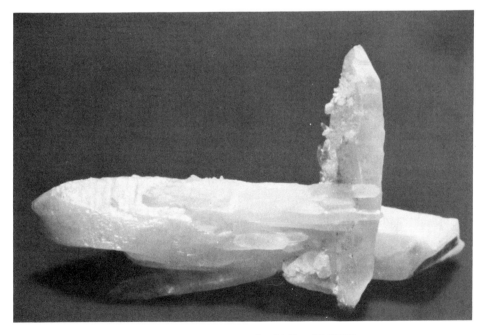

Fig. 4–21.   Quartz, Portland Mine (JM#288).

The report of the Colorado Division of Mines for 1976 shows the Portland Mine as being worked.

Ouray Manganese District

Manganese deposits of Recent age occurred within the city limits of Ouray. One deposit, near the south end of town, was mined for manganese oxides during World War II. Witherite occurred in vugs in manganese oxides and as much as one percent tungsten oxide was detected in some samples.

Grizzly Bear Mine

The Grizzly Bear Mine, possibly the same group known as the Grizzly King, Silver Bear, Black Bear, or the Yellow Jacket, is on upper Bear Creek, south of the Amphitheater and southeast of Ouray. It can be reached only by the Bear Creek pack trail which junctions the Horsethief pack trail in upper Bear Creek and continues over the Divide and down Henson Creek to Lake City. The mine is shown on the U.S.G.S. Ironton quadrangle sheet.

Not much is known of this mine, however, Aurand (1920), reported green fluorspar associated with quartz, rhodochrosite, galena, pyrite, and sphalerite.

Burbank under late Tertiary deposits, gave a suite of minerals that seems to fit under baritic lead and silver deposits.

This mine is credited with about $0.6 million in production. All of this was brought down the mountain by pack animals as no roads extend to this area. Supplies were brought to the mine over the same steep trail. Ransome reported rhombohedral crystals of rhodochrosite and this mine has been a famous location for pink rhombohedral rhodochrosite specimens.

Minerals of the Grizzly Bear Mine are:

Ore Minerals	Gangue Minerals
pyrite	quartz
sphalerite	barite
galena	rhodochrosite
chalcopyrite	calcite
tetrahedrite	sericite
stephanite or polybasite	chlorite

The ore was primarily a high-grade silver ore.

POUGHKEEPSIE GULCH AND MINERAL POINT

Veins of the Poughkeepsie Gulch and Mineral Point district contained all the common sulfide and gangue minerals of the San Juan Mountains. In addition they had soft gray minerals generally classed as sulfobismutites containing high silver values. These minerals were given names such as alaskaite, from the Alaska Mine, which were later discredited when it was found they were generally a mixture of minerals. Alaskaite proved to be a mixture of matildite, aikinite, and other minerals.

Grybeck found two specimens in the Colorado School of Mines collection marked alaskaite to be pavonite, monoclinic, with subordinate chalcopyrite, tetrahedrite, and pyrite. One sample was marked Alaska Mine, San Juan County, Colorado and the other Poughkeepsie Gulch, Ouray County, Colorado.

He also found a specimen labeled beegerite (Dana location for this discredited species) from the Old Lout Mine, Ouray County, Colorado, to be matildite.

Burbank and Leudke found beegerite from the Old Lout Mine to be schirmerite.

Dunmore Mine

According to Hillebran and Kelley the Dunmore lode is one of the most varied and complex in the vicinity of Ouray. It could well be the most interesting deposit in the San Juans.

The original fault zone offset the beds of the Uncompahgre formation by at least 2,800 feet before the San Juan formation was deposited, according to Luedke. Displacement after this, as shown by the San Juan beds, was 80 feet, vertically. In the quartzites of the Uncompahgre formation, the lode is 100 feet wide and exposed for 800 feet in length. Above, in the San Juan formation, it is only a few feet wide. In the north part of the lode Precambrian slates have been mineralized and dragged past truncated quartzites in the pre-San Juan formation faulting. To the south, the lode is largely siliceous barren vein material. Post mineral faulting has crushed and brecciated the ore.

Between the upper and lower workings there is a breccia chimney and a tungsten ore shoot. This shoot was 8 to 20 feet wide and 40 to 50 feet long and consisted of a breccia of fine-grained quartz, sericite, and kaolin cemented with hubnerite, coarse-grained quartz, and minor sphalerite, galena, hematite, and barite. Hubnerite was probably the last mineralization stage and it is also found sparingly in that part of the vein that extends up into the San Juan formation.

A second chimney or pipe occurs west of the upper mine portal. It is more like other breccia pipes of the adjacent Red Mountain district than the first pipe. Fine-grained siliceous material is replaced by specular hematite. It could be a potential source of iron ore. Within the hematite chimney, near the west side, is a copper-ore chimney. A prominent yellow knob of altered rock, largely barren of mineral, stands above it.

That part of the lode in Pce rocks is suggestive of the earlier Tertiary stage of mineralization found in the Ouray district, to the north; however, mineralization in the San Juan formation was of late Tertiary age. This fissure was probably one of the most important feeder channels for mineralization in the district.

Breccia pipes of the Dunmore Mine had fragments of slate and quartzite in the walls and in radiating breccia dikes. The dikes had pyrite, quartz, and kaolin but no metals of value. The Dunmore Mine ore was chalcopyrite and aikinite superimposed on siliceous specular hematite. Rhodochrosite, chlorite, and white barite were gangue minerals. Barite was a common gangue in this district.

Michael Breen Mine (Mickey Breen)

A jeep trail leaves U.S. Highway 550 near the confluence of the Uncompahgre River and Red Mountain Creek and goes south-eastward up the lower part of the Poughkeepsie Gulch about 1-½ miles to the Mickey Breen Mine.

This mine was worked in the 1880s and has operated intermittently since that time. It was active during the World War II years, 1942 through 1948. Ore worth $300,000 was said to have been shipped from the Mickey Breen Group (about 16 claims) during 1917. The Mountain Monarch, one of the claims of this group, has been credited with 1,226 tons of ore through 1943.

Mineralization in this area is associated with and influenced by the Dunmore Fault, a mineralized fault that has a horizontal displacement of as much as 4,500 feet, according to Kelly. Veins in the area strike N-S and are at right angles to this fault. They ranged from six inches to several feet in width.

The Mickey Breen Mine ore deposits contain quartz, galena, sphalerite, chalcopyrite, pyrite, tetrahedrite, and quantities of rhodochrosite. Gold and silver values are associated with these minerals. Aurand reported green fluorite.

Alaska Mine

The Alaska Mine is in Poughkeepsie Gulch in the Red Mountain Creek drainage. It is listed by Burbank as one of the more productive mines in the Poughkeepsie district. In this area swarms of veins extend outward from the northern border of the Silverton caldera. Over 100 miles of outcrops have been mapped. The Alaska Mine would get lost in the many small mines and prospects except for having a now discredited mineral specie named after it, alaskaite, a lead–silver bismutite. The Director of the Mint reported in 1884, that seven men were employed and a crosscut was being driven from a 170 foot shaft on a strong vein. The property had produced $2,500 worth of ore at that time. Production from the only ore shoot was said to have totaled about $90,000 in silver-bearing ore. Burbank and Luedke show the Alaska vein as a strong vein at the head of Poughkeepsie Gulch. Much of the vein is above 12,000 feet altitude.

The Alaska Mine is high on a saddle-like divide between Ouray and San Juan Counties at the head of Poughkeepsie Gulch. The Old Lout Mine is in the same area. It would be easy to get the county wrong. Between $0.3 million and $0.4 million worth of bismuth-bearing silver ore was produced from the Old Lout Mine which was the largest producer in the area.

REFERENCES

A–4, A–5 Ridge, (Burbank), D–1 (Burbank), (Traver), C–6, E–3, E–10, F–3, G–1, G–5, G–52, H–9, J–40, P–3 Baldwin, (Hillebran), (Kelly), K–16, L–1, 1959, 1960, 1964, Q–17, R–13, R–14, S–3, S–12, S–14, S–15, S–20, S–52, S–85, S–99.

SILVERTON AREA

The San Juan volcanic field is a large erosional remnant of a larger composite volcanic field that covered much of the southern Rocky Mountains in Oligocene time. Volcanic and other igneous activity of the Laramide uplift had been largely eroded by 35 m.y.B.P., when major volcanic activity started. Between 35 and 30 m.y.B.P., a composite volcanic plateau, about 0.6 miles thick developed in the San Juan Mountains. Ash-flow eruptions started in the western San Juan Mountains about 28.4 m.y.B.P. and the Uncompahgre and San Juan calderas collapsed shortly after that. The Silverton caldera formed in the older San Juan caldera 27.5 m.y.B.P. after eruption of the Crystal Lake Tuff (Fig. 4–22).

Subsidence of the Silverton caldera was from 1,500 to 2,500 feet, as estimated from offset volcanic units. Exposed rocks in the Silverton caldera are pyroxene–andesite; however, the rims of the caldera are formed of older rocks of the same volcanic group.

Mineralization associated with the Silverton caldera occurred from 30 to 10 m.y.B.P. Ores in the Silverton area are thought to have been deposited from 5 to 15 million years after the Silverton caldera collapsed, when quartz porphyry intrusions were emplaced in caldera-related structures such as the ring fault zone and adjacent faults.

Two of the most continuous vein systems in the Silverton area, the Shenandoah Dives and the Nevada-Silver Lake, have accompanying dikes and are in the ring fault zone of the Silverton caldera: Minerals of the Silverton area are:

Quartz	Massive or hexagonal prisms terminated by rhombohedrons, enclosing chlorite, minute sulfide minerals, and fluid inclusions.
Barite	Tabular, white, and massive replaced pseudomorphs of quartz. In Zuni Mine with zunyite and guitermanite, in kaolinite.

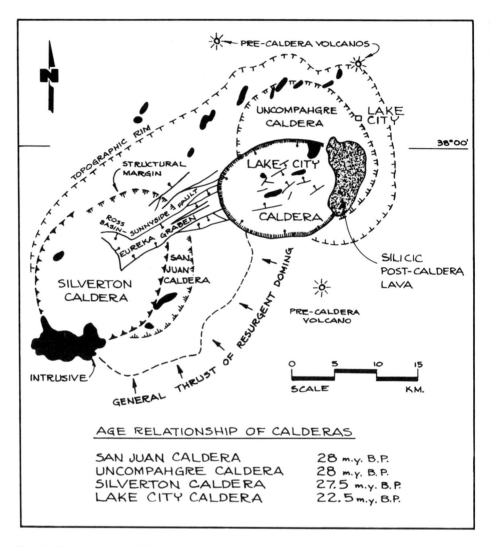

Fig. 4–22.   San Juan and Uncompahgre caldera complex, Western San Juan Mountains, Colorado. Adapted from U.S.G.S. Jour. Res. Vol. 1, No. 6, 1973 and U.S.G.S. P.P. 958, 1976.

Calcite	Rhombohedrons, scalenohedrons, or prisms; white, occurs at Osceola Mine as a pseudomorph of tremolite.
Dolomite	Curved rhombohedra.
Rhodochrosite	Massive, rhombohedral, with quartz in gangue of rich free gold ore of Golden Fleece Mine.
Kaolinite	At Zuni Mine with crystals of pyrite, slightly modified octahedra.
Fluorite	As fluorspar, at Sunnyside Mine an indicator of gold

Rhodonite	Massive (Note: Rhodonite was used in the old literature and is used with the understanding that it has been identified as pyroxmangite. See ahead under minerals of Sunnyside vein system.)
Zunyite	Tetrahedral, colorless crystals 3/16 inch in diameter, on Anvil Mountain associated with guitermanite, pyrite, enargite, bournonite, kaolin, and barite.
Chlorite	In vein quartz, with sericite, epidote, and zircon as microscopic constituents of ore.
Pyrite	Pyritohedrons, octahedrons, cubes, and modification of each.
Tetrahedrite	Gray copper, massive
Tennantite, var. Freibergite	Widespread
Chalcocite	Massive
Chalcopyrite	Sphenoidal, yellow copper, massive
Galena	Crystals rare, gold in galena in Sunnyside Mine
Sphalerite	Massive, tetrahedral and modified forms
Bournonite	Steel gray to black
Zinkenite	Massive, steel gray, from Brobdignag Mine
Guitermanite = jordanite = baumhauerite	Bluish gray, massive, encloses tetrahedrons of zunyite. Alters to anglesite in Zuni Mine.
Stibnite	Clusters of radiating prisms from North Star Mine, Sultan Mountain
Proustite	Ruby silver, red rhombohedral, hemimorphic
Bismuthinite	Lead gray, in slender prismatic crystals, with specularite in quartz, at Neigold claim, Galena Mountain, Cunningham Gulch area.
Argentite	Blackish lead-gray, brittle silver
Molybdenite	Scales, compact, in Sunnyside Extension containing free gold.
Hematite	Var. specularite.
Sulfobismuthinites	Cosalite, alaskaite, a mixture, beegerite, a mixture, kibellite.

Tellurides	Detected by chemical analysis in four mines.
Gold	Irregular hackly particles, arborescent sheets in quartz and rhodonite in Golden Fleece vein, Sunnyside extension as implanted crystals on faces of quartz crystals in vugs, embedded in yellow sphalerite and molybdenite. At Sunnyside embedded in sulfides, quartz and fluorite.
Silver	Wire, rarely seen.
Copper	Plates and branching forms, Royal Tiger and Tom Moore Mines, Sunnyside extension, Tom Moore in quartz with hubnerite crystals.
Hubnerite	Blades prisms often radial, Adams lode, Bonita Mine

Dana gives a formula for guitermanite and the type locality as the Zuni Mine, Silverton, Colorado. Eckel says that the species is in doubt and identifications have not been definite.

Burbank and Luedke list the ore and gangue minerals of the Eureka and adjoining districts as: pyrite, chalcopyrite, sphalerite, galena, tetrahedrite, tennantite, gold, silver, argentiferous tetrahedrite, sulfobismutites, silver sulfosalts.

Manganese and iron are higher in vein sphalerites and germanium, tantalum and indium are higher in chimney deposit sphalerites.

Quartz, rhodonite, rhodochrosite, calcite, fluorite, barite, and adularia are associated with late quartz veins.

Friedelite	In orange to rose-red tabular crystals to 0.13 mm. The chlorite was determined to be in excess of the arsenic, therefore, it is not arsenic variety schallerite.
Alleghanyite	Grayish-pink 1.6 × 0.3 mm, with tephroite forms gray to greenish-gray patches recognizable in hand specimens.
Tephroite	Gray
Helvite	Yellow
Alabandite	Distributed in grains, up to 0.75 mm, in silicate minerals.
Cosalite	Orthorhombic
Bismuthinite	Orthorhombic

Rhodonite was found in vugs, up to 1.0 mm crystals; however, it was massive in general.

In the old Golden Fleece Mine near Silverton, free gold was found in rhodonite. A slab of this material was seen in 1975. It came from an old estate.

Roberts, Rapp and Weber in *The Encyclopedia of Minerals* have color illustrations of hubnerite (p. 65) rhodochrosite (p. 102), from the Silverton area and zunyite (p. 128).

Treasure Mountain Group

The Treasure Mountain group of mines is on the slope of Treasure Mountain, north of the Sunnyside Mine. They are 12 miles north of Silverton. Included in the group are the: San Juan Queen, Scotia, Golden Fleece, and Santiago claims which were worked in late 1880s and early 1890s.

Treasure Mountain Gold Mines Company was formed in 1937, and the Company extended the Santiago tunnel 1,600 feet to the Scotia vein. A drift 600 feet along the vein did not disclose any ore so a 650 foot drift toward the Golden Fleece vein was driven, but no ore was found. When a diamond drill hole was drilled 148 to 162 feet to the vein, the inflow of water from old workings through this hole was so great a mucking machine was used to put the rods back into the hole. Operations were suspended in 1947.

Ore bodies in these veins were up to 125 feet wide and contained vuggy quartz, fine-grained galena, and rhodonite. Ore with rhodonite was of higher grade. Old records show hand-sorted ore sent to the smelter ran as high as $50 per pound (2-1/2 ounces gold/pound).

Gold King Mine

The Gold King Mine is about a mile north of the old silver camp of Gladstone. There was a railroad to Gladstone before the Silver Panic of 1893 made it a ghost town. This mine is in the south fork of Cement Creek drainage, high on Bonita Peak. Gold and silver were the metals mined in the period 1898 and up to 1918. Only about 60 percent of the ore value was recovered and it was estimated $11 million in gold and other metals was discharged into Cement Creek, thereby forming a man-made placer deposit.

In 1900, Gold King Consolidated Mining Company built a tramway from the mine to the mill at Gladstone and improved the mill. Production was 250 tons per day and the ore was free milling. (The gold could be saved in the free state and was not locked up in other minerals.) Later, a tunnel was run from the mill under the mine workings. It was to be 1,700 feet long.

About 80 percent of the underground workings were in the footwalls side of the Bonita Fault, which was a zone about 1,000 feet wide at this location. Some workings were also in the hanging wall. The Red vein, within the Bonita Fault, displaced other veins. It was composed chiefly of rhodonite. The Gold King Tunnel was driven about 1,300 feet below the old workings and was later driven to the Sunnyside Mine workings and known as the American Tunnel of Standard Metals Co.

Rhodonite in the Eureka District.

From time to time the possibility of producing manganese from rhodonite has been advanced. In World War II, the government gave encouragement to such a possibility by sponsoring several programs. Actual production did not become necessary, however, one of the programs that did develop in the 1950's was a pilot plant study on ores from the Eureka district.

Large veins of rhodonite outcrop in the Bonita Fault-Ross Basin area and most mines in the Eureka district have rhodonite gangue.

By 1957, manganese compounds were produced in a pilot plant in West Orange, N.J., from rhodonite ore mined in the Eureka district, by the U.S. Managanese Corp. They used a process called the Hierarc Process and although the process was a success the cost was probably not competitive.

Sunnyside Mine and American Tunnel

The Sunnyside Mine is at the head of Eureka Gulch in Sunnyside Basin. It is at the junction of the Sunnyside-Cinnamon Fault and the Ross Basin Fault, two fault systems that form one side and the toe of a boot-shaped block within the Eureka Graben. The Toltec–Anaconda Fault to the south-east and the Bonita Fault to the southwest form the side and sole of the boot. The Eureka Graben with numerous parallel faults and veins connects the Silverton caldera to the Lake City caldera and is cut by this younger caldera.

The Sunnyside claim was first worked for gold in 1875, but this discovery was made while the area was still in possession of the Indians. Rich surface ores were worked for gold until 1896.

An amalgamation mill was built on the shore of Lake Emma, but this mill saved only the gold and tailings were flumed into the lake. Table concentration was initiated into the mining industry when Wilfley invented his table in 1895 and a new plant, using concentration tables, was erected in 1896 at the Sunnyside Mine. By 1916, concentrate production of 400 tpm was being made by use of the Wilfley tables, flotation, then a new process, and electrostatic separation.

Sunnyside Mining and Milling Company was organized in 1917, and by 1918, had the first selective flotation mill in North America. The new mill with a capability of 500 tpd, which was doubled in capacity in 1928, was at Eureka where Eureka Gulch junctions the Animas River. An aerial tramway 2-3/4 miles long connected the mine and mill. Between 1918 and 1938, the mine was closed twice due to low base metal prices and in 1938, the Sunnyside closed and was sold under bankruptcy proceedings in 1948. In the 15 most productive years the mine produced $50 million and for many years it was the largest mine in the San Juan Mountains. Low grade of ore, severe winter conditions in the Sunnyside Basin, and high operation costs were blamed for the closing.

The Shenandoah-Dives Mining Co. closed their 700 tpd mill on the Animas River above Silverton in 1952 after 26 years of production. During this time they mined and milled 4.1 million tons of ore. March-Shenandoah Corp. renovated the mill in 1958 and produced ore from the Gary Owen Mine to run the mill. In 1959, they leased the Sunnyside Mine, which had been closed since 1938, and drove 4,800 feet of tunnel, 4,000 feet of drifts, and 480 feet of raises. Standard Metals, Co., formerly Standard Uranium Company, emerged as the operating company and in 1960, they extended the American Tunnel toward the Sunnyside and also produced ore from the old Shenandoah–Dives property.

Standard Metals continued work on extending the American Tunnel to the Sunnyside workings; worked on the Washington vein and the Belle Creole vein, and completed the Washington vein shaft to serve between the Terry Tunnel (F-level) and the American Tunnel by 1962. Renovation of the Shenandoah mill was completed and ore from the American Tunnel started to flow through the mill August 6, 1962. Ore from the Sunnyside-Belle Creole Group, and the Silver Lake Group (of the old Shenandoah-Dives lease) was milled in 1963. A lease on the Brennerman Mine gave the company a 2.5 mile long continuous vein system to mine.

In 1964, Washington Mining Co. was formed with U.S. Smelting, Refining and Mining Co. with Standard Metals having 20 percent control and U.S.S.R. & M. Co. the remaining. Standard Metals retained ownership of the renovated 600 tpd Sunnyside Mill (old Shenandoah-Dives Mill). Work on the Silver Lake Group was phased out as the flow of ore through the American Tunnel increased in the late 1960s. Standard Metals emerged as the operating company.

In the Sunnyside, the Washington ore shoot was almost a thousand feet long and 1,400 feet in vertical distance. The No Name shoot was the longest shoot at 1,500 feet. Workings extended almost 7,000 feet along the vein system and a vertical range of about 3,000 feet was explored. The vein was from 20 to 50 feet wide and some stopes were 50 feet wide.

In 1971, free gold ore was rediscovered in the Sunnyside and Standard Metals rose from fourth in production of gold in Colorado in 1970, to second in 1971, and first in 1973, with 49 percent of Colorado's total gold production. Gold production from the Sunnyside Mine from 1902 to 1974 was 417,416 ounces; of this 28,498 ounces of gold were produced in 1974. Capacity of the mill was increased to 1000 tpd in 1976.

About 6:00 p.m. on Sunday, June 4, 1978, the water of Lake Emma broke through into a stope that was supposed to be 85 feet below the lake. The first mill on the Sunnyside vein, which was said to have been worked as early as 1873, was on Lake Emma. Gold was the only mineral sought at that time and the tailings were discharged into the lake. This mud and water, with a head of 1500 to 1700 feet crashed down through four main levels and into an unknown amount of old workings to the American Tunnel level and was squeezed the two miles to the portal at Gladstone to explode into the air.

Eyewitnesses, who had to walk up to the mine because three bridges were washed out, describe the portal as discharging pipe and mine timbers into the air in a continuous stream. Black mud and water roared down Cement Creek in a wall said to be eight feet high in places.

Fortunately, the miners were not working Sunday and no one was in the mine. About 145 miners worked underground on a normal work day. A local payroll of about $3 million was disrupted for almost a year while a small crew reopened the mine.

Silt and muck was five feet deep at the portal when the flood subsided. Where Lake Emma had been, a hole 500 by 850 feet and about 70 feet deep was all that was left. A maelstrom developed that cleared all brush and loose soil for a distance of about 250 feet from the old shore line of the lake.

When news of the breakthrough reached Ouray that Sunday night a small group of people rushed to Siverlton to pan for gold. The stope was known to be in rich free-gold ore and a small gold rush developed. Results of the effort were not posted; however, some people seemed pleased with their effort and there were a few smiles.

Before the end of a year the mine was operating at full capacity.

The Sunnyside vein system is credited with about $75 million in metals. This famous mine group developed a mineral deposit at the junction of the Sunnyside Fault and the Ross Basin Fault within the Eureka Graben and, in part, within the Silverton caldera (27.5 m.y.B.P.) and the larger San Juan caldera (28 m.y.B.P.). Mineralization did not occur until 10 to 15 m.y. after the caldera activity was completed.

Ore in the Sunnyside vein (fault) had been dated at 13.0 to 16.0 m.y.B.P. On the other side of the Eureka Graben, ore in the Shenandoah-Dives vein has been dated at 16 to 17 m.y.B.P. The caldera activity and development of the Eureka Graben formed an area of faults receptive to the later mineralization.

Casadevall and Ohmoto in their fluid inclusion studies of ore from the Sunnyside Mine found that the ore forming fluids were potassium-sodium-calcium solutions of small concentrations with small concentrations of metals. Data suggested hydrothermal fluids were predominantly meteoric water which underwent exchange of isotopes with country rock. Ore fluids were scavenged from the Tertiary volcanic rock and from Precambrian rock. Paleozoic sedimentary rock may have contributed and the last of six periods of mineralization contained many odd-mass hydrocarbons.

A model was suggested that accommodated a recharge area for ore-forming solutions to the southwest of the calderas in the area of Mesozoic and Paleozoic sediments.

Hulin recognized three stages of ore deposition in the Sunnyside vein:

1. Quartz and pyrite
2. Quartz, sphalerite, and galena
3. Rhodonite, some quartz, and minor sulfides.

Gold was later than the bulk of the sulfide minerals and was found in fractures in the rhodonite. Rhodonite occurred in lenses up to 30 feet thick near

Eureka and on Treasure Mountain in the same general area. Rhodochrosite replaces rhodonite and is later than alabandite or rhodonite.

Burbank made these additions to the mineralogy of the Sunnyside veins:

Manganese Minerals of the Sunnyside Veins

Alabandite	Distributed through friedelite, alleghanyite, and rhodonite as microscopic grains and veinlets. Up to 0.75 mm in diameter.
Alleghanyite	As grains; grayish-pink, 1.6 / 0.3 mm at largest.
Friedelite	Translucent, rose-red or brownish-red, tabular crystals, 0.06 to 0.13 mm in diameter, rhombohedral.
Helvite	Honey yellow grains.
Rhodochrosite	Not manganocalcite by test.
Rhodonite	Crystals up to 1.0 mm found in vugs.
Tephroite	Manganese olivine . . . gray.

Casadevall and Ohmoto recognized six periods of mineralization:

1. Pyrite—Quartz
2. Banded Quartz—sulfides
3. Massive galena—sphalerite–chalcopyrite–bornite–hematite
4. Gold—telluride quartz
5. Manganese
6. Quartz—fluorite–carbonate–sulfate

They further note alabandite occurred as greenish-black anhedral grains adjacent to gray to deep maroon patches of tephroite. Pale pink friedelite occurred intimately mixed with pyroxmangite. Hubnerite as tiny, lathlike blades of brownish-red color occurred in vugs with quartz or with pyroxmangite. Fluorite crystals occurred as knobs with etched and corroded faces suggesting it was partly dissolved after formation. Trace amounts of barite were found.

There are several occurrences of quartz: milky in first and second periods of mineralization, cloudy due to minute fluid inclusions and scattered dust-like particles, and fine grained milky quartz/sulfides in period three. Quartz with gold in fourth period ores is fine grained, massive, and appears milky to clear-purplish and when with butter gold and wet, it has buttery appearance. There is also fine grained milky quartz in fourth period ores and drusy quartz in vuggy cavities in fifth period.

Pyroxmangite, pink manganese silicate, is most abundant in the ore of the fifth period. It is fine grained and was mistaken by earlier workers as rhodonite. No rhodonite was found when identifying the minerals by x-ray diffraction. This last observation is of utmost significance as it undoubtedly applies to all San Juan "rhodonite." This material will now be called pyroxmangite and the burden of proof will be to discredit this for any specific San Juan Mountain location.

Ore and gangue minerals in order of abundance in the Sunnyside Mine were found to be: quartz, sphalerite, galena, pyroxmangite, pyrite, rhodochrosite, chalcopyrite, tetrahedrite, fluorite, and calcite.

Less abundant minerals are: hematite, gold, petzite, calaverite, alabandite, hubnerite, tephroite, friedelite, helvite, anhydrite, sericite, aikinite, barite, and gypsum.

Mineral specimens from the Sunnyside vein system that came through the American Tunnel have been numerous. Sulfide minerals, quartz and calcite specimens were the most plentiful.

Large red rhombs of rhodochrosite on calcite came from the American Tunnel in the period 1960–5 and a small number of specimens came out in 1975–6. Some rhodochrosite in selenite came out at the same time, but that from the first period was far superior. It is a real collectors item seen only at the Tucson Show and in private collections.

In 1969–70, some large clusters of calcite crystals sprinkled with minute pyrite crystals came from the American Tunnel. Like most of the minerals from single large vugs, they disappeared into collections.

Green fluorite in small cubes, 1/2 to 3/4 inches, and in badly corroded nobs of crystals occurred frequently in ore from the American Tunnel. Some larger green crystals coated with quartz started coming from the upper stopes in 1971. This fluorite continued to come from the mine in small quantities through about 1974. By 1975, it was getting scarce. These crystals reached a size of about four inches on an edge but most were only half a crystal reliefed on massive green fluorite. They were mostly slab-type specimens; however, a large group about two feet high and 14 to 16 inches in diameter was seen in a collection (Fig. 4–23).

Quartz cast pseudomorphs of barite with rhodochrosite crystals occurred.

Fig. 4–23.   Quartz over 3 inch fluorite cubes, American Tunnel (JM#904).

Rhodochrosite was both deep red and pink in color and most often in rhombohedral form. Hexagonal pinacoids, discus-shaped, were occasionally found.

Bitter Root Mine

The Rio Grande Railroad Special, Durango to Silverton and return, came to an unscheduled stop just 3.6 miles below Needleton station and a small man with a twinkle in his eyes got off with his bag of supplies. He waved to the trainman and headed for some buildings nearby. Oscar was back at the Bitter Root Mine for a new season.

Oscar Schaaf's family were immigrants from Germany who, after several moves, settled in Durango in 1898. As a boy, he and his brothers and sister, Olga, broke wild horses, for use of the miners of the area. He became familiar with the mines and prospecting just naturally followed.

The Bitter Root Mine produced some excellent samples of wire gold and some scheelite was said to occur in the small quartz vein, but the rare mineral, alstonite, a light yellow-colored barium-calcium carbonate was the real prize of the mine.

Oscar's was a small-scale mining operation. Mostly it was hand digging and prying at the cracks. It is not known how much gold was produced and run through Oscar's mini-scale mill, complete with Wilfley-type table which he had at his home near Durango, but it could not have been any sizable amount.

What he did produce, however, was some of the finest alstonite specimens ever found in the United States. Palache and others give three locations in England and no other mention of localities where this rare mineral, as Dana terms it, is found.

Most of the alstonite went to a local dealer and was probably widely distributed. The prize specimen, a large cluster of crystals weighing possibly thirty pounds, was either stolen from the dealer's shop or sold to a southeastern museum with the rest of the dealer's collection. A fine specimen of modest size is still in the area, with a smaller collection that was acquired by a local bank, and is on display at the Ft. Lewis State College at Durango.

The smaller of the collections has a history of its own dating back to at least 1924, when Bill Little, Olga's husband, had a heart attack and took up lapidary work and mineral collecting full time. Olga helped her brothers break wild horses and drive visitors to the mines in buggies. In the spring of 1909, Frank Rivers had to get much needed supplies up to the mine called the Rivers–Gorman Ruby Mine. He talked Olga into leading a pack train with supplies up to the mine. By the time she reached the mine it was dark and she had to sit up all night with the mine superintendent as there was no place for a lady packer to sleep. On her return trip, she pulled her packstring off the trail just below the Neglected Mine so she could get some sleep. Pack trails led to all the mines in those days because making a trail required only running a pack string over it a few times. As Olga got back on the trail, along came J. Ball, superintendent of the Neglected Mine. Like all mines, one of the big problems of the Neglected Mine was to get supplies to it as men were scarce. The men were all employed as miners where the wages were good. After some serious persuasion, Olga came away from her meeting with J. Ball with a three year contract to haul supplies to the Neglected Mine. This started a 30 year career of packing supplies to almost every mine in the LaPlata Mountains.

When Olga married Bill Little, a miner at the Neglected Mine since 1910, she promptly made a packer out of him. Together, they packed many tons of supplies to the mines. At one time they each had a string of forty burros capable of moving about four tons to the mines in one trip. They bought a ranch at May Day, just above Hesperus, Colorado, and ran the ranch with their packing business. When Bill had to quit going up into the high country, Olga continued and became famous as the "Lady Packer." She was given many honors and much publicity and it was a highlight of Durango's annual Spanish Trails Fiesta to see Olga and her burro string leading the parade.

Bill and Olga also attended mineral shows and they maintained Bill's collection in a museum at the ranch. After Bill's death in 1969, and Olga's a year later, the small collection was sold in an estate settlement.

Alstonite is given as dimorphous with barytocalcite by Fleisher. This mineral from the Bitter Root Mine was first called bromlite, a name no longer in use. The name bromlite came from the Bromley Hill Mine, a type locality near Alston, England, where it was first identified. Bitter Root Mine alstonite has only tenatively been identified.

Dana and Ford show two views of a bromlite crystal in their Figures 640 and 641.

Rossman and Squires first reported an American occurrence of alstonite coating pyramidal crystals from the Minerva No. 1 Mine Cave in Rock, Illinois. The mineral had previously been reported from three localities in England, at Alston, Hexham and Durham. The American occurrence was found in the summer of 1971 as colorless to gray, transparent, sharply terminated pseudo-hexagonal pyramids up to 2 mm lining cavities in veins of waxy yellow benstonite, (trigonal), fine-grained calcite and cm sized witherite crystals.

Cunningham Gulch Area

Ore from the Cunningham Gulch–Galena Mountain area was largely base metal sulfides and silver was the most important precious metal. Wire silver in masses was reportedly shipped from the Pride of the West Mine to Del Norte, over Stony Pass in 1874. Galena, sphalerite, chalcopyrite, pyrite, tetrahedrite, and wire silver were the chief minerals. After the oxidized ore was depleted, mill-grade ore was responsible for most of the production from the Dixie Lynn Mines.

F. L. Ransome, pioneer geologist, for whom the Ransome Mine was named, mentioned calcite as a pseudomorph of tremolite in the Osceola Mine. Quartz, fluorite and calcite were the common gangue minerals. Rhodochrosite occurred in the Gary Owen Mine. Gold occurred in tetrahedrite ore according to one report.

Bismuthinite occurred in slender prismatic crystals with specularite in quartz at the Neigold claim on Galena Mountain.

Dixie Lynn Mines.   A number of individual claims and groups of claims, most of them worked in the early days of mining in the area by numerous owners, were worked by the Dixie Lynn Co. from about 1967 to 1971. Some may have been worked by this company earlier, as the Galena Mountain Co. These claims centered about Galena Mountain and Cunningham Gulch. Among the mines and claims worked were: Galena Mountain mines, Old 100 Mine and group, Osceola, Veda Madre, Gary Owen, Green Mountain, Pride of the West, and Ransome.

Varnes describes the Pride of the West fracture zone, which is more than 100 feet wide, as typical of the vein systems of the area. Ore occurs along discontinuous veins within the fracture zone where tension fissures opened between individual faults. Cunningham Gulch via Stony Pass to the Upper Rio Grande and down the Rio Grande to Del Norte was one of the early routes to the Silverton area. It would be expected that this area was prospected first. The Pride, as it is usually called was U.S. Patent No. 42 and the Old 100 group was largely made up of Patent numbers in that range. Production on the Pride was continuous for 70 years with production from 1901 to 1956 recorded as $6.3 million.

The Director of the Mint reported in 1884, that the Pride of the West Mine had one of the strongest veins in the district. It was 30 feet wide and had been traced for 3,000 feet with 1600 feet of adits and four tunnels working.

The Hayden Survey visited the mine and reported ore had been shipped in 1874, making it one of the oldest mines in the Silverton area.

Ransome mentioned a strange banded ore with sheets of finely crystalline sphalerite and galena separated by vitreous quartz about 2 mm thick.

The Galena Mountain Co. worked the Old 100 group above the 2,200 tunnel level and later, as the Dixie Lynn Co., in 1967, drove an adit, 9 feet by 9 feet in cross section, 3,100 feet to cut the Veda Madre, Gary Owen, Sterling and other veins. A second adit, 900 feet above, was in 1,600 feet by 1968, and being extended. A raise was projected to connect the two.

History of production from mines of this group is spotty, as shown by *Minerals Yearbooks* for the 1940s through 1973. Ownership or leasing arrangements are constantly changing and some mines are worked each year. The Pride Mill, at Howardsville, was working through most of the 1970s on ore from various mines of the area.

Shenandoah–Dives.   A structural block, delineated by the ring fault zone of the Silverton caldera on the north and a fracture zone within Precambrian rocks on the south, contains the most mineable vein systems and veins in the south Silverton area. The ring fault zone is displaced about 1,700 feet in this area along many individual faults. Largest vein systems in this block are the Shenandoah–Dives and the parallel Silver Lake.

The Shenandoah–Dives system contains the Mayflower, North Star and Morgan veins and the North Star vein system extends into the Highland Mary Mine. In 1925, a consolidation of the Shenandoah–Dives, North Star and Mayflower holdings was formed as the Shenandoah–Dives Mining Co. Holdings extended 8,100 feet along the vein system to the Highland Mary Mine.

These vein systems outcrop high above the Animas River and partly in Arrastra Gulch. Volcanic rocks of the San Juan volcanic field lie on Pce rocks and the Shenandoah–Dives vein complex follows an andesite dike, 15 to 20 feet wide, for about 5,000 feet. Intersecting veins have helped localize the mineralization. In the Highland Mary Mine, the Pce rocks are exposed.

The veins are predominantly quartz which has been crushed by faulting. In places this made the ore gouge-like and gave problems in mining and formed excessive slimes in milling. Mineable ore width consistently was 8 to 8–½ feet, although the mineralization and vein zones were wider.

Excellent ore was found in the Slide claim in 1927, and this helped to make mining the marginal ore a success. Production prior to this had been $3.5 million from the group, of which $2 million was from the North Star and was produced prior to 1893, and $1.25 million from the Shenandoah–Dives. All of this ore had to be transported out by pack animals after it was hand sorted.

The Mayflower crosscut became the main operating tunnel with a portal safely below the cliffs to protect it from avalanches. Shops, transformers, compressors, and crushers were located underground. An aerial tramway, 10,000 feet long, connected the mine to the mill and it had a capacity of 80 tons per hour. All ore was crushed before it was sent down to the mill on the Animas River. Capacity of the mill was increased by 600 tpd.

In the Shenandoah–Dives vein system, much of the ore was crushed and mixed with gouge. It gave problems by sliming in the mill circuit. Ore minerals were galena, sphalerite, chalcopyrite, gold, and silver. The silver occurred as acanthite and as complex silver salts. Gangue minerals were quartz, calcite, manganiferous carbonates, and mixed carbonates, along with brown carbonates. Rhodochrosite also occurred.

North Star.   The North Star Mine was working from a 1,245 foot crosscut in 1884 that intercepted the vein 450 feet deep. Mineralization consisted of 28 inches of solid galena and tetrahedrite.

Silver Lake–Nevada Vein System.   This vein system is about 4,000 feet south of the Shenandoah–Dives vein system and is similar to it. It was leased and worked in conjunction with and through the Shenandoah–Dives workings. A 4,000 foot crosscut tunnel connected the two. In the early 1900s the Silver Lake Mine sold for $1.3 million.

Before aerial tramways were used to bring ore down to the railroad from the mines, all ore was transported downhill by burros to where wagons could pick it up and bring it in. Arrastra Basin Mines around King Solomon Mountain used many pack animals. Benham describes one packer who had 120 pack animals and a number of teams bringing in the ore in 1897. This operation used trainloads of hay and feed. The sure-footed and sturdy burros contributed a great deal to the early development of mining in the San Juan Mountains.

The boarding house at the Silver Lake Mine in 1889 was five stories high. The largest in the San Juans, it housed 500 men and the dining room seated 250 men at a time. It was difficult to hold men for extended periods in that high altitude with isolation and avalanches constantly present. Electricity, hot food, hot water, good wages, and all the latest conveniences available; however, made the place irresistable. San Juan boarding houses were built with A-frame-like roofs to shed the deep snowfall. As winter-time work at the mines was doubly difficult and hazardous from snow slides, most of the mines closed down after the first snows.

The Silver Lake Mill burned in 1906 and was replaced completely in eight months. This was a remarkable construction feat for this area in winter.

Both the Silver Lake and Nevada Mines had produced high-grade surface ores and in 1890, an attempt was made to concentrate low-grade base metal ores without much success. After a number of years of marginal or no profits, the Shenandoah–Dives Mining Co. closed down in 1957.

Production on the Shenandoah–Dives from 1901–57 was $29.3 million and the Silver Lake produced $7.8 million. The Highland Mary produced $3 million in the same period. The Shenandoah–Dives operation reportedly produced 4.5 million tons of ore from three miles of vein system in this interval.

Sometime between 1957 and 1960, Standard Metals reopened and started production from the Shenandoah–Dives properties; however, operations, continued on ore from the Silver Lake Group, the Sunnyside, Mogul, Belle Creole, and Brennerman claims of the Sunnyside Group. The mill is still used to process ores from the Sunnyside Group, which is transported through the American Tunnel.

Highland Mary Mine. Highland Mary Mine is in Cunningham Gulch and is the continuation of the Shenandoah–Dives vein system, which is over two miles long. An aerial tramway 1,200 feet long connects the mine to the mill, 1,000 feet below, in Cunningham Gulch. Bradley Tunnel cuts the vein about 900 feet from the portal and drifting along the vein had continued for 2,400 feet by 1950. First part of the vein is in Precambrian schist and the volcanic formations of the San Juan volcanic field form the walls elsewhere. Galena, sphalerite, and freibergite with some gold form the ore. Quartz, barite, and minor calcite are the gangue minerals.

Water from Highland Mary Lake, with a head of 832 feet, drove two Pelton wheels, one for electric power generation and one to run a 400 cfm compressor. To prevent snowslides from destroying the power lines, three cables were strung across Cunningham Gulch and droplines used to deliver the power where needed. Snowslides close the area in winter.

Anvil Mountain Pipes

The breccia pipes on Anvil Mountain are somewhat similar to the Koehler–Longfellow pipes higher up the valley and the Red Mountain breccia pipes over on the other side of Red Mountain Pass. They, however, have some minerals not common but present in a lesser degree in the other breccia pipes in the ring fault zone of the Silverton caldera.

Zuni Mine.   The Zuni Mine is on Anvil Mountain, about three miles north of Silverton and east of U.S. Hwy. 550. It was discovered in 1881. Burbank noted that the mines on Anvil Mountain were within altered rocks similar to those of Red Mountain to the north, but that the ore shoots were different. The ore was in a pipe-like mass 60 feet long and 15 feet wide at the surface. It was worked by a shaft, two tunnels, and an open cut. The upper tunnel branches and has one branch 156 feet long and the other 180 feet. A lower tunnel, 200 feet below, is 540 feet long.

Brobdignag Mine.   This mine is northwest of the Zuni Mine on Anvil Mountain. Two small adits, marked by dumps, are all that is left to identify the location of the first authenticated occurrence of zinkenite in the United States. Rare crystals in a 4 foot vein of barite and feldspar were reported.

Hillebrand and Cross reported zinkenite in the area in 1885 according to Eckel, but one analysis gave 5.64 percent arsenic. Guitermanite, was discovered at the Zuni Mine in 1884 as was zunyite. Guitermanite has been discredited as a species and seems to be a mixture of jordanite–baumhauerite and other minerals. The occurrence of thallium in jordanite is unique in the San Juan Mountains.

In examining a specimen in the Colorado School of Mines Museum, Grybeck found the guitermanite to be composed of sartorite, and fine-grained galena.

Zunyite was reported in crystals up to 2 inches by Groben, who also reported the occurrence of cosalite and pearceite. Zunyite was found to be fairly common in the Red Mountain district in association with dickite and other clay minerals.

Ransome reported quartz pseudomorphs of barite in kaolinite with zunyite and guitermanite. He also reported bournonite and enargite that had over 200 ounces of silver per ton. The bournonite was steel gray to black and occurred in small vertically striated prisms with pyrite and massive zunyite. The once accepted guitermanite enclosed tetrahedrons of zunyite and altered to anglesite.

At the Zuni Mine, ore in the oxidized zone was anglesite. A mass of anglesite containing numerous small tetrahedral crystals of unaltered zunyite changed to unoxidized jordanite and other gangue materials associated with zunyite. This ore occurred in a mass 60 feet long by 15 feet wide. Below No. 1 Tunnel, ore changed to six feet wide and became a copper ore with enargite, pyrite, kaolin, and barite. Enargite carried 216 ounces silver and 40 percent copper per ton.

In the lower tunnel, the ore body was 40 feet by 12 feet wide and consisted of a soft mass of kaolin, embedded pyrite and nests of enargite. Pyrite occurs chiefly in octahedral form and carries very little gold. Angular fragments of country rock occurred in the ore and small masses of this material, seemingly having no connection with the main ore body, occurred in the tunnel. These masses often contain small caves or vugs lined with crystals of quartz, barite, enargite, and barite. Country rock around these caves was often brecciated and filled with ore. Small prospects of similar chimney ore occur on Anvil Mountain but they are unpredictable in occurrence and limited so as not to be commercial.

REFERENCES

A–4 Lindgren Volume, (Burbank), (Base Metals), B–1, C–2, C–3, C–4, C–5, D–1 (Burank), (Traver), D–2, D–3, E–4, E–6, F–3, F–5, F–6, F–7, G–1, G–2, G–3, G–5, G–6, G–11, H–5, H–7, H–8, I–1, I–3, I–16, J–10, J–14, J–18, J–41, J–46, J–70, J–74, K–3, K–14, K–16, K–17, K–19, L–1, 1952–1973, N–3, N–4, N–5, N–7, N–13, N–18, P–3 Baldwin (Kottlowski), (Wengerd), (Kelley), (Silver), (Bejnar), (Kelley), (Vein), (Rosenzweig), Q–4, Q–5, Q–9, Q–11, Q–68, Q–69, Q–70, R–14, S–13, S–15, S–52, S–71, S–75, S–99, S–116, S–117, S–141, S–148.

Iron Springs District (Ophir)

The Iron Springs district is about ten miles south of Telluride on State Route 145, in San Miguel County. The old mining camp of Ophir is about two miles up narrow Ophir Valley from the highway in approximately the center of the district. Walls of Ophir Valley are cliff-like and rise about 2,000 feet above the valley floor. Winters are severe and snow-slides are a constant hazard.

This small mining district is on the western edge of the San Juan volcanic field and is centered around a quartz monzonite stock that cuts a thick sequence of mostly red-bed sediments. It is east of the San Miguel Mountains and north of the LaPlata Mountains on the western flank of the Needle Mountain uplift.

Principal mines were in the Silver Belle group and were worked for silver before the Silver Panic of 1893 left the camp deserted. The Director of the Mint report for 1884 mentioned their silver production but actual production is not known.

Silver Belle Group. The Silver Belle group of 58 mining claims was worked in 1945 by the Silver Belle Mining Company. Principal veins were the Ida, Bulter, and the Silver Belle. In 1902, a 50 stamp mill had operated on ore from this group; however, the mines had been closed most of the intervening time.

The veins cut a small intrusive center of quartz monzonite and were worked throughout a range of about 1,000 feet vertically. Production of base metals was made possible by high metal prices during World War II and for a short time thereafter.

The mine was typical of the small marginal mines that occur just outside of the main mineralized area of the San Juan Mountains. Its bid to importance was its production of tungsten.

In the Silver Belle Mine, ore minerals included galena, sphalerite, chalcopyrite, and tetrahedrite. Gangue minerals were calcite, barite, fluorite, siderite, and ever-present pyrite and quartz. Tungsten occurred in quantities sufficient of make a separate concentrate during World War II years.

The Ida and Butler veins in the Silver Belle Mine both contained hubnerite ore. Sixty tons of tungstic trioxide concentrates were produced and shipped in 1940 from the Ida vein. A small mill was built in 1952 to produce tungsten concentrates.

RICO MOUNTAINS

A party of about sixty trappers from St. Louis under Wm. G. Walton spent the summer of 1833 along the Dolores River and near Trout Lake, about 13 miles northeast of Rico and 5 miles southeast of Ophir. They reported on the area. Evidently they came into the area from the south or southeast.

Then in 1861, a Lieutenant Howard came over the mountains from what is now Silverton on the Animas River and prospected the Dolores River, returning to the Animas River. A first claim in the Rico Mountains, the Pioneer, was worked in 1869. This claim gave the district its name. Other claims were worked the following summers, as most of the miners did not stay over in the winters. A small adobe, Spanish-style furnace was built and three small bars of bullion were produced before it caved in. The Hayden Survey came through in 1874. Rich oxidized silver ore was found on Nigger Baby Hill in 1879 and a rush from neighboring camps followed. That same year a small shipment was made to Swansea, Wales. With freight rates from Durango $300 per ton, a smelter was brought in during 1880 and was producing bullion by autumn.

An expedition against a party of Utes was launched from the camp in 1881. They were overtaken near the LaSal Mountains, in Utah, and defeated with heavy losses of life on both sides.

As early as 1881, David Swickhimer began a shaft on the Enterprise claim. He and his partners sold it for a few hundred dollars worth of lumber. The success of two other miners in following small veins on nearby claims gave him second thoughts and he repurchased controlling interest. The story of the Enterprise is the real story of Rico.

The Rico Mountains are an elliptical group of mountains on the southwest edge of the San Juan Mountains. They are separated from them by a plateau about 10 miles wide and 11,000 feet high. The East Dolores River flows through a deep canyon that divides these mountains in half. Other streams radiate from them to join this superimposed river.

These mountains are in a thick sequence of Mesozoic and Paleozoic rocks that slope southwest to from the Canyonlands of the Colorado Plateau. Rico dome is the central structure and is on the western flank of the larger Needle Mountain dome. LaPlata dome is on the southwest flank of this same dome. Rico dome is about 5 miles in diameter and is made up mostly of sedimentary rocks into which intrusive dikes, sills and irregular bodies have been emplaced. A monzonite stock and a small body of Precambrian rocks, which is bounded

Formations in Rico Region, Colorado

AGE	FORMATION	APPROX. MAX. THICKNESS (FEET)
Late Cretaceous	Mancos shale	3,000
Late and Early (?) Cretaceous	Dakota sandstone	300
	Unconformity	
Late Jurassic	Morrison fm.	
	Brushy Basin shale mbr.	500
	Salt Wash S.S. Mbr.	300
	Wanakah fm.	
	(with Pony Express l.s. mbr. in eastern part)	200
	Entrada sandstone	80
	Unconformity	
Late Triassic	Dolores fm.	1,000
	Unconformity	
Early Permian	Cutler fm.	2,100
Middle Pennsylvanian	Rico fm.	325
	Hermosa fm.	
	Upper mbr.	830
	Middle mbr.	650
	Lower mbr.	880
	Quartzite of Larsen Tunnel area	
	Unconformity	
Lower Mississippian	Leadville limestone	170
Devonian	Ouray limestone	
	Unconformity	
Precambrian	Uncompahgre quartzite	1,000 (?)
	Metadiorite	?
	Greenstone	?
		11,415 Ft.

Adapted from Pratt Table 1., p. 85, Guidebook, 1956 Field Conf., N. Mex. Geol. Soc. 1968.

by faults, occupy the central part of the dome. Numerous sills and laccolithic structures increase the height of the dome with individual units as much as 200 feet thick. The area is at least 4,000 feet above the surrounding plateau. Some intrusive units may be early Tertiary or possibly late Cretaceous in age.

Formations in the Rico area are tabulated below because they are representative of those of the western side of the San Juan volcanic field and the adjacent Colorado Plateau.

Mineralization occurred in three general forms: as fissure veins with associated blanket deposits, at favorable horizons in the Hermosa formation as stocks or chimney deposits, and as large lead, zinc, and pyrite replacement beds in limestone.

Early day mining was from the fissure veins of Newman Hill, as the west slope of Dolores Mountain east of the town and between Deadwood Gulch and Silver Creek, was called. High-grade silver with lead and some gold occurred in small veins that often led to large blanket deposits in favorable beds.

The most favorable and, in fact, the blanket deposit that made the mining camp of Rico, was at the Enterprise Mine. Dave Swickhimer, a local miner of good reputation, bought a half-interest in the Enterprise Mine from G. Barlow and agreed to develop that property for another quarter interest. A shaft was started but Dave soon had to do work on other claims in the group to hold them. Funds were short of those required and although ore stringers or veinlets in the Enterprise shaft were encouraging, thousands of dollars were owed to the miners for wages and to other creditors. The merchants decided against any more credit and the miners quit. Just as things looked bleakest for Dave, Mrs. Swickhimer was notified she had won $4,000 in a Louisiana lottery. Some supplies were bought, food for some of the miners helped and Dave plunged his shaft deeper. At 262 feet a 15 inch blanket of $300 per ton ore was cut in 1887. This, the famous Enterprise blanket, directed prospecting in the late 1880s for the rest of the camp.

In 1891, the Enterprise production was $0.5 million and in 1892 it was over $1.5 million. The Enterprise Group was sold in September, 1891 for $1.25 million cash, after sparking a boom period that lasted about six years. By 1907, Rico was well on the decline and when the Rico State Bank suspended operations, President David Swickhimer's bank went into receivership.

Ore occurred in stocks or chimneys in the Johnny Bull and Gold Anchor Mines in the Horsecreek area. Although relatively unimportant for the ore produced, the occurrence is of significant interest to compare with the Red Mountain deposits near Ouray and Silverton.

The Johnny Bull stock was 10 to 15 feet in diameter and 120 feet deep. It was in sandstone of the Dolores formation near several dikes and irregular intrusion of porphyry. The sandstone was silicified and pyritized and ore minerals were enargite and small amounts of kaolin, sericite, and other minerals. Enargite was not found elsewhere in the Rico district. A second stock occurred under this one in the Gold Anchor Mine. It was chiefly pyrite.

Large replacement beds of massive pyrite with galena and sphalerite occurred in the Ouray and Leadville limestones and in a massive bed of limestone near the top of the Hermosa formation. Galena and sphalerite also occur as massive beds with little or no gangue minerals.

In 1907, it was reported that in the Atlantic Cable Mine, at a depth of 185 feet a great deal of gas was giving trouble. Carbon dioxide was found in a number of the mines and blowers had to be used to prevent suffocation. It bubbled out of the Dolores River at one place to the extent that small animals and birds that came too close were suffocated.

In the Rico district pyrite, galena, sphalerite, chalcopyrite, tetrahedrite, argentite (acanthite), proustite, polybasite, stephanite, native silver, and native gold are the ore minerals. Magnetite has been mined as a flux. Quartz, specularite, rhodochrosite, calcite, fluorite, barite, and gypsum are common gangue minerals. The ore is thought to have formed prior to the erosion surface on which the Telluride Conglomerate was deposited. This places it in the same general age as the deposits northeast of Ouray. These deposits have not been dated but are two of the oldest mineral deposits in the San Juan Mountains.

In his report for 1898, the Director of the Mint said the veins were narrow but high in grade, containing a great variety of the true silver ores and carrying a large amount of metallic gold, frequently found as a network of threads permeating a mass of silver glance.

George reported rhodochrosite and manganiferous limonite carrying some gold and silver occur in considerable quantities. Rhodochrosite did not occur as individual crystals but as banding with quartz and as rough banding in the vein. Gold in rhodochrosite was reported. All of the ore in veins had distinct banding with rhodochrosite and late quartz near the center.

In the Enterprise Mine blanket, beds of gypsum up to 30 feet thick may have been displaced by ore minerals; overlying shales were brecciated and irregular subsidence occurred.

In the Atlantic Cable Mine, metamorphosed limestones contain garnet, wollastonite, vesuvianite, pyroxene, chlorite, epidote, and hematite as gangue minerals.

Eckel had the following to add about the minerals of the Rico district: acanthite occurred in the Enterprise Mine associated with stephanite, polybasite, tetrahedrite, pyrargyrite, and common sulfides all set in bright pink rhodochrosite; allophane occurred as a pale blue mass with kaolinite in a limestone cavity; Calico Peak porphyry has been changed to almost pure alunite; anglesite was found in near-surface ores, copper was found near the head of Iron Draw, dolomite with celestite was found near the Enterprise blanket ore body, silver halides were common in the Puzzler Mine, some gypsum recrystalized to variety selenite; pyrite occurred in thick blanket-like replacement deposits in limestone, and the rhodochrosite was not crystalline but massive and banded.

Rico–Argentine Mine

The Rico–Argentine Company's St. Louis Tunnel is about a mile up the Dolores River from Rico. A company was formed in 1937 from several former operations and the Blain Tunnel, two miles up Silver Creek, was opened to develop a large replacement body of lead–zinc. In 1938, a 135 tpd flotation mill was built and the company expanded so that by 1948 they had over 3,000 acres of holdings in the Rico district. In the fall of that year, the operations were curtailed and a crew of 200 men was reduced to 50. Demand for sulfuric acid in the uranium industry produced a ready demand in Durango and in mills on the Colorado Plateau. The company had massive replacement beds of pyrite in its holdings and built a 150 tpd acid plant at the St. Louis Tunnel site in 1953. An enlarged plant was built in 1956; however, it was partly destroyed by fire in 1960. The State closed the acid plant in October, 1964, for polluting the Dolores River. Vegetation had been killed by the fumes along the valley and adjoining hillsides.

The year 1958 was the first time in 20 years that the Rico–Argentine failed to ship either ore or concentrates of lead–zinc. Development work was done however and ore recovered was concentrated and stockpiled. Production continued on lead–zinc ores in the 1970s and the mill and a leaching plant were reportedly working in 1976.

REFERENCES

A–4 Lindgren Volume, D–1 (Burbank), D–3, F–1, F–2, F–3, F–5, F–7, G–5, G–7, J–13, J–64, L–1, P–5 Shomaker, (Chapin), (Pratt), (Engel), R–3, R–14, S–3, S–21, S–25, S–52, S–99, S–100, S–142.

LAPLATA MOUNTAINS

The LaPlata Mountains are west of Durango on the high divide between LaPlata and Montezuma Counties. They are on the southwest flank of the Needle Mountain dome and are between the San Juan volcanic field and the Colorado Plateau.

The principal peaks of the LaPlata Mountains are in a mass about nine miles in diameter and are twenty miles southwest of the main San Juan Mountains. Drainage is radial from this dissected dome. The Tertiary and Cretaceous formations were removed by erosion exposing lower Mesozoic strata and intrusives into them. Headward erosion by the LaPlata River has deeply cut the mountains into two segments.

These mountains are a dome having a horseshoe-shaped hinge fold in the center with LaPlata River valley occupying the center of the horseshoe. Rocks of Pennsylvanian to Upper Cretaceous age dip away from the dome at steep angles on all sides. They have been intruded by laccolithic-type igneous masses and have numerous stocks, sills, and dikes that have protected the entire mountain so that it rises above the surrounding area.

Sedimentary formations are comparable to those in the Rico area and the igneous rocks are considered to be late Cretaceous or Tertiary in age. They are of two general types: porphyritic and non-porphyritic. Porphyritic rocks are between diorite and monzonite in composition and are the oldest, occurring mostly as stocks, sills, and dikes. The nonporphyritic rocks are syenites, monzonites, and diorites and occur as stocks and dikes.

Placer mining and prospecting was started as early as 1861 in the LaPlata Mountains, but it did not last long. Not much prospecting for lode mines occurred until 1873 when the Comstock and other mines at the head of LaPlata Valley were opened. High grade telluride minerals were discovered in 1893 in the Neglected Mine but it was closed by the end of the year. Most of the ore was pockety but of high grade. The May Day Mine was discovered in 1902, or 1903 by some accounts, and reached peak production by 1907. Next to this mine, the Valley View or Idaho Mine, which was located in 1902, produced extremely high grade ore in 1910-1. Production of the district up to this time was about $4.5 million with the May Day and Idaho having produced over half of this amount.

Galbraith characterized the lode deposits of the LaPlata Mountains as follows:

1. Disseminated chalcopyrite, in two syenite stocks, containing native platinum and palladium.
2. Gold with sulfides, as contact-metamorphic replacement bodies, as gold-bearing pyrite in veins, replacement bodies, and as breccia bodies, and mixed sulfides with silver and native gold.
3. Chalcocite-bearing veins.
4. Ruby silver-bearing veins.
5. Telluride-bearing veins and replacement bodies.

Limy beds in the central part of the district are highly metamorphosed. Associated minerals are: andradite, augite, magnetite, hematite, and a little gold.

Gold-bearing pyrite deposits have sericite, kaolin, and chlorite associated with them. These deposits occur as veins, replacements, and as breccia filling. Mixed sulfides with gold and silver also occur in breccia zones, some up to 40 feet in width. Pyrite, chalcopyrite, galena, sphalerite, and tetrahedrite are the ore minerals. Chalcocite veins associated with monzonite porphyry dikes in the Dolores formation have also been mined.

Ruby silver-bearing veins, the most important one being in the Cumberland Mine, occur in a zone about three miles long and a half mile wide. Proustite, pyargyrite, stephanite, argentite, and probably sulfosalts of silver with minor gold are minerals found in these veins. Telluride veins and replacement bodies occur in three general areas. Two of these areas lie along the hinge fold that encircles the dome and the third is within a belt of east-west faults across the south end of the dome. The replacement deposits are within 50 feet of veins and in the Pony Express limestone member of the Wanakah formation. A similar occurrence in the same formation was in the American Nettie Mine at Ouray. An interesting but barren set of veins occur in syenite on Bedrock Creek. Coarsely bladed dark-green augite, intergrown with microcline feldspar is cut by veins of coarsely crystalline calcite, white to clear crystalline quartz, and blue chalcedony. Some chalcopyrite and pyrite occurs in irregular masses. These calcite veins in a syenite mass may be unrecognized carbonatites, with silica and sulfides introduced later.

Gold was said to be abundant in the Neglected, May Day–Idaho, and Comstock Mines and other mines in the near-surface workings. It occurred with amalgam and with native mercury also. Grybeck reported kobellite from the Comstock Mine.

Below LaPlata townsite a black muck in a swampy area contains native copper in grains up to a cm in length.

Sphalerite is said to have replaced quartz, pyrite, and carbonate gangue. Calcite occurred in the eastward extension of the MayDay–Idaho Fault in solid bodies 10 to 20 feet wide. This may again be evidence of carbonatite occurrence. Roscoelite occurs widespread with fine-grained quartz and gives it a dull green color. George reported aikinite and other minerals but this species has not been confirmed. Masses of mixed tellurides several feet thick have been found.

Two random samples of ore from the Copper Hill Mine dump indicated that ore in place might have the following mineral values as determined by assay:

Copper	2 to 4 percent/ton
Platinum	0.02 to 0.06 oz./ton
Palladium	0.02 to 0.04 oz./ton
Silver	0.14 to 0.76 oz./ton

Minerals of the LaPlata Mountains:

Andradite	Dickite	Petzite
Anglesite	Enargite	Platinum
Ankerite	Epidote	Proustite
Argentite	Fluorite	Pyrargyrite
Arsenopyrite	Galena	Pyrolusite
Augite	Gold	Pyrite
Azurite	Gypsum	Quartz
Barite	Halloysite	Realgar
Bismutite	Hematite	Rhodochrosite
Bornite	Hessite	Roscoelite
Calaverite	Kobellite	Sericite
Calcite	Krennerite	Siderite
Cerussite	Limonite	Silver
Chalcanthite	Magnetite	Stephanite
Chalcopyrite	Malachite	Sylvanite
Chlorite	Marcasite	Tellurium
Cinnabar	Miargyrite	Tetrahedrite
Coloradoite	Mercury	Tourmaline
Copper	Orthoclase	Tremolite
Covellite	Palladium	

Minerals whose presence have not been definitely established:

Aikinite	Cosalite
Amalgam	Pearceite
Benjaminite	Polybasite
Cerargyrite	Troilite

May Day and Valley View (Idaho) Mines

The May Day–Idaho vein system is in strong E-W faults that are closely related to the horseshoe-like hinge fold that is in the center of the LaPlata dome. The mines are about two miles up LaPlata dome, and are located about two miles up LaPlata River from Hesperus, near May Day. By 1943, the Idaho had produced 47,962 + ounces of gold and 383,004 ounces of silver and the May Day 74,914 + ounces of gold and 758,984 ounces silver. Principal workings totaled over five miles. A specimen of ore is shown in (Fig. 4–24).

Two faults in the system, the Idaho and the May Day are reverse faults. Vertical displacement is 350–475 feet and horizontal displacement is 1,000 to 2,000 feet to the east. Vein and replacement deposits occur and the ore is principally tellurides with some base metal mineralization. The most productive part of the May Day vein was stoped continuously for 455 feet. Wall rocks ranged from Entrada sandstone up into the Morrison formation. Some of the best ore was in the Pony Express limestone member of the Wanaka formation. Some shipments of ore contained several thousand dollars worth of gold per 100 pound sack. Local legends persist that as much was high graded (unauthorized removal) as was shipped. Probably only legends—a lunch bucket will only hold so much.

Fig. 4–24.   Calcite on banded cerussite and hemimorphite, May Day Mine (JM#23).

Red Arrow Mine (California Mining District Montezuma County)

One of the last significant discoveries of free gold at the surface of a vein in Bonanza proportions and in the tradition of the old time prospector became the Red Arrow Mine. The mine is nine miles northeast of Mancos, Colorado, on the southwest flank of the La Plata Mountains. It is on the north side of the East Mancos River, about a mile north of the Montezuma–La Plata County line. An unnumbered truck-trail leaves the Echo Basin Road, Route 44, about a mile north of its junction with U.S. Highway 160 and continues seven miles to the vicinity of the mine at 9,100 feet elevation.

When news of the strike reached the press in November, 1933, some extravagant claims were made and a rush to the district began after the heavy winter snows were gone. This influx of miners was said to have resulted in the expenditure of at least $750,000 by January of 1935. Knowledgeable mining men who visited the mine proclaimed it to be the greatest gold discovery in Colorado since Cripple Creek.

Although production of the mine was about $400,000 and small in comparison to Cripple Creek, important quantities of free gold were found in pockets. Sheets of gold "as big as your hand and weighing up to a half pound" were found. Nuggets sometimes had chalcocite in the creases so as to give them an "antique" and rather attractive look. Seven thousand dollars (about 200 ounces at $35 per ounce) worth of free gold was mined from a gouge-slip in one day by the son of one of the owners, according to one report.

Gold ore valued from $10 to $30 a pound was said to be stored in local bank vaults. Records show 256 ounces of gold (over 21 troy pounds) and 50 ounces of silver in the form of nuggets and high grade ore was sold in 1934. Some specimens reached mineral collectors.

Nuggets by the handful worth $75,000 were said to have been scooped up from the surface and a first shipment of three tons was expected to bring $200,000 according to news accounts. Actually, this three tons brought $2,000 per ton—a case of confused decimals. Recorded production from 15 shipments of ore was $30,000 by January, 1935.

The gold was relatively free of silver and contaminating substances; however, reports of "4-9," or gold that was 99.99 percent pure, were exaggerated. A vandal was reported to have chiseled a piece of gold the size of a half dollar from an outcrop. This not only spoiled a good specimen, it distorted the production records as well.

Some miners considered the Red Arrow and Red Arrow Extension to be the continuation of the famous May Day Mine which had been sought for 50 years. As the May Day Mine is about 5-1/2 air miles to the southeast this hardly seems plausible. Both mines worked E-W vein systems which, if projected, would not cross.

A press release by the U.S.G.S. in 1933 contained data furnished by the Red Arrow Gold Corp. and a team of U.S.G.S. geologists who were working in the area. It is the most complete account of the mine available and is extracted and given with other information below.

Some prospectors were panning gold on small bars of gravel in Gold Run Draw about 500 feet northwest of the East Mancos River on the west side of the draw when they found spectacular gold showings in their pans. Following the color upstream in the classic manner of prospectors, they found some coarse gold just below a fissure that crossed the draw in the redbeds. It is easy to speculate that the strike trace of this fissure resembled a red arrow and the claims were so named. The discovery data was given as June 3, 1933.

The LaPlata Mountains are formed by monzonite intruded into the sedimentary beds of the Colorado Plateau and they stand alone west of the San Juan Mountains. Similar to centers of igneous activity at Ouray and Rico, the three are about the same age and predate the volcanic pile that formed the San Juan Mountains.

Age of the ore has not been determined by K/Ar dating methods but is assumed to be much older than most of the ores of the San Juan Mountains.

A sequence of the sedimentary beds found near the Red Arrow Mine is given as follows. The section is not complete and is much thinner than elsewhere on the Colorado Plateau. Some formations may not have been recognized. Navajo sandstone and Windgate sandstone have been mentioned but the U.S.G.S. team did not find any evidence of them near the Red Arrow Mine.

Cutler Formation—Permian (oldest)
Dolores (redbeds)—Triassic
Entrada Sandstone—Jurassic
(the lower LaPlata of early reports)
Morrison Formation
(the Upper LaPlata of early reports)
The lower 150 to 200 feet is a white sandstone that contains the discovery level tunnel (1,200 feet) of the Red Arrow Mine.
Dakota Formation—Cretaceous
Mancos Shale
(The type locality is Mancos, Colorado)

As for the prospectors, further panning in the draw led to the footwall contact in the lower LaPlata sandstone (Entrada). This was probably the Red Arrow Extension vein which was worked at the same time as the Red Arrow vein. It was 500 feet south of the parallel to the Red Arrow vein.

Outcrop of the Red Arrow vein was found in a clump of scrub oak in the Upper LaPlata (Morrison Fm.) which was a white sandstone 150 to 200 feet thick at this locality. The outcrop of slickensided sandstone stood up about two feet above the other sandstone and was heavily stained with azurite and malachite. It panned free gold in exciting amounts. Later a sample of chalcocite from an open cut under the outcrop assayed 1,000 ounces silver/ton. The chalcocite found in the vein usually ran high in silver. This could have been derived from freibergite and other minerals of the district.

The vein dipped 60 to 70 degrees south and had an E-W strike. A tunnel, which was the main working level and referred to as the discovery level tunnel, was started 50 to 75 feet above a limestone marker bed that divided the LaPlata into an upper and lower member. About 75 feet from the portal of this tunnel, a two ounce nugget was found. This was the first of the coarse gold found. It occurred in nuggets, plates, and in foliated masses.

The tunnel was in 110 feet when the U.S.G.S team visited the mine. It was still in enriched and oxidized ore in a sandstone breccia with chiefly barite gangue. The face of the tunnel was in massive interlocking barite crystals with frequent vugs. Only some of the open spaces were filled with limonite, indicating they were originally filled with sulfides. There was no copper mineralization at this point, however, at other places along the vein there was much azurite, malachite, chrysocolla, and chalcocite associated with partly oxidized pyrite and chalcopyrite. Barite and sandstone breccia fragments were seamed with mineralization.

Free gold occurred on the vein walls with unaltered sulfides. The hanging wall streak was 20 to 30 inches wide and ran one to three ounces of gold/ton. The footwall had the most nuggets and coarse gold. Screenings of footwall material ran 4.4 ounces gold and 15.8 ounces silver/ton.

Limonite contained small amounts of tellurium and selenium, which was interpreted as locked up in tellurium oxides and tellurates of iron. There were traces of manganese. It was thought that only a small part of the gold and silver was derived from tellurides as gold derived from this source "usually yielded a finely divided 'mustard' gold." The gold was thought to have been derived mainly from destruction of pyrite and to have migrated down-vein to plate out on primary gold. This would account for its foliated form and appearance. Assays of silver in the chalcocite frequently ran 500 ounces/ton and copper ran as high as 18 percent.

Older reports on the LaPlata Mountains recognized three sets of fissure systems. One, the strongest, had an E-W strike; one NE striking system had large zones of crushed rock cemented by quartz and sulfide minerals; and the third set had a NW strike. The fissures were tight in the shales with only a small amount of mineralization, but this increased as they passed through sandstones and intrusive porphyries.

Minerals of the district, as listed by the U.S.G.S team were:

tellurides of gold and silver
gold
amalgam
freibergite
tennantite
stephanite
sulphantimonides of silver
sulpharsenides of silver
pyrite
marcasite
chalcopyrite (and secondary minerals)
galena

sphalerite
realgar
cinnabar
magnetite
hematite

Gangue minerals were: quartz, chalcedony, calcite, rhodochrosite, dolomite, barite, fluorite, chlorite, sericite, kaolin, and metamorphic minerals of the sedimentary-igneous contacts.

The mine was worked from its discovery continuously to 1942 when wartime restrictions caused it to be closed. After the war, it was worked continuously for five years. From time to time efforts have been made to reopen the mine. Inspectors for the state found the discovery level tunnel active in 1958 and again in 1960. It is closed at the present time but is said to be under option.

There is 2,500 feet of underground workings on three levels. The discovery level tunnel is 1,200 feet, a second level 300 feet, and a 365 foot crosscut tunnel that has not yet reached the vein.

Production from the Red Arrow Mine was given in 1947 by Vanderwilt as follows:

YEAR	ORE TONS	GOLD OUNCES	SILVER OUNCES	COPPER POUNDS	REMARKS
1933	21	170			
1934	124	435			
		256	50		High grade ore and nuggets
1935	81	270	562		
1936	216	1,593	3,414	2,000	
1937	214	1,929	2,383	1,945	
1938	638	1,744	3,447	2,500	
1939	839	943	1,102	500	Includes small production from adjacent mine
1940	3,000	1,355	295		Mill ore
	39	179	585		Shipped ore
1941	2,524	1,053	1,152		Mill ore and 24 tons shipped
1942	1,600	210	735		

After the Bonanza years of 1933 and 1934, with gold averaging over 8 ounces/ton in 1933, shipments of ore averaged 3.3 ounces of gold in 1935. The high water mark was reached in 1936, when the average of ore shipped was over 7 ounces gold/ton, and in 1937 when it exceeded 9 ounces/ton gold.

A drop to 2.6 ounces/ton in 1938 and to about an ounce per ton in 1939, ended the Bonanza years with a sudden realization that the ore must be up-graded by milling to pay; as the oxidized ore gave way to the primary sulfides, mill feed dropped from 0.4 ounces gold/ton in 1940 and 1941 to 0.13 ounces gold/ton in 1942. A spark of former greatness occurred in 1940 when 39 tons of 4.6 ounces gold/ton ore was shipped. This is the story of a small but interesting mine—it may or may not be the end of it; however, the rich Bonanza ore is gone.

REFERENCES

A-4 Lindgren Volume, C-1, D-1 Burbank, (Eckel), E-8, G-5, G-8, I-25, K-16, L-1, P-5 Shomaker, (Molenaar), (Eckel), Q-2, Q-3, Q-6, Q-7, Q-23 through Q-33, Q-54 through Q-58, Q-67, R-14, S-3, S-23, S-28, S-40, S-52.

CREEDE

After the Brunot Agreement with the Indians was ratified by the United States, the rush of prospectors and miners to the San Juan Mountains began. It is estimated at least 2,000 men swarmed the area the first spring and summer. The main route to Silverton was from Del Norte, which was founded in 1874, up the Rio Grande and by way of Stony Pass and Lower Cunningham Gulch to the Animas River. Lake City was reached from the Rio Grande by way of Spring Creek Pass and Slumgullion Pass. Both routes passed near Sunnyside and present day Creede. It is inevitable that someone would do a little prospecting along the way. The Alpha Mine was located at Sunnyside, two miles west of Creede, on April 24, 1883. The Bachelor property was staked July 1, 1884, but little work was done until after the rush to the district started. A prospector named Rheiniger picked up float and had it assayed in Del Norte. The resulting high assay values became known before he could get back to the site. In 1889, N. C. Creede, a Del Norte gambler, and his partner staked the Holy Moses. He soon sold it for $65,000 to Dave Moffat, President of the Rio Grande Railroad and the rush was on. Creede also located the Amethyst claim on the Amethyst Fault system and also the Solomon. The mining district was called the King Solomon district and today the Creede district combines the King Solomon and Sunnyside districts.

Within a few months, the Amethyst vein system was staked for two and a half miles and had been prospected for another two miles. Population of the area jumped to 10,000 and the railroad reached the camp in 1891. The Com-modore Mine had an aerial tramway 2,000 feet long that delivered ore from the upper workings to railroad cars on Willow Creek below. The rich wire silver ore in the upper parts of the veins soon boosted production from the Creede district. Production in 1891 was about $2.2 million and remained that much or more yearly up to 1956, (Steven and others, 1965, Table No. 1); in 1893 it reached \$4.1 million. The Silver Panic of 1893 took its toll and production declined to less than \$1.5 million for the next three years. Then four years of over \$1 million brought the camp up to the slump of the 1910s. The lowest year was 1922 with production at \$117,000.

The Creede Caldera and Mineralization

The Creede caldera formed after the eruption of the Snowshoe Mountain Tuff about 26.5 m.y.B.P. It is the youngest subsidence unit in the central San Juan Mountains and it obliterated the southwest margin of the older Lagarita caldera and the southern part of the Bachelor caldera (Fig. 4–25).

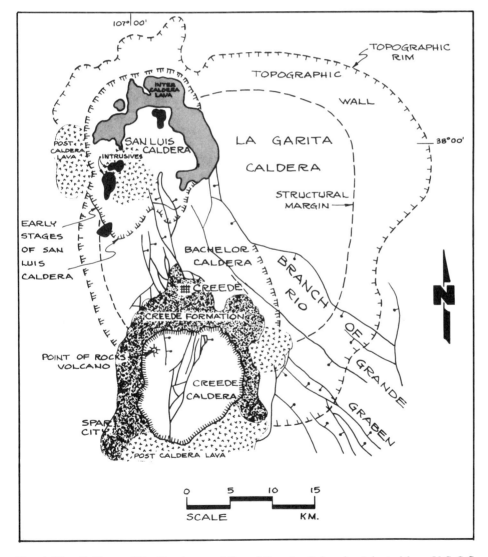

Fig. 4–25. Calderas of the Creede area, Mineral County, Colorado. Adapted from U.S.G.S. P.P. 958, 1976.

A complex graben that extends north-northwest from the Creede caldera contains the mineralization in the Creede district. Veins formed during a long period of activity and are along faults that were active in the last period of movement. Ores at Creede were deposited about 24.6 m.y.B.P. and are not considered to be a terminal phase of the subsidence of the caldera. They are related to a later totally different event.

A local stock was emplaced under the Creede district in early Miocene times, about 24.6 m.y.B.P. and mineralization took place in a graben in a near-surface environment. Faulting and mineralization were apparently related to emplacement of this graben. Ore was deposited along a zone where ascending and descending solutions mixed.

Adularia from the early stages of mineralization in the OH vein have been dated at 24.6 m.y.B.P., earliest Miocene time. Disruptions associated with mineralization resulted in local intrusion of magma beneath the Creede district. This intrusion caused faulting and may have been responsible for later mineralization. It formed a graben with considerable displacement.

Three of the four main mineralized faults cut the Creede (sedimentary) formation and mineralized it. Fisher quartz latite intertongues with the Creede formation and has been dated by K/Ar methods at 26.4 m.y.B.P. These two formations were deposited around the Creede caldera after resurgent doming of the core. Travertine occurs in the Creede formation.

The Alpha–Corsair Fault, which is partly in the Sunnyside district, and the Bulldog Mountain Fault are the mineralized faults on the west side of the graben. Amethyst Fault and Holy Moses Fault are on the east side. The most productive mines along the Amethyst Fault were the Bachelor, Commodore, Del Monte, Last Chance, Amethyst, Happy Thought and Park Regent. Prospecting and stoping has been carried on for about two miles along this fault and a vertical range of 1,200 feet has likewise been explored or stoped. Dip of the Amethyst vein is about 50 degrees W and in the late 1920s the numerous hanging wall splits were being investigated with considerable good luck. The OH vein was the most productive of these hanging wall veins. The P vein was also extensively worked.

Between 1917 and 1920, a period of extensive exploration was carried on to try to locate ore below the old Amethyst vein workings. In the Commodore workings an old shaft which had been sunk 375 feet below the No. 5 (lowest) level, was unwatered. Drifts were run along the vein 1,500 feet in both directions from a station 350 feet lower than the Nelson Tunnel. Of the 3,000 feet explored, the Amethyst Fault contained from 6 to 20 feet of brecciated white rock with small quantities of sulfide minerals and only a trace of silver. On the Bachelor claim, prospecting from a shallow shaft below the Nelson Tunnel level to the southeast indicated that the vein became smaller and ended up in a series of iron-stained gouge fissures. Minor amounts of sulfides occurred in the territory explored.

Work to determine depth of mineralization on the Amethyst claim was carried out 7,500 feet from the portal of the Nelson Tunnel. A winze inclined 70 degrees southwest was sunk to a depth of 120 feet and a drift was run 200 feet south and another one north, under the Happy Thought workings.

Under the big stope of the Happy Thought, which had produced much lead ore, some sulfide pockets occurred but the drift ended in a large barren crushed zone. A large inflow of water carried sulfide particles washed from this zone. In the south drift, the vein was three to four feet wide and ran 12 to 15 percent combined lead–zinc with only a little silver.

The richest ore in the district was from 200 to 800 feet below the surface.

Ore in the Bachelor came from the parallel footwall vein of the Amethyst Fault. In the Commodore, Last Chance and Amethyst Mines many small mineralized fractures were in the hanging wall. Fractures such as these in the New York, Last Chance and Del Monte expanded the hanging wall ore body to 100 feet wide. This was the richest section of the Amethyst lode.

Emperius Mining Company

The history of mining at Creede up to the late 1920s was one of multiple operators and leasees. In 1927, B. T. Poxson, a former Alamosa County Judge, and Herman Emperius worked the Amethyst vein. From this, the Emperius Mining Company developed. From 1927 to 1941, ten miles of workings were opened up and twelve levels developed along the Amethyst vein system. Main haulage level was the Commodore fifth level and it still is. In 1949–50, the value of combined lead–zinc exceeded the value of silver for the first time (Fig. 4–26).

The year 1958 marked the first major closing of the workings along the Amethyst vein, however, by November work was resumed on a limited basis. Principal mines worked during this period were the Amethyst, Wedge, Commodore, Aspen, Del Monte, and Equinox.

Minerals Engineering acquired control of the group in early 1973 and increased the mill capacity to 300 tpd. The old mill had burned in 1955 but had been replaced. A limited partnership with Statesman Mining Company, for control of the old Emperius group, and with Humphrey Mining Company interest gave minerals Engineering access to claims on the north end of the Amethyst vein system. In the late 1960s and early 1970s work was being done on the OH vein and on the P vein, both hanging wall splits of the main Amethyst vein. Due largely to increased chalcopyrite production from these veins, a significant copper production was recorded for 1966, 1967 (second in production in Colorado) and 1968 (in top three in production in Colorado). In 1971, the mine was fifth in gold production for the State; however, decrease in silver prices from $1.77 to $1.55/oz. forced a reduction in the work force. The mine was closed in 1976–77.

Bachelor Mine.   After discovery in 1884, not much work was done on the Bachelor until 1891 when many of the mines were opened. Four adits, the largest of which is the Nelson (Wooster) developed the Amethyst vein on its southern end. In the Nelson Tunnel, this vein was cut 1,175 feet from the portal. It is 1,375 feet vertically to the outcrop from the Nelson Tunnel. At tunnel No. 3 which is 330 feet below the highest tunnel (No. 1) there is an intersection

Fig. 4–26.   Mines along the Amethyst Fault at Creede, Colorado. W.H.

with the Copper vein. Production from the Bachelor up to 1923 was about $2 million.

Commodore Mine.   The Commodore is on the Amethyst lode between the Bachelor and the New York sections. The Archimedes, a fractional claim between the Commodore and the Bachelor, and Commodore claims occupy 1,600 feet of strike length along the vein. Production to 1912 was over $6.6 million and over 16 million ounces of silver were produced.

The Amethyst Fault and vein join near the south end of this part of the lode.

Ore did not occur near the surface but was found 200 to 500 feet below the surface. Stopes 1,500 feet long occurred between upper levels.

Last Chance, New York, and Del Monte Mines.   The Last Chance, New York, and Del Monte Mines overlap so that they cover only about a full claims length along the Amethyst lode. Rich ore found in the Last Chance is credited with starting the development of the Creede district. Early history included legal fights over apex rights and an involved and complicated ownership. Production, up to the early 1920s, was estimated to be $19 million. This was the richest section of the entire Amethyst lode and most of the production value came from the Last Chance. Ore occurred along the Amethyst Fault and not along the foot wall vein as in the Bachelor.

Amethyst Mine.   The Amethyst Mine was located in August, 1891, by N. C. Creede (who gave his name to the town). D. H. Moffat, pioneer tunnel builder, bought the mine and started a rush to the Creede area. Amethystine quartz rich in gold and silver was found practically at the outcrop. This claim lies between the Last Chance and the Happy Thought Mines. By 1912, the mine had about two and one half miles of underground working. Production was estimated to be about $4 million.

Happy Thought, White Star, and Park Regent Mines.   These mines follow the Amethyst Mine in order on the north end of the Amethyst lode. Mineralization is similar to that in the Amethyst with gold values increased. The iron-rich chlorite, thuringite, forms a greater part of the gangue.

Bulldog Mountain Project of Homestake Mining Company: Bulldog Mine

As early as 1960, Steven and Ratte had suggested that the Bulldog Mountain Fault zone would be a favorable area to prospect. Early reports from prospect shafts along this zone gave assays of up to 87 ounces of silver per ton. In 1964, prospecting was well underway and a great mine, one of the last Bonanzas, was "being found." Diamond drilling gave some good indications of ore and the Bulldog Tunnel was driven at an altitude of about 10,000 feet on Bulldog Mountain. At 800 feet, the Bulldog Fault was cut. A total of 4,000 feet of underground work was completed including a winze 460 feet deep. A second adit, 350 feet lower, was driven on the Puzzler vein by 1966. Ore minerals were found along 1,650 feet of drifts on the east strand of the Bulldog Fault (Puzzler vein) and an 850 foot section was probably unmineable ore. One raise above the Bulldog Tunnel level was in ore for 120 feet; however, two other raises ran out of pay ore at 66 and 83 feet. A diamond drill hole cut 7.7 feet of ore 70 feet below the Bulldog Tunnel level and substantial ore showings were found in a diamond drill hole 1,200 feet north of the face of the Bulldog Tunnel level. The Bulldog Mine was first in Colorado in the production of silver in 1969 and 1970 and in 1973 was first again with a production of over two million ounces silver. Larger pumps were installed and deeper mining continues on Bulldog Mountain, the modern Bonanza.

Of the five vein systems in the Creede district, the Bull Dog Mountain Fault was the last to be developed and the Amethyst Fault system was the most outstanding structural feature. Mineralization is similar in all the veins of the district; however, minor variations do occur.

The Amethyst vein system minerals were cerussite, anglesite, chlorargyrite, gold, copper, malachite, chalcanthite, smithsonite, chrysocolla, minor pyromorphite, rhodochrosite, siderite, argentite (acanthite), chalcopyrite, galena, silver, pyrite, sphalerite, stephanite, proustite, pyargyrite, marcasite, hematite, and pyrolusite. The more common gangue minerals were chlorite, variety thuringite, which alters to turgite (micaceous hematite), barite, (Fig. 4–27) white at depth but some pink in upper workings, quartz, blue, blue-gray, smoky, milky, amethystine; and chalcedony, as jasper, usually red and green, and chrysoprase; adularia, calcite, fluorite, kaolin, wad, goslarite, gypsum, jarosite, limonite, and melanterite.

Bonanza ores of the Creede area were oxidized or partly oxidized as deep as 1,200 feet below the surface. Some areas were more oxidized than others. In the Commodore section of the Amethyst vein hairlike wads of silver occurred in vugs on the No. 5 Tunnel level and in the wire silver stope which was 1,100 feet below the surface. (Fig. 4–28). Leaf silver formed bands with white quartz and red jasper and sheets and stringers were dispersed in three dimensional dendrites throughout the maxtrix. Much silver occurred in white barite and red

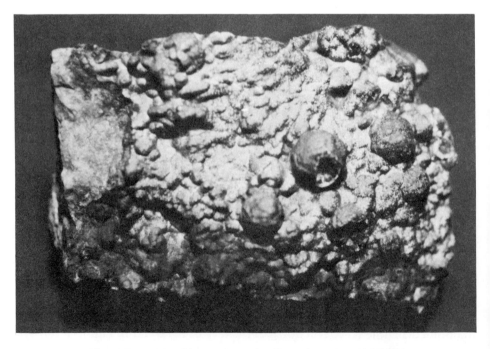

Fig. 4–27.   Acanthite on marcasite, Emperius Mine (JM#192).

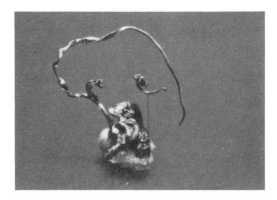

Fig. 4–28. Wire silver, Emperius Mine (JM#374).

jasper where sheets and flakes of silver were found. Cerussite, anglesite and pyromorphite were often associated with the silver.

At the intersection of the Copper vein with the Bachelor section of the Amethyst vein, barite, quartz, limonite, hematite, manganese oxides, copper carbonates, silver halides, and silver were the minerals. The main vein ore was valuable principally for silver and although gold was present it was more plentiful in the northern end of the Amethyst vein system. Highest gold values occurred in the Happy Thought section. A small shaft on the Copper vein had silver ore carrying about 20 ounces per ton of silver in amethystine quartz, barite, limonite, wad, and copper carbonates.

In the Happy Thought, White Star, and Park Regent sections, thuringite formed the principal gangue and gold values increased.

Old workings of the mine became lined with a coating of goslarite and melanterite, as a white to greenish slime. So much sulfate is found in the ore that cleaning specimens is often difficult as the white coating continues to leach out after several washings. Sphalerite at Creede occurs in rounded, corroded crystals over which later deposits reconstructed the earlier crystals according to Barton. Galena crystals with deep etchings, hopper-type structure and curved faces occur. Much of the galena is altered to anglesite (Fig. 4–29). Fine-grained galena of the type known as steel galena occurs. White fluorite occurred in the Holy Moses and blue cubes and octahedrons occurred in the Amethyst vein. Most of the fluorite has been leached out and octahedral casts are found in amethystine quartz.

Rhodochrosite is very rare but has been reported.

Chalcopyrite occurred in the Copper vein and in the OH vein and P vein splits of the Amethyst.

Thuringite, the ferrian variety of chamosite, alters to red mica like flakes of hematite or turgite (hematite with absorbed water). In the Park Regent floaters of pyrite, as twinned pyritohedrons, occur in pockets of thuringite.

The most interesting mineral found at Creede is possibly the silica, which occurs as quartz and chrysophrase. Chrysoprase was known at one time as Creede jade. It occurs in the sulfide ore and was probably the source of the red jasper found in the oxidized zones (see color section).

Fig. 4–29.   Anglesite over galena, Emperius Mine (JM#284).

Quartz was separated into four varieties by Emmons and Larson. A dark gray quartz is thought to be colored by finely disseminated pyrite, galena and sphalerite. It is generally barren and is sometimes capped with milky quartz. Milky quartz is a second variety. Quartz crystals occur on siderite in the Monte Carlo section of the Amethyst vein. The third variety, amethystine quartz, is

Fig. 4–30.   Barite, Bulldog Mountain (JM#245).

Fig. 4–31.   Electrum and silver in barite, Bulldog Mountain (#37).

sometimes found in vugs as amethyst crystals of light to dark purple color. It is apparently later than the chrysoprase and early mineralization and cuts these minerals in veinlets. It has been found to contain 0.0005 percent manganese oxide. The fourth variety is amethystine quartz banded with chalcedony and containing specks of native silver. This is the famous Sow's Belly agate of lapidary interest. The banding was thought to have been formed by descending waters.

Barton and others in their study of the environment most typical of ore

Fig. 4–32.   Silver and calcite, Bulldog Mountain (JM#952).

deposits in the OH vein, of the Amethyst vein system, determined the ore forming fluids were at a temperature of 250 C. at 50 bars pressure. They had a pH of 5.4 in principally an alkali chloride brine within a sulfur solution concentration of 10–1.7 molar.

They were convinced that this deposit is complex and any description must of necessity be an oversimplification.

Mineralization in the Bull Dog Mountain vein is similar to that found in the Amethyst vein system. Silver and other specimens are fully as spectacular as those from the Amethyst workings. White barite, sphalerite, galena, and ruby silver specimens are equally fine. (Figs. 4–30, 4–31, and 4–32).

In December, 1976, a refinery unit was added to the mill at the Bull Dog Mine and the first bar of silver, in excess of 400 troy ounces, was poured.

WAGON WHEEL GAP FLUORSPAR AND SPAR CITY DISTRICTS

The Spar City district is along the south part of the Creede caldera near an intersection of the caldera margin with a core graben that extends at least 15 miles southeast. Wagon Wheel Gap fluorspar district is a small district north of it near Wagon Wheel Gap.

On the east margin of the Creede caldera, fluorspar occurs at the intersection of the ring fault zone and a fault of the southeast trending graben. Fluorspar deposits are in close association with hot springs of the Wagon Wheel Gap district. This relationship suggests that the thermal activity related to mineralization is still active. The fluorspar deposits were formed prior to the end of the Pleistocene; however, vein fragments have been found high up in Pleistocene gravels of the area.

Four hot springs and two cold springs occur about a mile from Wagon Wheel Gap along Goose Creek. The largest, Boiling Spring, flows 50 gpm at 58° C.

Two hot springs, the main fluorspar deposit and a travertine deposit are in alignment. The travertine deposit contains 0.22 percent calcium fluoride and appreciable amounts of barium and zinc, and a temperature of 58° C.

The Wagon Wheel Gap Fluorspar Mine was operated in 1913 and operated intermittently until 1950. C.F. & I. Co. bought the mine in 1924. This deposit is 1–1/4 miles south of Wagon Wheel Gap Station on the Rio Grande Railroad. Production was about 50,000 tons from 1911 through 1921 and although production was intermittent, by 1928 a million dollars worth of ore had been produced. In 1936, 110,000 tons were mined for use of C.F. & I. Co. at Pueblo. Production of metallurgical grade calcium fluoride was valued at $674,000.

A fluorspar vein 6 to 8 feet wide with a maximum width of 35 feet was developed. This deposit can be traced for over a mile and has been mined to a depth of at least 700 feet.

In the Spar City mining district, which adjoins the small Wagon Wheel fluorspar district on the south, veins that cut the Creede formation and Fisher quartz latite, 24.6 m.y.B.P., contain galena, sphalerite, and manganese oxides in a gangue of quartz and barite. Production from this district was minor.

In the Wagon Wheel Gap fluorspar deposit the ore is mainly white fluorspar with a radiating fibrous structure. It is also botryoidal and mammillary in structure. Fluorite occurs as yellow, green, brown, lilac,and purple encrustations at places. Euhedral barite crystals occurred at the surface and to a depth of 25 feet where they became less plentiful.

Other minerals in the deposit were: pyrite, quartz, chalcedony, calcite, halloysite, beidellite, creedite, kaolinite, and gearksutite.

Beidellite, a clay mineral of the montmorillonite group, was first described from Beidell Creek in Saguache County, Colorado. Creedite was discovered at this type location in 1916. Gearksutite occurred in white balls of varying diameter.

REFERENCES

A-4, A-5 Ridge, (Steven), C-6, C-7, C-16, D-1, (Burbank), D-2, G-3, G-5, G-6, H-1, H-3, H-12, J-1, J-7, J-21, L-1, 1940-1973, N-2, R-19, S-10, S-22, S-34, S-35, S-69, S-115, S-116, S-119, S-120, S-121, S-123.

LAKE CITY DISTRICT

Harry Henson and three companions discovered the Ute–Ulay vein system on August 27, 1871, while the territory was still in possession of the Ute Indians. Mining on the veins did not start until after 1874, when the Treaty with the Utes was renegotiated. Up to that time prospectors were in trespass on tribal lands. The mine is located on Henson Creek about three miles west of Lake City, Hinsdale County.

Gold was said to have been found in the Lake City area in 1842 by a member of Fremont's party; however, the location of this find was never rediscovered. Hotchkiss discovered what was later to become the Golden Fleece Mine in 1874 while surveying a road from Saguache to Lake City and the news of a rich strike spread rapidly. By 1875, Lake City was a town of thirteen log cabins and the Crook smelter was started. It was 1878 before the smelter was in use and after a brief production, from 1878 to 1883, the smelter was closed in early 1884. About $60,000 worth of ore was processed in 1879. The first sizable shipment from the district was from the Mountain Queen Mine at the head of California Gulch in 1877. The ore contained 64 percent lead and 30 ounces silver per ton and pack animals carried 300 tons to Rose's Cabin on Henson Creek from which point it was picked up by wagons.

When the Ute–Ulay Mine was sold for $135,000 in 1876 the rush to Lake City really began. By November there were fourteen general stores, seven saloons and an assortment of banks, barbers, bakeries, brickyards, breweries, blacksmiths, drugstores, laundries, boot shops, hardware stores, billiard parlors, sawmills, meat markets, stables, hotels, assayers, a furniture store and very much more. Many people came only to leave in disappointment and to give way to new arrivals. A post office was established in 1875, and mail came from Del Norte, by way of Saguache, by stagecoach. Telegraph service came in 1876, and the telephone in 1881. By 1889, the Rio Grande Railroad completed a narrow gauge line to Lake City.

The Silver Panic of 1893 was a blow to the area but gold production increased; the years 1895 to 1897 were the peak years for gold, but total area production was over a half million dollars in 1892. The most productive years were 1885 through 1900; however, it fell to $60,000 by 1902. High base metal prices, such as in war periods, still bring flurries of activity to the district but the Bonanza years are gone.

Lake City Caldera

Ash-flow eruptions produced the Sunshine Peak Tuff in the Lake City area about 22.5 m.y.B.P. A large block nested within the older Uncompahgre caldera began to subside to form the Lake City caldera and a ring fault along which this collapse occurred is continuously exposed for about 300 degrees of arc around the caldera. A simple dome was produced by resurgence and formation of a graben reflects reactivation of the earlier Eureka Graben system. This graben was related to resurgence of the Uncompahgre and San Juan calderas. After the Lake City caldera was formed, the only major volcanic activity in the western San Juan Mountains was development of the Hinsdale formation. The moat area of the Uncompahgre caldera was filled with igneous rocks 18 m.y.B.P. Thin flows of olivine basalt were wide spread, however, erosion has removed most of this material. Ages of the various stages of mineralization have not been established but veins were recurrently opened and filled with vein material of contrasting composition.

Ute–Ulay Mine and the Hidden Treasure Mine.

Although the Ute and Ulay and Hidden Treasure Mines were never worked in the early days as a group, they are on the same veins and their workings are interconnected. Workings on the four parallel veins these mines develop are the most productive and extensive in the district. An inclined shaft on the Ulay vein had eleven levels with the most production coming from the ore shoot on the bottom five levels. The Hidden Treasure vein is about 500 feet northwest of the Ulay and almost parallel to it. A shaft 265 feet deep was sunk on the vein before pay ore was found. The third level on the Ute is the No. 5 level of the Hidden Treasure. The Ute No. 4 level is the No. 6 level on the Hidden Treasure.

Production to 1911 from the Ute and Ulay was between 10 and 12 million dollars in lead–silver ore and from the Hidden Treasure it was $0.7 million dollars.

Veins of these mines were in the volcanic series of the San Juan volcanic field. Mineralization was principally filling of open fissures and as cementing material for breccia zones. Veins varied from a small fracture to 20 feet wide with the average width being about four feet. Splits in the veins were common.

Irving and Bancroft classified the minerals of the Lake City area in the following order:

Minerals of Oxidized Zone: kaolinite, limonite, hematite, silver, gold, copper, malachite, azurite, cerussite, anglesite, chalcopyrite, and pyrolusite.

Minerals produced by secondary sulfide enrichment: covellite, bornite, galena, proustite, pyrargyrite, and argentite.

Minerals of moderate and shallow depths: sericite, hinsdalite, jasperoid, barite, rhodochrosite, tetrahedrite, and bismuth compounds.

Persistent minerals: quartz, calcite, fluorite, chalcopyrite, galena, sphalerite, stibnite, tellurides, and pyrite.

Although this listing does not conform to present stages of understanding, it was one of the earlier attempts to establish the genesis of San Juan minerals and is of interest from a historical standpoint.

A division of ores in the Lake City area by vein types was given by George and Lindgren as follows:

1. Tetrahedrite–rhodochrosite
2. Quartz–galena–sphalerite
3. Tellurides

Silicification of the vein walls was followed by two periods of mineralization. The first period of mineralization deposited quartz, rhodochrosite, tetrahedrite, galena and quartz in that order. A second period of mineralization deposited quartz, barite and minor galena and quartz.

Base metals occur in roughly two classifications: a quartz–galena–sphalerite group and a tetrahedrite-rhodochrosite group. These groups overlap. A third group contains silver and gold tellurides and hinsdalite. The Golden Fleece Mine at Lake City was the type locality for hinsdalite.

Rhodochrosite made up the bulk of the vein filling on the northern end of the Hidden Treasure Mine. This mine is on the Ute–Ulay vein system. Lipman and others give the age of ore in the Ute–Ulay at 20.3 m.y.B.P.

In the Monte Queen Mine, south of Lake City on the western side of the Lake Fork River, rhodochrosite occurred in a lens five feet thick. In this mine, a peculiar dark-brown, fine-grained, massive, rosin-like sphalerite, mixed with fine steel galena and averaging about 75 ounces in silver and notable percentages of bismuth occurred.

About 12 to 14 miles up the Lake Fork of the Gunnison River, toward Burrows Park, Muilenburg reported a large vein of rhodochrosite. It was near vertical, in a lava flow, from two to ten feet wide and could be traced on the surface for 600 feet. Some of the vein was altered to pyrolusite. Masses of pyrolusite when broken open showed crystalline rhodochrosite. The vein was nearly free of sulfides.

Golden Fleece Mine

The Golden Fleece Mine is located about a half mile west of the north end of Lake San Cristobal at an elevation 1,000 feet above the lake. Outcrops of the veins are 20 to 30 feet above a wide draw and form a conspicuous ridge.

Although a well-defined vein, the mineralization occurred as stringers cementing broken blocks and breccia, in the Golden Fleece Mine. Gray and white quartz and siliceous fragments of rock caused the vein to stand in relief on the mountainside and it was stained yellow with an occasional reddish cast.

In the upper levels, the vein seemed to have no walls but was a zone. At the main tunnel level, walls were present and at the face mineralization consisted of light pink rhodochrosite with comparatively few metallic particles. In the high grade ore, petzite, tetrahedrite, and other minerals were fine-grained and disseminated throughout the gray quartz. Pyrargyrite occurred in bunches above the third level and as much as 1,200 feet below the surface.

The ore shoot of the Golden Fleece Mine was 750 feet along the level, but pinched out with depth. A central interior shoot, unusually rich in tellurides, was found at the approximate intersection of the Ilma and Gold Fleece veins.

History

In 1874, Enos F. Hotchkiss while working with a survey party running an alignment for a road from Saguache to Lake City saw the outcrop of a vein standing out in bold relief above Lake San Cristobal. He located the Hotchkiss Mine after examining the outcrop and had some work done on it while he finished the survey. A year later, it was relocated as the Golden Fleece Mine by G. Wilson and C. Johnson, but after starting the No. 1 tunnel they found only small stringers of rich ore and stopped work. Other prospectors tried their luck but gave up. O. P. Posey found several hundred pounds of rich ore in an outcrop above the No. 1 tunnel and it was carried by pack animals to Del Norte and from there sent to the Pueblo smelter. J. J. Crooke, who built the local smelter, took a lease and extracted about $30,000 worth of ore from the outcrop above No. 1 tunnel between 1876 and 1878.

Due to litigation the annual assessment work was not done on the mine and some miners jumped the claim in 1884. They found some ore and started working it. In 1889, C. Davis took a lease and after prospecting along the high outcrop sank a 30 foot shaft. This shaft hit a high-grade pocket which yielded $40,000 in ore in a very short period of time. In 1889, the mine was sold to G. W. Pierce for $50,000 and he started extensive exploration. He soon found out that Davis had mined all the ore in sight. Most of the work to that time had been to the north and it was thought the vein faulted in that direction. The new owners drove a crosscut south from the No. 2 tunnel and the vein was found, but it contained little ore at first. Within a year, rich ore was found and it was mined up to the No. 1 tunnel level. If the No. 1 tunnel had been driven an additional ten feet by Wilson and Johnson the ore body would have been found.

One lot of ore gave the phenomenal assay of 125 ounces of gold and 1,255 ounces of silver per ton. A branch railroad was completed to Lake City in 1889, and soon after this a car of telluride ore from the Golden Fleece was said to have brought $50,000. The Golden Fleece Bonanza brought a great deal of activity to the district and in the late 1890s much work was done on mines around the Golden Fleece. The Lake View, Black Crook, Golden Fleece Extension, Contention and others produced ore. The Golden Fleece shipped $100,000 worth of ore in 1900. By 1911, the district had produced $12 million in mineral wealth. In the years 1893 through 1897, the most gold was produced with over $274,000 produced in 1895, the peak year. By 1910-1, Irving and Bancroft found the mine caved and inaccessible. Production of the Golden Fleece Mine up to 1904 was given by G. W. Pierce as $1.4 million.

Minerals of the Golden Fleece Mine were: pyrargyrite, proustite, rhodochrosite (pink), hinsdalite (pale green to dark green from inclusions) pyrite, galena, tetrahedrite, barite, and probably calaverite, sylvanite, krennerite, petzite (disseminated in gray chalcedonic quarts) and hessite. An oxide of tellurium was thought to cause the red color in the oxidized zone of the mine.

Other than the Bonanza ore of the Golden Fleece Mine and the large base metal deposits of the Ute–Ulay and Hidden Treasure Mines, the Lake City area was primarily a marginal base metal mining district.

Champion Mine

The Champion Mine is near the top of Cinnamon Pass at White Cross, on the Hinsdale County side of the trail from Lake City to Animas Forks, in San Juan County. The upper part of the Lake Fork of the Gunnison River has been known as Burrows Park since the early 1870s when Charlie Burrows built the first log cabin after prospecting the area in 1873. After the treaty with the Ute Indians other prospectors came into the area and Sherman was established at the junction of Lake Fork and Cottonwood Creek. Burrows Park Village was up the Lake Fork and White Cross, named for a white quartz outcrop on the mountain, was 1/4 mile further with Tellurium and Sterling all strung out between Sherman and Cinnamon Pass. White Cross was six miles from Sherman. It is about six miles to Animas Forks and 20 miles to Lake City from the general Burrows Park area.

The Champion was probably worked in the early 1870s and production was made in 1877. By 1883, it was considered one of the best developed mines in the area and had a vein four to six feet in width. Five hundred tons of ore was said to be on the dump and in December of that year a shipment described as 20 tons (two car loads) was sent to Spanish Bar (Idaho Springs, Colo.) for metallurgical testing.

By 1885, a new tunnel had been driven 400 feet above the old workings. At 15 feet from the portal the ore was found to be different in character from ore in the older workings which had been primarily a copper ore. This ore contained galena and carbonates and the vein was ten feet wide. By September, 1885, copper ore was being sorted for shipment from the big ore dump.

Population in Burrows Park declined in the early 1880s and in 1882, the post office was moved to White Cross from Burrows Park Village. Mines active in the White Cross area in the 1880s and 1890s were the Tobasco, Bon Homme, Cracker Jack, and Champion. Most of the mines were inactive in the winter due to deep snows and the isolation of the area.

By 1901, a shaft 160 feet deep with two drifts at the 100 foot level, all in mill ore, had been driven and the ore put on the dump at the Champion Mine. Crosscuts had been run on the 100 foot level to try to find the vein walls. One side located the wall in 18 feet and the other was driven 10 feet and stopped. This was a 28 foot width of milling ore. The owners hoped to get a mill to treat the deposit that evidently proved to be a large deposit of mill grade ore.

Several years prior to this, the owners of the Black Wonder Mill at Sherman milled a sizable tonnage of ore from the dump of the Champion Mine. This supposedly low-grade ore was later found to have 17 to 19 percent copper; $8 to $9 in gold; and 30 ounces of silver per ton. It was worth $63.00 per ton at then current prices. (No record of how this was settled was found.)

The Champion vein was on the extension of the Bon Homme vein on which a strike was made that assayed 48 ounces of gold per ton. This evidently gave encouragement to those mining the Champion because they worked through June of 1901. Management problems caused the mine to close in 1901, and it was not reopened until 1916. If anything was done on the Champion in the next 60 years it is not known; however, some rhodochrosite specimens from the mine reached mineral dealers in about 1976. The quantity was probably less than a dozen flats and then the supply stopped. Local inquiry at Lake City disclosed only that: (1) the mine had closed, (2) it was in litigation, and (3) it would probably not be reopened.

REFERENCES

A-4 Lindgreen Volume, C-12, D-3, F-3, G-5, G-6, G-8, H-8, J-9, J-18, J-46, J-74, L-1, Q-19, Q-20, Q-21, Q-22, Q-49, Q-50, Q-51, Q-52, S-52, S-57, S-59, S-75, S-116.

PLATORO AND SUMMITVILLE CALDERAS

The Platoro caldera and nested younger Summitville caldera are in the northern part of Conejos County and the southern part of Rio Grande County west of the San Luis Valley in the San Juan volcanic field. The area is centered roughly 35 miles west of Alamosa and 25 miles southwest of Monte Vista, just east of the Continental Divide.

A thick pile of volcanic rocks was built, 35 to 30 m.y.B.P., by the Conejos fm. This formation was then eroded to a low relief on the San Juan volcanic field when a huge body of magma was emplaced near the surface and caused doming in the Platoro–Summitville area. Platoro caldera formed as a result of the ejection of the La Jara member of the Treasure Mountain Tuff, 29.8 and 29.1 m.y.B.P. The Summitville caldera formed some time within this interval.

Volcanic rocks that filled the ring fracture zones of these two calderas have been dated from 29 to 20 m.y.B.P.

A major northwest trending structural lineament, that can be traced for 35 miles as a major fault zone, provided access for the magma and controlled placement of the calderas, according to Bird (1972). This lineament, the Platoro lineament, passes through the Lake City and Mt. Hope calderas and along the edge of the Creede caldera.

The Platoro dome collapsed leaving a depression about 15 miles in diameter. Resurgent doming, a second collapse, and a second resurgence formed the Summitville caldera and resurgent dome within the Platoro caldera. All this activity took place in less than 2 m.y. with volcanic activity extending over a period of 5 m.y.

Mineralization in the Platoro–Summitville mining districts, which are usually linked together because of their similarity and location, occurred in the late stages of volcanic activity. This was during the span of eruption of the Fisher quartz–latite, the youngest unit of the San Juan volcanic sequence. Summitville ore has been dated at 22.4 m.y.B.P.

Summitville is within the younger caldera and the mineral deposits were formed in a shallow volcanic environment within a volcanic dome of coarsely porphyritic quartz–latite. This dome, South Mountain, is in a north-trending fracture zone in which intensely altered volcanic pipes and irregularly tabular masses of quartz–latite were replaced with quartz–alunite rocks. Surrounding the quartz–alunite are zones of illite-kaolinite and propylitized rocks of a montmorillonite-chlorite zone. Intense leaching of the quartz–alunite rocks allowed deposition of pyrite and enargite mineralization to form in vugs.

Mineralization occurred during the eruption period of the lower rocks which are highly mineralized. The upper lavas lie uncomformably on an erosion surface and are unaltered. Alteration resulted from shallow solfataric activity and is similar to that in the Red Mountain district of the western San Juan Mountains. Two periods of hydrothermal activity are recognized. A large oval mineralized pipe occurred in the Aztec vein zone, at Summitville.

Platoro Area

The old mining camp of Platoro, a combination of Plata (Spanish for silver) and Oro (Spanish for gold), was founded in the early 1880s, about ten years after Summitville. The largest mine was the Mammoth in which the vein was up to 50 feet wide. This mine produced about a quarter of a million dollars between 1889 and 1906. The camp of Platoro then became a ghost town until the 1930s when the Mammoth reopened. There was a fire that burned the mill in the early 1930s and this closed things up once more.

In 1959, the Mammoth-Revenue group of claims, was reopened and a mill was built in 1966. By 1970, the mine produced over 500 ounces of gold and in 1973 over 20,000 ounces of silver. The mine is still active.

One other interesting development in the area is a breccia pipe with gold-bearing ore. This pipe has the same characteristics as other breccia pipes in the San Juan Mountains. Gold values are as high as 6 ounces per ton but values are spotty.

In the Valley Queen Mine, on the Mammoth vein, an 18 inch streak of high grade ore occurred in a quartz vein 34 feet wide.

Minerals reported from the Platoro caldera are: marcasite, pyrite, arsenopyrite, sanidine, penninite, sericite, magnetite, hematite, petzite, argentite (acanthite), pyrargyrite, epidote, rutile, leucoxene, apatite, zircon, diopside, hypersthene, proustite, quartz, gold, silver, electrum, sulfur, orthoclase anorthite, albite, biotite, ilmenite, tetrahedrite, famatinite, chalcopyrite, barite, gold tellurides and silver sulfosalts, galena, sphalerite, molybdenite pyrrhotite, chalcocite, digenite, miargyrite, andorite, zinkenite, covellite, enargite, luzonite, calcite, chalcedony, anhydrite, and allophane, an amorphous hydrous aluminum silicate.

Summitville Mines

Arrastras were used by the Spanish miners for crushing ore to release the gold. One found near Summitville may be mute evidence of their early day work on the gold bearing outcrops of the district. First recorded discovery of gold in the district was in June of 1870, by James L. Wightman and his party of prospectors in the South Mountain area of Wightman's Fork of the Alamosa River. Placers were worked in 1871, but when a large rush of people to the district proved the placers unprofitable most of them left. A few lode claims were staked in 1872, and a new wave of people returned in 1873 and some of the richest mines were located at this time.

The Aztec Mine was located in 1872. The Aztec claim was 50 by 1,500 feet and also known as Summit Lode. The Little Annie, Del Norte, and Margaretta Mines were located in 1873. A small lot of ore for testing was shipped in 1874 and the first mill erected the next spring. Summitville was occupied for the first time in the winter of 1875–76. By 1877, the population was 250.

Placer mining continued on the early claims from 1870 to about 1880 in the short summer season and nuggets up to one inch in diameter were found.

Early production from the mines soon reached $1,000,000. The San Juan, Odin, Little Annie and Golconda Mines had aerial tramways to various mills. By 1883, there were nine stamp mills "dropping" 155 stamps in the district. In 1884 the Annie Mill, with 12 batteries of five stamps each, and 16 Frue vanners for concentrates, was the only mill running in the district. Gold was caught on the copper plates as amalgam, retorted, and gold bricks cast for shipment to the Denver Mint. This gold was .900 fine, some reported to be .980 fine, and brought $19.00 an ounce ($20.00/oz. gold). This was an unusually high fineness as most gold carries iron, silver and other impurities.

On August 26, 1878, a rich deposit of flour gold was discovered on the Margaretta. Ore from the Little Annie also contained flour gold, not visible to the unaided eye; however, specimens ran as high as $160,000 per ton. Up to

1875, this mine had produced the finest specimens of free gold. Raymond, as quoted in Henderson, found the settlement in 1875 to have 50 log cabins roofed with earth and a population of 200 people.

At a depth of 100 feet the Little Ida Mine, on the same lode as the Del Norte and owned by the Little Annie Mining Company, had a vein 17 feet wide, of which ten feet was decomposed quartz. In 1881, the ore was said to run $1,500 to $2,500 per ton and in four months a quarter of a million dollars worth of ore was mined.

The Aztec Mine, also known as the Summit Lode Mine, was the oldest lode mine on South Mountain. By 1884 it had three shafts and two tunnels. The ore was reported to be "decomposed jasper, carrying black sulphurets, free gold and tellurium". Ore shipped for the period 1882–3 averaged over $200 per ton and the mine produced $2 million in gold between 1873 and 1887. By 1887 all the rich surface ore had been mined and the mills were not equipped to mill the low-grade sulfide primary ore. By 1893, the district was almost deserted and total production was $621, down from a high of $289,739 in 1881.

The many surface cuts, small adits and, in general, shallow workings, made it convenient to group the South Mountain mines into three groups—the Aztec, near the top of the mountain, the Bobtail, and the lowest group, the Little Annie. In 1897, the Golconda Tunnel was started to develop the Golconda Mine and Aztec group at depth. It was completed to 2,780 feet by 1917, but initial work was suspended in 1906 with intermittent work being done after that.

At 1,600 feet a copper vein was cut; at 2,000 feet four to five feet partly of covellite was cut, and at 2,700 feet the Tewkesbury vein was cut. At this level the vein carried low grade pyrite but high-grade gold was mined in the oxidized zone. Later, the tunnel was abruptly turned to the southwest to form an approximately 30 degree interior angle and followed the Tewkesbury vein in this direction through the Bobtail ground into the Little Annie ground.

In 1914, the mines were consolidated under one ownership as the Summitville Gold Mines, Inc. Production during the next eleven years was unimportant. In 1926, Jack Pickens, who reportedly had seen a rich outcrop in a wagon road rut 20 years earlier and who had waited to get a lease without arousing any suspicion, reported a strike of high grade gold ore on a lease he shared with Judge Wiley.

Between 1926 and 1931, this lease produced over a half million dollars from 864 tons of hand-sorted ore. Production declined abruptly and by 1934 it was unimportant.

In this same year, the Summitville Consolidated Mines, Inc. built a new mill of 100 tpd capacity and a new phase was entered by the old camp. A year later the capacity was tripled. Production from 1934 to 1947 exceeded $4 million. At one time the mill was producing over 2,000 ounces gold per month. In the early World War II years, the mine was closed as were all predominantly gold-producing mines; however, the ores had started to be predominantly copper ores. A section of the mill was reopened in 1948 to test copper–gold ores from the dumps. No production occurred from 1949 to 1958. After a period of development work and exploration, additional ore bodies were discovered with chief values in copper. A $2 million joint venture composed of Cleveland-Cliffs Iron Company, U.P.R.R. and W. S. Moore Company formed to work the mine in the late 1960s. A new mill and a 630 foot shaft were constructed. The mill was completed in 1971 and closed in 1972 for lack of ore reserves. By 1975, exploration for more ore reserves was well underway and is continuing. A camp such as Summitville does not die that easily.

Summitville, the camp that changed from a gold-mining area in the oxidized zone to a copper-mining area with depth, can boast of many of the minerals given for the Platoro caldera. In the early period of mining, the Summit lode (Aztec) was said to be composed of jasper with "sulphuretes," and quartz, of a dark ebony color containing fine gold and tellurium.

In the later workings, pyrite and enargite with covellite were the principal ore minerals. In the last period of mining pyrite, enargite and covellite were the principal ore minerals. Covellite occurred in massed, bladed crusts up to six inches thick. The bottom side of these crusts were massive blue-purple covellite; however, the tops of the bladed crystals were in a clay-feldspar gangue and terminated individually as blue-purple and golden varities. The finest and rarest specimens from this last period of activity were up to 1/2 inch crystals of deep blue-purple covellite in small vugs. Some large enargite crystals in matrix were of museum quality. Sulfur, barite, galena, and sphalerite were associated with the copper ore. Phenocrysts of sanidine up to 2 inches long occur in the Golconda vein; quartz pseudomorphs of the sanidine also occur. Enargite occurs as tabular to prismatic black to sooty crystals and as compact aggregates. Casts of phenocrysts of ferromagnesian minerals are sometimes lined with enargite crystals or pyrite crystals. Luzonite, the tetragonal dimorph of enargite, also occurs.

Sulfur is generally massive but occasional crystals occur. Barite is often coated with quartz or pyrite. Pyrite is generally a combination of many forms but pyritohedron and cube faces can be recognized. Microsized octahedrons have been found on the dumps. Gangue minerals are: quartz, calcite, penninite, a pseudo-trigonal variety of clinochlore, sericite, magnetite, hematite, limonite, jarosite, pyrite, epidote, rutile, chalcedony, clay minerals, ilmenite, leucoxene (altered ilmenite) apatite, zircon, diopside, hypersthene, orthoclase, anorthite, albite, and biotite.

Gold Boulder of Summitville

In October, 1975, while bulldozing at Summitville for ASARCO Co., Inc., Robert Ellithorpe picked up a glint of metal in a 114 pound boulder. On closer inspection it turned out to be gold in matrix and was estimated to be at least 350 troy ounces, or nearly 30 troy pounds of the metal. The specimen was a foot thick 14 inches high and 21 inches long. It is not a solid nugget but is crystalline gold in veinlets. This specimen was donated by the family of A.E. Reynolds, who first consolidated the mines of Summitville into one group in 1915, and ASARCO, Inc., to the Denver Museum of Natural History, City Park,

Denver, Colorado. This gold boulder of Summitville became part of the museum's permanent display. It was valued at $350,000, in 1975.

REFERENCES

A-1, A-4, Lindgren Volume, A-5, Ridge, (Steven), C-15, F-3, G-5, J-11, J-22, L-1, 1968-1973, P-7 James, (Calkins), (Lipman), (Buchanan), Q-65, S-52, S-74, S-76, S-116, S-118.

CHAPTER 5
UPPER ARKANSAS VALLEY

SALIDA AND PONCHA PASS AREAS

Precambrian rocks of the Salida and Poncha Pass area are less metamorphosed than most Precambrian rocks of central Colorado. They include both metasedimentary and metaigneous forms and may represent remnants of a younger Precambrian sequence.

Amphibolite masses are conformably interlayerd in a complex of rocks of predominantly sedimentary origin. Foliation and recrystallization have obliterated the original texture of these amphibolites and they are now in the almandite-amphibolite facies of regional metamorphism. Originally they were metagabbro sills and metabasalt flows. Green hornblende now forms about 1/2 of the metagabbros and about 3/4 of the metabasalts with plagioclase constituting the remaining.

Metasedimentary rocks of the area are amphibolitic schist, biotite schist, phyllites, quartzites, arkosic gneisses, quartz plagioclase–sillimanite–garnet micaceous schist, quartz-plagioclase-cordierite schist, and skarn, a contact-metamorphic rock containing garnet and epidote. (Fig. 5–1).

Poncha Pass

The Poncha Pass scheelite claim is east of U.S. 285 in Chaffee County near the top of the pass and about 12 miles from Salida. A small shaft along the highway exposes mica schist and greenstone schist, of Pce age, containing almandite, quartz, calcite, and minor scheelite mineralization. Maximum width of this mineralization was two feet and a sample was said to have assayed 0.17 percent tungstite.

Fifty feet higher up the hill and about 1,500 feet distant the Lucky Two scheelite claim, still in Chaffee County, exposes a vein in Pce schists which can be traced for about 60 feet. A 15 foot open cut disclosed a one inch streak of nearly pure scheelite.

Further up U.S. 185 on the Saguache County side of Poncha Pass, a quarry was opened in 1974 on a deposit of sericite schist. This material was stockpiled

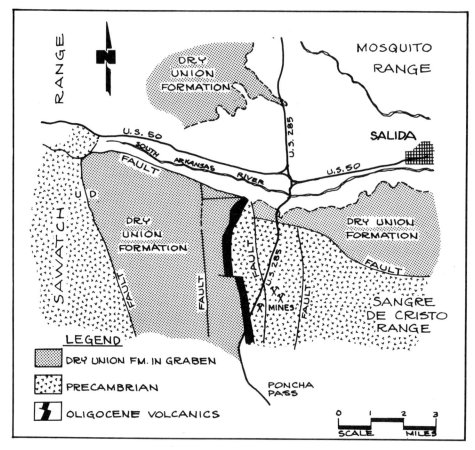

Fig. 5-1.   Location map with generalized geology of Salida-Poncha Pass area. Adapted from U.S.G.S. P.P. 750-B, 1951.

for ceramic use at Golden, Colorado, however, only a small amount was shipped. Earlier workings on this deposit produced a mica product for use as an artificial snow for Christmas decoration use. This did not prove to be a success probably because of the clay found in the flakes.

A thin streak of fuchsite occurred as a discontinuous parting in the sericite near the top of the deposit on a small ridge. Such an occurrence could be repeated in this unique geological environment. In localized areas, the cordierite schists contain zoisite, phlogopite, talc, chlorite, gahnite, tourmaline and garnet, mostly almandite. Magnetite, sphene, apatite, and zircon also occur. Copper minerals, scheelite, and traces of nickel are found in the Poncha Pass area. This area should be of interest to micromounters.

SALIDA AREA

The Salida area has long been of interest to mineral collectors and has had its share of reports of unusual mineral occurrences. In the early history of the

Sedalia Copper Mine, one of the most famous mines of this area, it didn't seem possible that oxidized ores similar to those of Leadville could occur. Where was the blue lime they asked? But occur they did and in a large variety of minerals.

Some unusual mineral is always showing up. In 1971, a request was made by the U.S. Geological Survey for study specimens of a pale blue, hexagonal, micaceous mineral occurring with serpierite and linarite from the Salida area. After World War II, at Buena Vista, Colorado, just north of Salida, a pale blue mineral was seen in a store window. It was of immediate interest; it was said by the storekeeper to probably contain uranium and had been left temporarily by a prospector but was not available for close examination. Someone may locate such a mineral in this area.

Aurichalcite has been reported from the Salida area. No location is given but it could have come from the oxidized zone of the Sedalia Copper Mine where aurichalcite was reported.

Specimens of tetradymite, trigonal, from the old camp of Whitehorn were examined by Hillebrand.

The Whitehorn district, east of the Calumet Mine, extends into Fremont and possibly Park Counties, as well as Chaffee County. If any mining activity occurs in this old camp this would be a good mineral to watch for.

Van Alstine describes botryoidal manganese oxides coated with botryoidal and stalactitic calcite from the Longs Gulch area, about 4 1/2 miles northwest of Salida. This is in the Sedalia Copper Mine vicinity.

South of Salida in the Poncha Springs area, fluorspar was mined in the early 1950s by Reynolds Metals Co. A mineralized zone, trending north – northwest, over 100 feet wide, and several thousand feet long was exposed. Mineralization was fluorspar, quartz, and calcite in brecciated Precambrian rock. This and another deposit nearby are considered Tertiary in age and were localized by faulting in the rift.

Ute Trail Creek. Ute Trail Creek has been of interest to miners and mineral collectors for many years. This creek was a favorite route of the Indians and early prospectors for crossing from the Upper Arkansas Valley to South Park. Prospect pits, many large to small adits, and various size quarries mark the area. The Calumet Mine, several old ghost towns, and the old Turret Creek mining district are accessible from this area.

At Midway Springs on Ute Trail Creek, a brown and white banded onyx, aragonite of local usage, occurs. It has been used for lapidary purposes and much rejected material is scattered around the deposit. Native sulfur also occurs. Tremolite (asbestos), and small pseudomorph cubes of goethite after pyrite are found.

Pegmatite deposits in the Ute Trail Creek vicinity have produced beryl, mica, feldspar, ornamental stone for building purposes as well as crushed for decorative uses, and small quantities of pegmatite specimen minerals. Individual pockets of pegmatite have produced up to 20 tons of beryl. Columbite has also been produced in small quantities.

Calumet Mine. The Calumet–Hecla–Smithville magnetite deposit, now known as the Calumet Mine, was discovered in 1880. It was covered by six mining claims. The mine is about 12 miles northeast of Salida in the Turret Creek mining district. Calumet City and Turret were camps near the mine and Whitehorn developed as a gold camp nearby in 1896 and 1897, with a population of 600 to 700. Stagecoaches made daily runs to Salida when the mines were active. A spur line was extended five miles up Railroad Gulch from the main line, of the Rio Grande Railroad at Browns Canyon station, to the mine. (Fig. 5-2).

Rich surface gold ores soon ran out at Whitehorn and by the early 1900s, the

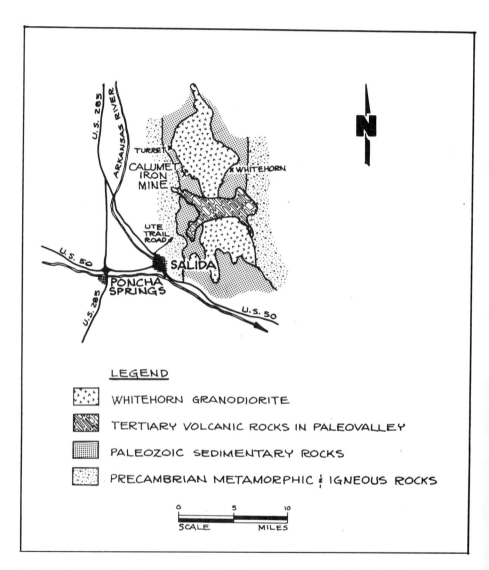

Fig. 5-2. Relation of Calumet Iron Mine to Whitehorn granodiorite pluton of Cretaceous age. Adapted from U.S.G.S. Bull. 1394, 1974.

camp was a ghost town. The Calumet Mine probably produced through 1905 but after a testing program indicated the remaining ore was high in sulfur (pyrite) work was discontinued. Sulfur is an unwanted element in steel making for which the ore was used. Local historians say the mine was closed by a cave-in that trapped seven miners; however, no documentation of this was found.

After the deposit was discovered, development was slow at first. By 1882, production of 40 tpd was shipped to the Colorado Coal and Iron Company's plant at Bessemer, South Pueblo. This company later became the C F & I Steel Company.

At this time, 75 men were working a 354 foot deep east-dipping incline shaft with a 60 foot crosscut at the 206 foot level. A tunnel lower on the mountain had been driven 500 feet with another 200 feet needed to intersect the incline. This tunnel was 10 feet wide at the bottom, 9 feet at top, and 8 feet high so that railroad cars could be filled from stopes underground. Pneumatic drills were used to advance the tunnel four to five feet per day. This was an advancement in mining for this period.

An incline rail system was used to lower ore from the collar of the incline shaft to the loading ramps 400 feet below on the railroad. The crosscut tunnel was to replace the extra handling of the ore.

In May of 1882, three carloads of ore and one of quartz were being shipped daily. Five carloads of ore per day were being shipped by February, 1883, with production expected to reach 20 to 30 carloads per day.

During this period, an iron ore body 40 to 50 feet thick was being mined and the hanging wall of the lode had not been reached. Iron content of the ore was 58 to 64 percent. A width of 500 feet and continuation downdip for 1,800 feet was claimed for the ore body. As mining proceeded downdip, the pyrite content increased and in the late 1890s an unsuccessful attempt was made to roast the sulfur from the pyrite. The last ore mined contained only 43 percent iron.

The Calumet Mine ore body was a replacement of Leadville limestone and associated vein in regionally metamorphosed rocks. Baked shales of the Weber formation rest on top of the Leadville limestone (the blue lime of the Leadville district) and below the ore was a sill of granodiorite which had its source in a plug-like mass, satellite to the Whitehorn stock of granodiorite. The plug was termed the Calumet stock by Behre but more recent work by Wrucke terms the Whitehorn granodiorite a new formation consisting of the main pluton and three satellite bodies. One satellite body is a plug, one is sill-like, and the third a complex form. Composition of the Whitehorn formation ranges from syenogabbro to quartz monzonite. It was intruded into Paleozoic rocks in late Cretaceous time and is thought to have a steep feeder conduit, which formed a floor on upper Paleozoic strata. This formation has been dated at 69.4 to 70.4 m.y.B.P.

The contact metamorphic iron deposits of the Calumet Mine are in Leadville limestone in part between two granodiorite sills along the west side of the Whitehorn stock. Shale beds of the overlying Weber formation have been metamorphosed and contain cordierite, sillimanite, and andalusite. Carbonaceous shales have been altered to graphite that has been mined from the general area.

Paragensis of the deposit was given by Behre as follows:

1. Calcite from original limestone recrystalized.
2. Tremolite, diopside, and epidote formed along with other silicates.
3. Magnetite and hematite formed massive replacement ore; some veins were also formed.
4. Pyrite and chalcopyrite were deposited in veins.
5. Calcite and quartz were deposited in veins.

Faults are marked by zones of schistose rocks, slickensides (polished wall rock due to fault movement), and brecciated or altered rocks containing veinlets of epidote, chlorite, quartz, and grains of chalcopyrite.

Diopside occurs as selective replacement of the limestone and in the old workings it occurred as spheroidal masses, with radiating blades, up to a foot in diameter. Epidote formed massive replacements and also occurred as crystals in veins with quartz. Scapolite occurs in the veins at the Calumet Mine. Introduction of fugitive constituents, such as chlorine, carbon dioxide, and sulfur trioxide into regionally metamorphosed rocks is thought to be the origin of the scapolite.

Minerals of the Calumet Mine are: epidote, massive; fibrous and crystals; uralite (Fig. 5-3); garnet, (var. hessonite); diopside; actinolite; tremolite,

Fig. 5-3.   Uralite, Calumet Iron Mine (PR#12–1) T.E.C.

golden amphibole of local terminology (var. asbestos); calcite; magnetite; hematite (Fig. 5–4); pyrite; chalcopyrite; scapolite; biotite, brown and green; and quartz, sagenitic with chlorite or fibrous epidote, as long tapering crystals up to 6 inches long and as Japanese-Law twins.

Eckel described the occurrence of sapphires near the Calumet Mine. They were discovered in 1886 and it would be doubtful if any remain except for an article in the *Minerals Yearbook* (U.S. Bureau of Mines, 1943, p. 568):

> Guy B. Ellermeier, of Denver, reported that at the old Sapphire locality near Turret, Colorado, first discovered in 1886, the stones occur in a bed of corundum schist one foot thick lying on garnetiferous metamorphic limestone. While the corundum stones are a fine blue, they are too small to be of commercial interest.

About .3 miles down the old R. R. grade, from the old Calumet loading platforms there is a small deposit of magnesite.

Sedalia Mine.   The Sedalia Mine, a copper-zinc deposit, is about 3½ miles northwest of Salida in Chaffee County. A poor road from Belleview station on the Rio Grande Railroad and State Highway 291 leads to the mine (Fig. 5–5).

An early account in the Director of the Mint report for 1884, relating an account of a new strike reported in the *Denver Tribune,* gave this insight of the Sedalia Mine workings. At the base of the first foothills on the east bank of the Arkansas River, about four miles above Salida, are the Sedalia and Hidden Treasure claims. An outcrop 20 feet above the surface and almost that wide can be traced for about 100 feet; the claims extend 3,000 feet northeast. Development consisted of a discovery shaft at the top of the hill and an adit about 200 feet downhill, about the center of the hill.

Although the mine was located in 1881 it was 1883 before the shaft was down

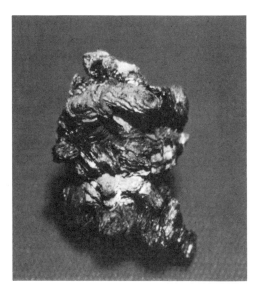

Fig. 5–4.   Hematite roses, Calumet Iron Mine (JM#947).

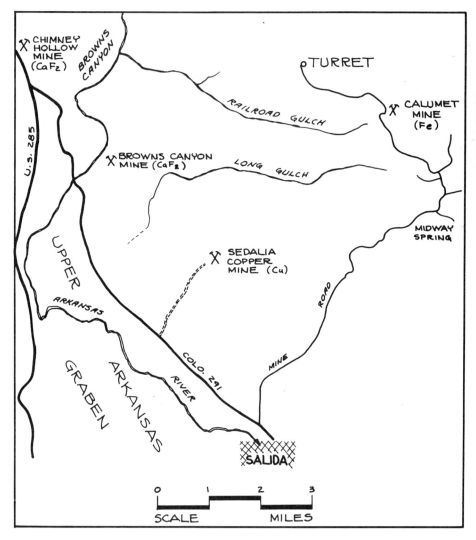

Fig. 5-5. Salida area mines, location map, Chaffee County, Colorado. Adapted from U.S.G.S. 15 Min. Series Poncha Springs Quad. and Cameron Mountain Quad., 1956.

50 feet with a 22 foot drift at that level. A tunnel extended 75 feet from the outcrop toward the shaft. At this point, a 35 foot crosscut of the deposit was made.

This development uncovered an ore body of lead carbonate and because this find was not in the familiar blue lime–porphyry contact, such as occurred in Leadville and other camps to the north, a great deal of excitement was aroused in the mining community.

The discovery occurred just a day before expiration of the bond on the property, May 1. The leasees, not having the money to take up the bond, secured an extension for another three months. With the deed in escrow, the discovery was then announced.

The first 15 feet of the crosscut was estimated to contain ore with 20 to 25 percent copper, and the first 20 feet could be shipped without sorting. The next ten feet was lean and contained only syenite and wernerite. Next came carbonate of iron, chunks of galena, copper carbonates, talc, sulphides, oxides, etc.

Later reports gave the winze, probably the discovery shaft, as being 100 feet deep with drifts running north and south in ore. The south drift was 70 feet long and showed black oxide of copper and pyrite assaying 38 to 55 percent copper and 9 to 10 ounces of silver per ton. The copper was relatively pure and had no arsenic or antimony.

In November, 1898, the lease was transferred and by December the working face on the third level showed almost solid copper. Copper-zinc ore was shipped to a zinc–lead paint plant in Canon City in 1907. A leaching plant at the mine had been replaced by a 50 tpd concentrating plant the year before. High zinc content drew penalties at the copper smelters and the copper and incompletely oxidized zinc ore made it difficult for the zinc plants to treat it.

Production from 1884 to 1908 was between 60,000 and 70,000 tons of ore containing 5 percent or more of copper and $1.00 to $2.50 per ton in gold and silver. A small amount of native silver was found in the lower workings. Intermittent activity occurred until 1923 with especially good years reported for 1916, 1917, and 1918, due to the high prices of metal during and after World War I. In 1953, it was examined for uranium by the Empire Zinc Co., division of the New Jersey Zinc Company, apparently without any favorable indication.

Old company maps made in 1917 show about 8,100 feet of drifts, crosscuts and raises with three levels.

This mine, which has produced a wide range of minerals for almost a hundred years, has been the subject of numerous interpretations as to its origin. Some are presented as a matter of interest. Cross, in 1895, described the deposit as a thick bed of actinolite schist impregnated with copper minerals. Lindgren, in 1908, advanced the following hypothesis of the origin of the Sedalia deposit, which he refined in 1930:

In Precambrian times, a large body of basic rocks, diabase or gabbro, intruded metasedimentary rocks that were probably dolomitic sandstones and shales. This intrusive magma contained copper, zinc, and lead.

A dike from this body intruded the folded metasedimentary rocks, in part parallel to the bedding. The metasedimentary rocks were converted into crystalline shists and the dike into amphibolite. Ore minerals were recrystallized and migrated through the wall rocks and intruding granites of Precambrian age and further metamorphosed the deposit near the contacts. Continuing metamorphism made the granites shistose in part.

A large dike of granite-pegmatite cut the deposit in two and acted as a barrier to movement of minerals during subsequent oxidation of the deposit. Below the pegmatite dike, the sphalerite and chalcopyrite were only partly oxidized.

Lindgren in 1933, considered that the sedimentary series was contact-metamorphosed by later granite intrusions and still later altered to amphibolite. A nearby large, coarse mass of diabase was the source of the dikes. Chalcopyrite, sphalerite, and magnetite are intergrown with amphibole, garnet, spinel and labradorite. Oxidation of the upper 200 feet of the deposit produced supergene zinc and copper minerals which made ore bodies in the second 100 feet of the deposit.

Singewald, considered the ore body to be a flat lens 800 feet long by 150 feet wide of chlorite and amphibolite schist representing an extremely metamorphosed off-shoot of a diabase or gabbro intrusion. It was regarded as a magmatic differentiate of a parent magma rich in copper sulfides. Primary ore minerals were magnetite, chalcopyrite, pyrite, sphalerite, and minor galena.

Heinrich and Salotti regarded the deposit as a pyro-metasomatic skarn replacing an amphibolite layer in gneiss. Heyl regarded the deposit as a massive replacement of non-carbonate schist. He added these refinements. Willemite, the earliest supergene mineral was formed under arid conditions and like hydrozincite and auricalcite it may have formed in the early Pleistocene and possibly in the Pliocene ages. It occurs in small white, gray, or light brown cystals and as hexagonal prisms. It is often coated with ferroan-smithsonite, (var. monheimite), hydrozincite and later oxidation minerals. It was first described in 1894.

Hemimorphite and malachite were probably the last minerals deposited and were thought by Heyl to have been deposited in a more humid climate, probably in the Pleistocene and Recent periods. Hemimorphite is more abundant in partly oxidized ores below the pegmatite dike.

Van Alstine in describing a similar deposit about 700 feet above Railroad Gulch, near Turret and known as the Ace High and Jack Pot prospect, says that the deposit resembles some gahnite-bearing copper–zinc deposits once worked in adjacent areas, which Lindgren regarded as magmatic segregates in gabbro dikes regionally metamorphosed to amphibolite.

The Cotopaxi Mine, about 20 miles southeast of Salida, is considered a deposit similar to the Sedalia Copper Mine deposit and was termed a pyrometasomatic skarn deposit by Heinrich and Salotti. Galena was found to be 1,300 ± 100 million years old which places it in the later part of the Precambrian age.

Characteristic minerals of deposits similar to the Sedalia deposit are: chalcopyrite, pyrite, pyrrhotite,sphalerite, and molybdenite as sulfides and magnetite and specularite as oxides. Gangue minerals are the contact-metamorphic silicates garnet, epidote, vesuvianite, diopside, tremolite, and wollastonite. Recrystallized, sometimes coarse, calcite is abundant; quartz is not abundant and the ore minerals are later than the silicates. Van Alstine points out that the genetic connection with limestone and dolomite has not been established to make the deposit a replaced skarn; however, some skarn may have been formed by regional metamorphism.

Van Alstine lists the following wallrock minerals in the Sedalia Copper Mine: actinolite, andalusite, anthophyllite, apatite, asbestos, beryl, bytownite, calcite, chlorite, clinozoisite, cordierite, corundum, cummingtonite, diopside, epidote, gahnite, garnet, hornblende, idocrase, kyanite, labradorite, microcline, phlogopite, quartz, rutile, serpentine, sillimanite, sphene, talc, tourmaline, tremolite, and zircon.

Other minerals are: anglesite, auricalcite, azurite, barite, calcite, cerussite, chalcanthite, chrysocolla, cuprite, galena, gold, gypsum, hematite, hemimorphite, hydrozincite, limonite, magnetite, malachite, marcasite, melanterite, opal, psilomelane, pyrite, pyrrhotite, quartz, rosasite, silver, smithsonite, sphalerite, tenorite, willemite, and an unnamed yellow sulfate of lead and copper that Lindgren reported in 1908.

Tweto found scheelite in the Sedalia Copper Mine and in the nearby Cleora district which has similar mineralization. The most famous mineral from this mine is the dodecahedral alamandine, which occurs in chlorite schist. Crystals up to 15 pounds have been found.

The top 100 feet of the deposit was leached to a gossan of limonite, jasperoid, malachite, and yellow, earthy sulfates of lead and copper. Minerals of the second 100 feet were willemite, smithsonite, limonite, jasper, anglesite, cerussite, tenorite, hydrozincite, hemimorphite, auricalcite, and rosasite.

Brown's Canyon Fluorspar. The Brown's Canyon fluorspar district is in the Poncha Springs northeast quadrangle and is considered one of the major fluorspar districts of the United States because it has produced $5 million in calcium fluoride concentrates and it has large reserves.

The main fault through the old Sedalia Copper Mine extends four miles northwest as a cross fault of the Upper Arkansas Graben. It is on the southwest side of a horst block of Pce rock that extends northwest across the graben.

The down-faulted graben south of it and the graben to the north of it contain an unknown thickness of Dry Union formation. The Precambrian rocks of this horst block are overlain by lower Tertiary volcanic rocks, Miocene tuffaceous siltstone of the Brown's Canyon formation and Dry Union formation.

The Brown's Canyon formation is a tuffaceous siltstone which was deposited in the general rift area of Brown's Canyon. Fossils of Miocene age have been identified from this distinctive siltstone. Locally, it is mineralized with fluorite.

Faults and joints in this horst contain northeast and northwest-trending quartz–specularite veins. The main fault on the southwest side of the horst is mineralized with fluorspar almost continuously for 3,000 feet, and is the main deposit of the Brown's Canyon fluorspar district. This fault has parallel deposits; the east branch has Precambrian rocks for wall rock and has been the most productive. The west branch has an east wall of Pce rock; however, a wall of ash–flow tuff of Oligocene age occurs on the west. Faulting occurred after the deposit was formed. Vugs 4 feet by 8 feet by 30 feet high occurred with a filling of wad and clay.

The veins have fluorite, microcrystalline, and chalcedonic quartz, with only minor coarse grained quartz, opal, calcite, barite, pyrite, marcasite, black manganese oxides, iron oxides, and clay minerals.

Some fine-grained fluorite is rippled so as to suggest slight down flow of gelatinous material; much is botryoidal. Chocolate-brown, purple, red, pink, green, yellow, gray, white and colorless fluorite were observed in the mines but colors fade if weathered. All varieties were tested with ultraviolet lamp but none fluoresced according to Van Alstine. Ribbon spar is made of layers from 1 mm to more than two feet thick. Nodular ore is formed of nearly concentric layers of fluorite around breccia fragments, fluorite, country rock, or chalcedony. An origin for such formation has been suggested by Van Alstine as rotation of the fragments and deposition of additional fluorite. Well-formed crystals of fluorite are scarce and generally less than 1 mm. The occurrence of multiple crystal habits together is of interest.

Cubes; octahedrons; dodecahedrons; octahedrons modified by cube, dodecahedron, trapezohedron, trisoctahedron, tetrahexahedron, and hexoctahedron; dodecahedron modified by cube, trapezohedron modified by cube and octahedrons have been identified. Cubic, octahedral, and dodecahedral fluorite have been found together and evidently were deposited simultaneously. Cubes and dodecahedra, and dodecahedra and octahedra modified by cubes have been found together in specimens.

The Chimney Hill Mine is between Brown's Canyon and Nathrop in the rift. In a speciman from the Chimney Hill Mine fluorite crystals less than 0.04 mm in diameter had the following four habits: cube, octahedron, cube-octahedron and dodecahedron. Within recent years, an exploratory diamond drill hole produced warm water under artesian pressure. This fluorspar deposit has green, cream, brown, white and purple fluorspar.

REFERENCES

A–4 Lindgren Volume, (Singewald), A–5 Ridge, (Graton), (Sec. 81), C–7, D–3, F–4, G–1, G–5, H–2, H–14, J–1, J–15, J–46, J–56, K–4, K–5, L–1, L–1 1948, P–7 James, (Bruns), Q–17, Q–18, Q–44, Q–45, Q–46, Q–48, R–2, R–11, S–10, S–40, S–52, S–55, S–56, S–72, S–134, S–135, S–137, S–138, S–139, S–146.

MONARCH–TAYLOR GULCH AREA

Monarch–Taylor Gulch area is in Chaffee County on the southeastern flank of the Sawatch Range. The South Fork of the Arkansas River drains this area which is east of Monarch Pass and about 13 miles west of Poncha Springs where U.S. Highway 50 goes E-W through the old Monarch mining district. Taylor Gulch is north of Garfield and access is by a jeep trail that follows an old mine road (Fig. 5–6).

Gold prospectors were in this area as early as the 1860s. A shop was built on the site of Maysville in 1870 and the twin settlements of Crazy Camp and Maysville were soon established. Growth soon merged the towns and the name Maysville was adopted. According to some, the wrong name was chosen and Crazy Camp would have been more appropriate.

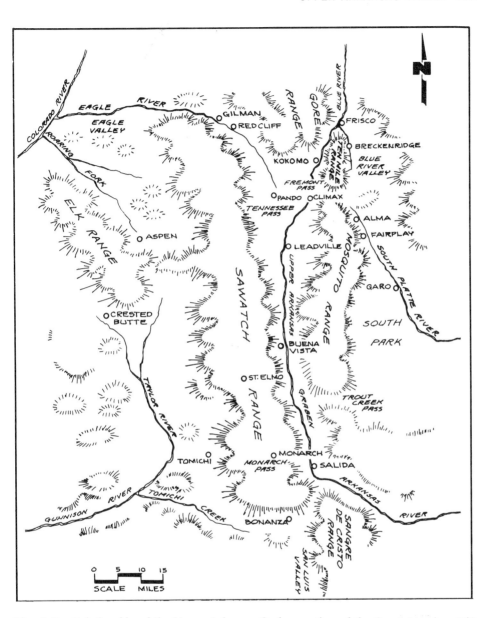

Fig. 5-6. Relationship of the Upper Arkansas Graben section of the Great American Rift zone to other topographic features of this zone in central Colorado. Adapted from U.S.G.S. P.P. 235, 1953.

Ore was discovered on the Great Monarch claim in 1878 and other mines, including the Madonna, were soon located and established. A minor discovery at Cree Camp north of Taylor Gulch brought about 3,000 people into the area in early 1878; however, Cree Camp did not last long.

As early as 1872, Hayden had predicted that the area within a ten mile radius of Monumental Peak would be one of the richest mining areas of Colorado. This had a stimulating effect on prospecting in the Monarch–Taylor Gulch and

Cree Camp areas and many prospects and small mining camps, such as Shavano on Mt. Shavano, in the Monarch mining district and along the Sawatch Range were opened.

Chaffee City was platted in 1880 but the name was changed to Monarch in 1884. The railroad was extended from Maysville, which it reached in 1881, to Monarch in 1883 and limestone and marble quarries were opened. A blue marble was found near the head of Taylor Gulch and some marble from the area was said to have been used in the State Capitol Building.

Junction City was founded in 1879 where the wagon road up Taylor Gulch to Cree Camp and Alpine Pass junctioned the one to Monarch and Monarch Pass. A disastrous fire in 1883 occurred while the male population had gone to Salida to vote. The town was rebuilt and renamed Garfield.

Arbor Villa, or Arborville, a small nearby village of 150 population in 1885, was the location of a large dance hall and the only brothel in the area, a distinction that did not last very long.

Most of the larger mines were producing by 1882. The Madonna produced continuously until 1893 when silver dropped from $1.27 to $0.70 per ounce (the Silver Panic). Mining in the district was minimal from 1893 to 1906, however, the Madonna was still shipping three carloads a week in 1898; by 1901 total prodcution of the district was over $9 million in lead–silver–gold ore. Production of the district from 1901 to 1957 in lead–silver–gold–zinc–copper ores was $4,195,000 over half of which came from the Madonna Mine.

Oxidized zinc ore was first produced in the district in 1902 and production continued until 1922 with production also in 1926 and in 1930. Estimated production in this period was 25,000 tons of zinc carbonate ore containing 18 to 35 percent zinc.

H. E. Burton of Leadville made the first zinc carbonate ore shipments. He later found zinc carbonate ore in the May Queen lode at Leadville. Due to heavy limonite staining the zinc carbonate ore was difficult to recognize and, at Leadville as well as elsewhere, it was not recognized for many years after mining began.

During and for a short period after World War I, a small production was made from the Garfield Mine in Taylor Gulch. A shipment of 457 tons of ore was made in 1950. Prospecting and diamond drilling on the lower levels of the Madonna Mine failed to locate mineable ore bodies in this same period of activity.

Other than the large limestone quarry of CF & I Company, and a small production of crushed marble for decorative landscaping use from Taylor Gulch, the district has been inactive since World War II.

The Monarch–Taylor Gulch area is on the west side of the Upper Arkansas Graben, the Great American Rift, and is on the east side of and extends into the Sawatch Range. Basement rock units of the district are Pce gneisses and schists which were intruded by granites and diorites, also in Pce time.

An upper Cambrian quartzite, the Sawatch, was deposited on an irregular land surface of these old Pce rocks and then mostly removed by erosion. Sections of only a few inches up to tens of feet thick are recognized in the mines. The Sawatch quartzite is 105 feet thick at Leadville, according to a section given by Behre.

Manitou fm. (Manitou dolomite), Harding sandstone (quartzite), and Fremont fm. (Fremont limestone), of Ordovician age, rest unconformably on the Sawatch quartzite. Chaffee fm., Parting quartzite, and Dyer dolomite of Devonian age are next in sequence. Leadville limestone (dolomite), of Mississippian age; Belden shale of Pennsylvanian age; and Minturn fm. of Penn-Permian age complete the Paleozoic section which is less than 1,000 feet thick in most places within the Monarch mining district.

These Paleozoic rocks were twisted into a tight synclinal fold and, in late Tertiary time, intruded by quartz monzonites and related igneous rocks of the Mount Princeton batholith. Locally chonoliths, stocks, sills, and dikes are common forms of these intrusions. Faulting occurred prior to deposition of the ore that occurs in fissure veins and as replacement bodies in the adjacent limestones. The Manitou and Leadville limestones were particularly receptive host rocks for replacement ore beds.

Most of the steep to vertical sides of the synclinal folds were tipped on edge and form ridges in the Madonna Mine and particularly in the mines of Taylor Gulch. Adits were driven to the Pce contact zone that frequently contained mineralized replacement zones of the best ore.

The Madonna, Mayflower, and Hawkeye Faults were the most productive veins and pipe-like bodies as well as replacements of the limestone beds were confined to their proximity.

Madonna Mine

The Madonna Mine was by far the largest and most productive mine of the district. In 1878, Mark Gray found a thin seam of silver chloride ore on the Cherubim claim. G. L. Smith joined Gray and together they found lead carbonate ore on the sideline of this claim and located the Madonna claim. A 30 foot shaft was sunk on Monarch Ridge on this outcrop in 1879. C. B. Richards purchased a third interest in the two claims in 1879 and he and his son with Smith and Gray put down three more shallow shafts in 1880, one of these shafts also encountering lead carbonate ore. In the fall of 1880, a New York group bought out Smith and Gray and with Richards as superintendent sank a 60 foot shaft and drove the first Madonna level, which developed about 80 feet of lead carbonate ore along the lode (Fig. 5–7).

This ore averaged 30 percent lead and 0.10 ounces of silver and was too low grade to ship to the Pueblo, Colorado smelter. Two small inefficient smelters were reported operating in the area as early as 1880; one at Maysville and one at the site of what was later Garfield. The Madonna Mining Company, however, built one in 1881 and treated a small tonnage in 1882. This proved to be unsuccessful due to the high cost of coke which was hauled from Salida and due to a lack of silica in the ore.

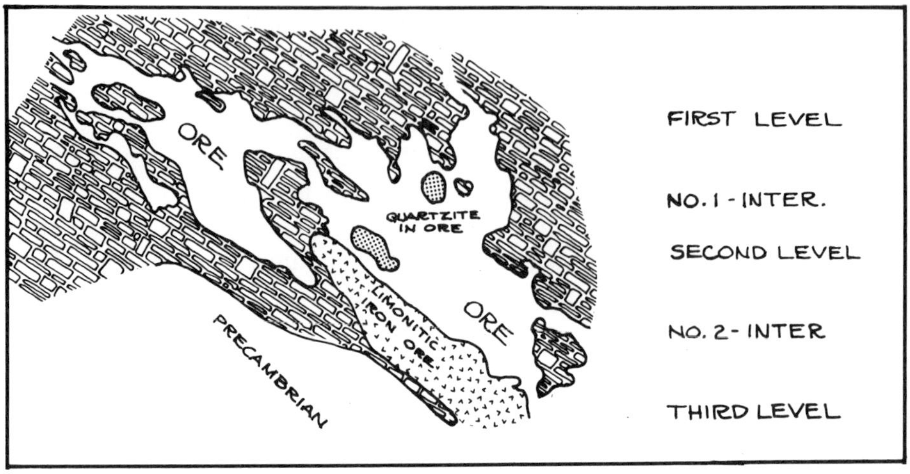

Fig. 5-7. Cross section of ore shoot in Madonna Mine above third level. Monarch mining district, Chaffee County, Colorado. Adapted from Colo. Geol. Sur. Bull. 1, 1910.

A. Eilers, a metallurgist of Leadville, was given a half interest in the company to erect a smelter at Pueblo, Colorado, to treat Madonna mine ore and siliceous ores from other areas. A successful operation resulted and the Madonna Mine was worked continually until 1893, when the Silver Panic curtailed activities. Production of up to 30 carloads a day, with 300 men employed, was reported. In 1884, production was reported as 10 to 14 cars per day with 65 men working.

By 1884, two tunnels 350 feet long were driven into Monarch Ridge. Raises and winzes were driven to connect these workings and by 1850 there were seven levels; eight sublevels, with raises and winzes; 12,000 feet of drifts; and workings throughout a vertical distance of 1,525 feet. The ore deposit was worked for a dip or pitch length of 2,650 feet.

The Madonna No. 7 level was 450 feet below the No. 5 level and it was driven along the Precambrian-limestone contact for 1,500 feet. Access to the lower workings was by a shaft at the No. 6 level, which was 70 feet above the South Arkansas River.

By 1885, a 3,000 foot aerial tramway, one of the first in Colorado, had been built on a 40 degree incline, to replace an army of teams and teamsters that crawled up and down Monarch Ridge to bring ore to the railroad below at Monarch. About ten cars of ore a day were going to the Colorado Smelting Company at Pueblo, Colorado, at that time. It was said that $7 per ton ore could be mined at a profit and Madonna ore was averaging $24.20 per ton. Some of the upper levels were producing sand-carbonate ore which could be mined by shoveling. This type of oxidized ore also occurred at Leadville and at the Eagle Mine at Gilman, Colo., in limestone replacement pockets.

In 1910, the Madonna Mine was equipped with electric hoists, lights for underground, and electric drills, which were used only on development work. This was advanced equipment for that time.

Madonna Mine was worked intermittently until 1924 and remained idle until

1942. Exploration for new ore bodies was carried on at various times until 1953; it was not successful. The mine has been used as a tourist attraction in recent years and limited tours are conducted.

The Eclipse Mine, along the Mayflower Fault; the Hawkeye Mine, along the Hawkeye Fault; and in Taylor Gulch, the Wilson, Lilly, and Garfield Mines all had similar geologic settings. Ore occurred in replacement beds in the Manitou dolomite and along the Pce contact; in the Chaffee fm; and in the Leadville limestone. It also occurred as veins and in breccia zones. Lower parts of the veins were massive sulfide bodies.

Great Monarch Mine

Great Monarch Mine was discovered in 1878 and produced the first ore from the district that was hauled by wagon to Canon City, Colo. This ore was high grade silver, up to 200 ounces per ton, in a brown limonite gangue. Walls of the vein were of a black dolomite. Rich silver ore occurred with dark gray to black smithsonite; however, the vein was only inches wide and a 200 foot shaft was the deepest working.

Lilly, Garfield, and New York Mines

The Lilly Mine in Taylor Gulch had a tunnel 2,530 feet long and produced for a number of years, including after World War II. A production of $23,000 was recorded for 1957. It produced an ore chiefly of copper carbonates and some chalcopyrite. An aerial tramway 7,174 feet long brought the Lilly Mine ore to the railroad at Garfield.

In this mine chrysocolla formed linings of small caves. One cave had a chrysocolla lining one inch thick and another one had an underground stream. Small caves were numerous in the Taylor Gulch mines. Mimetite occurred in the Lilly Mine as a yellow to green earthy mineral. The ore carried an average of 10 percent copper.

The Garfield and Lilly Mines were the most productive in Taylor Gulch. They contained more copper and more sulfide mineralization. In the New York Mine, at the head of the Gulch, the ore was characteristically that of a contact-metamorphic deposit. This was true to a lesser degree in some of the other mines. Mineralization was considered to be associated with placement of the intrusives into the Mount Princeton batholith.

Ore in the Garfield Mine occurred as replacement bodies at the contact of the Precambrian rocks and the Manitou dolomite. Pyrrhotite occurred with lead–zinc–copper sulfides. More copper occurred in the Taylor Gulch mines than in the Madonna Mine. Only one mill operated in the Monarch–Taylor Gulch district and that for a short time as the ores went directly to the smelters.

Sphalerite in the New York Mine was associated with actinolite, diopside and andradite. The sphalerite altered directly to smithsonite, an uncommon alteration as it usually migrates down vein as a soluble sulfate to be precipitated as a carbonate much lower in limestone deposits.

Anthophyllite, mountain wood, was found in Taylor Gulch and tremolite, marble, garnet, epidote, massive and as spherules, and other metamorphic minerals occur (Fig. 5–8).

Just north of Taylor Gulch on the east slopes of Taylor Mountain limonite cubes, pseudomorphs of pyrite, occur. On Missouri Hill, a granite contains smoky quartz. A shipment of gold ore from a pegmatite in Green Gulch, in the Monarch district, was made. This gulch could not be located.

Minerals of the Monarch–Taylor Gulch district were: cerussite, mostly limonitic with 5 to 7 ounces of silver per ton; however, massive crystals were found in the Madonna Mine. Smithsonite, dark gray to black, yellowish to brown, with small crystals were found in vugs. Chlorargyrite and anglesite as water-clear crystals up to 2 inches in massive galena, were found in the Madonna Mine (Fig. 5–9): A classic occurrence of lead is called woody anglesite and is unique to this area. Brochantite, minium, molybdite, native copper, silver, gold, sulfur, and plumbojarosite, formerly lead–antimony ocher, azurite, malachite, chalcocite, cuprite, copper pyrite (possible cubanite), pyrite, chalcopyrite, covellite, bornite, tenorite, limonite, hematite, magnetite, calcite, wulfenite, as yellow crystals on galena were found in the Hawkeye Mine. Hydrozincite and stephanite were from the Little Charm Mine. Gahnite, in rhombic dodecahedrons up to 1/4 inches came from the Bon Ton Mine. Ankerite, blue–black, in veins, argentite (acanthite), limonite (a minor iron resource), turgite, and dolomite crystals coated with black to blue-gray ankerite, were all known from the Madonna Mine and Monarch Ridge quarries. Chalcophanite, pyrolusite, and other manganese oxides were also known. Brochantite was said to be deposited from sulfate solutions in the mine. Calcite occurred as coarse crystals on the Madonna No. 6 level.

The greatest part of the ores from the Monarch district were silver-bearing lead carbonate ores. Samples containing as much as 816.25 ounces of silver per

Fig. 5–8. Spheroidal epidote, Taylor Gulch (JM#170).

Fig. 5-9. Woody anglesite, galena, and cerussite, Taylor Gulch (#3-190).

ton, 16 percent lead, and 1/2 ounce of gold were obtained from the No. 5 level of the Madonna Mine; however, the average value was much less than this. Streaks one inch to six inches wide on the lowest level carried 65.10 ounces of gold; 5,974.9 ounces silver and 24.3 percent lead per ton. Oxidized ores made up the largest percentage of production from the district. Sulfide ores came from the deeper workings of the mine.

A zone of secondary gold–silver enrichment occurred between the oxidized and sulfide ores. Chief sulfide minerals were silver–bearing galena, gold-bearing pyrite and chalcopyrite. Oxidized zinc ore bodies occurred in the main deposits as hemimorphite and smithsonite envelopes around silver-lead oxidized ore pods and as replacements of the limestones. Hemimorphite was more common in the upper workings and smithsonite in the lower ones. The mineral occurrences were similar throughout the district.

CF & I Co. Quarry at Monarch

Limestone for the Pueblo, Colo. steel mills has been mined at Monarch for many years. The limestone beds, which are part of an eroded synclinal fold, dip down Monarch Ridge at an angle of 45° toward the South Fork of the Arkansas River.

Dyer dolomite, Ouray of former usage, of Devonian age, is mined for the steel mill because of its purity. The Manitou dolomite, Tomichi of former usage, of Ordovician age, is too siliceous. The quarry, one of the largest in Colorado, is capable of shipping over 30 carloads per day.

The quarry, being on highly mineralized Monarch Ridge, has opened old mine workings and mineralized zones. At one time, a 20 foot mineralized zone had a streak of galena two feet wide in it. This material was waste and went to the dumps as it only interferes with selective mining of the limestone.

Fig. 5-10. Dolomite with bluish-gray ankerite coating, Monarch Quarry (JM#283).

Dolomite in coarsely crystallized rhombohedrons occurred in the quarry. A black to bluish-gray variety of ankerite was found in veins and as coating on dolomite crystals (Fig. 5-10).

REFERENCES

C-10, E-12, F-4, F-5, G-5, G-8, J-14, J-18, L-1, 1950-1957, Q-47, R-11, S-27, S-52, S-55.

MOUNT ANTERO BERYLLIUM AREA

Mount Antero beryllium area is in the Sawatch Range, Chaffee County. This area is on the upper slope of Mount Antero and Mount White, well above timberline. Chalk Creek lies to the north of the area and the Upper Arkansas Valley is to the east. St. Elmo, formerly Forest City, a mining camp in the Chalk Creek drainage established to serve the Mary Murphy Mine in 1880, is the nearest inhabited community.

A small quantity of aquamarine, the local variety of beryl, was found on Mount Antero in 1884 or 1885 and a small production of gem aquamarine was continued into the 1890s. This area is accessible for only a few summer months a year and mineral collectors visit it annually.

In the 1950s and early 1960s, a government support program to encourage production of beryllium ore resulted in claims being filed on low-grade beryllium deposits on Mount Antero and Mount White. A small production was made from this area but without government support the mines were not profitable. A short work season and severe conditions for operating at a high and remote location also contributed to the failure of the venture.

The CYCA Group of 73 mining claims was staked on the upper slopes of Mount Antero. A large open pit and numerous open trenches were started in 1959. A truck–jeep trail was built to the workings and another jeep trail was extended southwest 1.3 miles to the Atlas Group of 15 claims on the north side of Mount White. Numerous pits and prospect holes were made on these claims.

Mt. Princeton batholith occupies this part of the Sawatch Range and the Mount Antero leucogranite, the latest of the Oligocene granite intrusives of the batholith, contains the beryllium deposits of Mount White and Mount Antero.

Mount Antero leucogranite has a (K/Ar) age of 30.8 m.y.B.P. and is the youngest of seven intrusives that make up the Mt. Princeton batholith. It occurs as two stocks which are on the eastern edge of the Mt. Princeton batholith.

Five variations of the Mount Antero leucogranite have been mapped that represent cooling or crystallization stages. Two of these stages have mineral assemblages that are somewhat different, yet overlapping. Mount Antero summit and the west peak of Mount White have the latest stage which has miarolitic structures and pegmatites that are thought to be from lower in the batholith or deeper seated than these structures.

In Mount Antero leucogranite that has been greisenized, (changed to quartz, mica and feldspar) fluorite, molybdenite, pyrite, ferrimolybdite, muscovite, brannerite, tourmaline, and ferberite occur. Late-stage greisenization has changed feldspar to muscovite and beryl to phenakite. Albitization was common.

In the CYCA group of claims beryl crystals up to 2 inches in diameter were found. Phenakite, bertrandite, fluorite, limonite, and malachite occurred in pods up to four feet in diameter. Beryl blebs in the granite as much as six inches in diameter occurred with bertrandite; these two minerals also occurred in veinlets two inches thick and up to 50 feet long. A vein three feet thick and 300 feet long containing iron–manganese oxides and pyrite in quartz also contained beryl.

Minerals of the Atlas group of claims on Mount White occurred in miarolitic cavities, blebs and in veinlets two inches wide and up to 50 feet long. Beryl, phenakite, and bertrandite were the most common minerals. A banded quartz–orthoclase rock, ribbon quartz, is distinctive of this deposit.

Minerals usually associated with Mount Antero are: beryl, (var. aquamarine), which was made Colorado's official gemstone in 1971, phenakite, bismutite, brannerite, fluorite, calcite, cyrtolite, spessartine, topaz, and quartz, smoky, clear, with inclusions, and smoky with amethystine interiors. Quartz with pronounced growth hillocks and vicinal surfaces is common. Many specimens are doubly terminated or distorted and some contain chlorite inclusions. Frondel described quartz specimens from Mount Antero, "toward

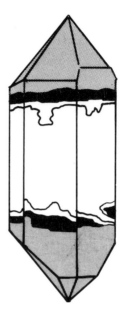

Fig. 5-11.   Smoky quartz with milky quartz capping, Mount Antero.

the base of which smoky color planes surround a very faintly amethystine interior.'' (Figs. 5-11, 5-12, and 5-13).

A quantity of gem aquamarine and phenakite was reportedly produced in 1955. Phenakite crystals from Mount Antero occur in both the rhombohedral and prismatic habits. Yedlin pointed out that the prevailing form, as shown by Dr. G. Switzer's study of the Mount Antero phenakites, is that shown in Dana p. 603, diagram 899. (Fig. 5-14)

A specimen of orthoclase and microcline from the western slope of Mount Antero is shown. (Fig. 5-15)

California Mine

The California Mine is on the southwestern side of Mount Antero about 25 miles from the CYCA workings. A jeep trail connects the two and continues to St. Elmo. The mine is on the divide between Brown's Creek and Baldwin Creek.

This mine is in the Mount Pomeroy quartz monzonite of Eocene (?) and Paleocene (?) age. This quartz monzonite is greenish-gray in color and has been slightly chloritized and epidotized; it forms the wall rock of the tunnel of the California Mine. Mineralization along a prominent vein is considered to be related to the Mount Antero leucogranite.

Prior to World War I molybdenite was mined from the California Mine and reportedly sold to Germany for making alloy steel. The mine was also worked in 1917 for the same purpose. A 90 foot crosscut to the vein was driven in 1917. Other work at that time consisted of 350 feet of drifts and an inclined shaft of

Figure 5-12   Figure 5-13

Fig. 5-12.   Distorted quartz crystal, Mount Antero.

Fig. 5-13.   Quartz from Mount Antero showing growth hillocks (top) and vicinal surfaces (bottom).

50 feet. At a point 141 feet from the crosscut, the vein was faulted and displaced 30 feet to the north. An operator in 1960 reported a block of inferred beryllium (aquamarine) ore about 750 feet long and 265 feet deep below the tunnel level.

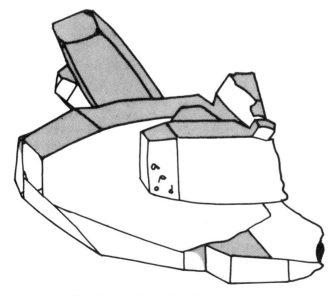

Fig. 5-14.   Phenakite, Mount Antero.

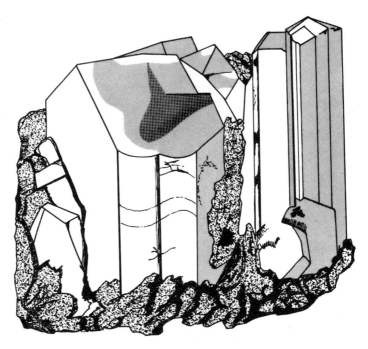

Fig. 5-15.   Orthocase and microcline specimen from western slope of Mount Antero.

The grade was estimated at 1 percent beryllium oxide. Extent of the work done in this period is unknown; however, it probably was not extensive as it was mapped in 1962–3, by Sharp of the U.S.G.S., and looks to be substantially the same as described in 1919 by Worcester.

In the California Mine, molybdenite and ferrimolybdenite occurred as chunks of mineral one inch to two inch thick and six inches to two feet long along the vein wall. Flakes occurred up to ½ inch in diameter. White quartz crystals up to 12 inches long, pyrite, and clear to opaque aquamarine were the associated minerals. Pockets of 20 to 30 pounds of pure molybdenite were found. Tourmaline, brannerite, magnetite, topaz, columbite, muscovite, and rutile are also found.

Adams describes beryl crystals containing inclusions of molybdenite or of mica. The color of the beryl may be blue, bluish–green, colorless, or pale straw yellow. Isolated crystals of beryl formed in vugs have the most perfect crystal form but are also comparatively rare. Simple combinations of pinacoids and prisms predominate but first and second order pyramids have been found on these crystals.

REFERENCES

C–18, E–12, G–1, G–5, J–25, J–56, J–62, J–66, K–5, L–1 1955–1971, R–17, S–1, S–2, S–27, S–106.

Mary Murphy Mine

The Mary Murphy Mine is on the southwest side of Chrysolite Mountain, about two miles south of St. Elmo. Originally called Forest City, which seemed inappropriate after the local forest was depleted, St. Elmo is in the Chalk Creek (Romley) mining district, Chaffee County. It is about four miles by road up Pomeroy Gulch to the main tunnel, No. 14 or the 1,400-foot level of the Mary Murphy (Fig. 5-16).

This mine was possibly in operation as early as 1870. Legend has it that one of the early locators was nursed back to health in a Denver hospital by Mary Murphy; however, this does not account for Pat, May and some of the other Murphys for which the veins of the multiple-vein lode were named. The mine was worked continually until 1925 and more or less intermittently until 1952.

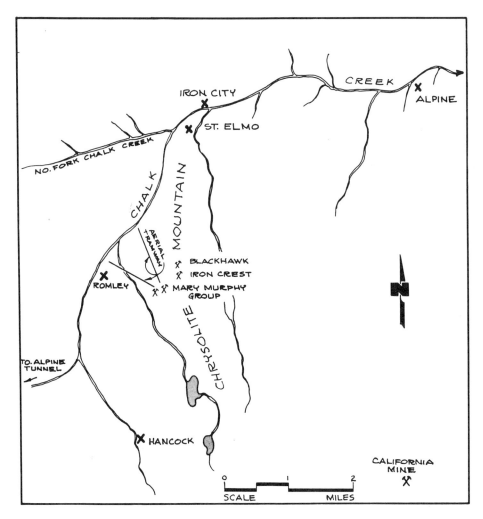

Fig. 5-16.   Location of Mary Murphy Mine, Chalk Creek mining district, Chaffee County, Colorado. Adapted from U.S.G.S. Bull. 1135-C.

Production of this famous old mine is about $14 million in ore that contained values in gold, silver, lead, zinc, and copper. Due to the early use of the leasing system, with individual leasees sometimes operating their own mill and shipping ore or concentrates to smelters at Black Hawk, Denver, Alpine, and other Colorado smelters, production is hard to trace and some unofficial estimates place the vein system's production as high as $60 million.

A smelter was built at the mine as early as 1875 and evidently one was in operation at Alpine by 1880. These were inefficient operations at best.

Some idea of early production of metals from smelted ore (and in this case, lode mining preceded the lode mining for carbonate ore at Leadville by probably four years) can be obtained from the following report of 1870 on production of matt (or matte) at the works of the Boston and Colorado Gold Smelting Company, Gregory Gulch, Black Hawk, Colorado, by James D. Hague.

Matt consists mainly of sulfide of copper with sulfide of iron. The copper content may vary from 50 to 60 percent and gold and silver may be from 40 to 50 ounces gold and 100 to 400 ounces silver per ton of matt.

The matt was shipped to Swansea, Wales, for refinement as there was no refinery to separate the metals in Colorado at that time. A refinery was being planned by this company, however.

In this process of making matt, the metal contained in 30 tons or more of ore could be concentrated into one ton to save shipping and treatment costs. Sulfur was important in this process as copper sulfide collected the gold and silver allowing the iron and other impurities to go off as slag. As excess of sulfur allowed an excess of iron in the matt and a lack of sulfur allowed a loss of copper to the slag. Control of the ores mixed in a batch was critical to success of the process. The process was to break with hammers or to crush the ore to size; weigh and sample it; roast it in heaps in the open air; recrush it with Cornish rollers; and smelt it in a reverberatory furnace.

After the ore was broken to size, weighed and sampled, it was roasted in heaps of 30 to 40 tons in the open air. A bed of cordwood 16 feet square was made as the base of a pyramid. Larger pieces of ore were placed on the wood with finer material covering it so as to form a pyramid. A wooden chimney 9 to 10 inches square was set in the center extending through the wood and the ore to the top. Then a quantity of charcoal was put in the bottom of this chimney and lighted. Draft was controlled because the fires would go out if the heap burned too slowly and the process would have to be repeated; If it burned too fast the ore would slag. Quantities of fine ore or concentrates were roasted on a grate in a furnace the capacity of which varied from one half to four tons per day. Each furnace consumed a cord of wood per 24 hours and required two men to stir the charge with iron rakes.

After roasting the calcined ore was recrushed by passing through 26-inch Cornish rollers. Matt too low grade to ship, usually recovered from the bottom of slag billets, was also crushed and added to the smelting charge.

The reverberatory smelting furnace which received this charge had a large cast iron skimming plate nine inches thick at one door. The liquid metal was tapped just below this plate and cast into molds and the slag was skimmed with iron rakes from a door near the stack and also cast into molds. Charge was fed through a feeding door.

Usually four or five charges of four to five tons each were required to make a ton of matt. The matt remained in the furnace and was not tapped until about a ton accumulated.

It is of interest to also note that gold, at $20 per ounce, was paid for, as were other metals, on a sliding scale. Two-ounce gold per ton ore was paid for at 20 percent of value; six-ounce gold per ton ore at 50 percent; and ten ounce gold per ton ore at 60 percent of value. Treatment charges were an additional amount per ton. Only Bonanza-type ores could be moved any distance for processing because of the cost.

Alpine, about three miles down Chalk Creek from St. Elmo, was a support center for mining in the area and for prospectors and miners going into the Gunnison country with its bustling camps such as Tin Cup and Pitkin, in 1877. By 1880, it had a population of 500 and was the railhead for the Denver, South Park, and Pacific Railroad. The rails were extended to St. Elmo in 1881 and, in turn, it became the center of activity.

In 1883, the Denver, South Park, and Pacific Railroad completed its line to Murphy's Switch below the Mary Murphy Mine. Murphy's Switch was later called Romley. This railroad, from Denver by way of South Park and Trout Creek Pass to Buena Vista, used the Rio Grande Railroad tracks from Buena Vista to Nathrop. At this point the route continued up Chalk Creek to Murphy's Switch. In January, 1880, the Alpine Tunnel was started at an elevation of 11,523 feet. It was completed in two years and the route continued on to Gunnison.

Timbers in the Alpine Tunnel were 12 by 12 inch hearts of redwood. When the old tunnel was re-entered in August, 1961, eighty years after it was started, the timbers were found to be sound. The tunnel had been closed since 1910, as the high cost of snow removal and seasonal use made it too costly to maintain. This tunnel was in use during the most productive years of the Mary Murphy Mine. By 1883, the Mary Murphy Mine was in full production and several hundred miners were working.

There were five main veins and several smaller ones worked in the Mary Murphy, the Iron Chest, and the Black Hawk, all mines on the same vein system. These veins are in quartz monzonite of the Mount Princeton batholith, a large intrusive mass made up of seven major units that occupies the central portion of the Sawatch Range. The quartz monzonite is Oligocene in age and the mineralization is younger.

The Director of the Mint's Report for 1880 listed the Pat and the Mary Murphy Mines working and the Black Hawk starting to work. Production was also reported from the Lady Murphy, May Murphy, and Pat Murphy Mines in 1882.

By 1882, the Mary vein was known to extend for 5,000 feet on the surface. Later it was followed for another 1,000 feet and it was mined and explored underground for 5,000 feet and mined through a vertical range of 1,400 feet. Through the Golf Tunnel it was possibly mined for another 1,000 feet in depth. The Iron Chest was an extension of the Pat vein of the Mary Murphy vein system. It was worked underground for about 2,000 feet. This vein can be traced on the surface for about 4,000 feet.

Development work reported in 1884 on the Mary Murphy was a discovery shaft 130 feet deep, and four winzes each 30 feet deep, connecting four levels. Level No. 2 was 500 feet long; No. 3 was 750 feet long; and No. 4 was 850 feet long. Contractors had just completed a winze 240 feet deep, at a point 600 feet from the portal, from the No. 4 to the No. 7 level. The ore body was 6 feet to 11 feet wide. A width of 10 feet in the winze assayed $40 per ton.

A gravity-activated aerial tramway 4,996 feet long, one of the first in the State, brought the ore from No. 4 level of the Mary Murphy to Romley for loading on the railroad. Ore was shipped to smelters in Denver, Black Hawk, and Alpine in 1880, 1881, and 1882. Production in 1884 was 2,635 tons of ore valued at $92,246. In 1884, the Mary Murphy was also reported to have shipped 81 tons of bullion to Denver. Bullion of early mining terminology was lead containing gold and silver in varying amounts. If it was free of iron and other impurities it was called soft, if not, it was hard.

Production in 1885 was 50 to 70 tons per day of ore that averaged $30 per ton. Due to the leasing system in use by the mine it was difficult to get a composite picture of actual mining and of production. One leasee's mill was burned in 1896 and throughout the years other mills were destroyed.

In 1908, a 20 stamp Pawnee amalgamation and concentration mill was in operation. An English syndicate bought the mine in 1909, and spent $800,000 on developments which included a crosscut tunnel 5,800 feet long that cut the lode 800 feet below the old workings. By 1916, this tunnel was double-tracked and a second aerial tramway, a mile long, was constructed. In 1911, a 200 tpd mill was successfully treating lower grade ores; the process included cyanidation. Production peaked before 1917 but continual operation was until 1925 or 1926 and intermittent operation by leasees, especially during and after World War II, extended until 1952.

In the Mary Murphy vein system ore above the 400 foot level was oxidized and contained cerussite, smithsonite and anglesite in a limonite and quartz gangue. Pyrolusite, psilomelane, azurite, malachite, and chrysocolla occurred as stains and in small vugs.

Between the 400 and 900 foot levels the ore was a mixture of oxidized ore and sulfide ore. Below the 900 foot level there was only sulfide ore. The ore occurred as cementing material for quartz monzonite breccia. Stringers and veinlets of quartz–rhodonite–rhodochrosite were present. Primary sulfide minerals were pyrite, chalcopyrite, galena, and sphalerite. Rhodochrosite and rhodonite occurred as fine-grained mixtures and as vein filling with calcite and barite without sulfides.

Old timers who worked in the Mary Murphy and Pat Murphy have told of rhodochrosite in large crystals going to the mill and over the dump.

RUBY MOUNTAIN

The Ruby Mountain area, east of Nathrop in Chaffee County, has long been known to mineral collectors for garnet, (var. spessartine), and topaz, of gem quality.

Nathrop, at the junction of Chalk Creek and the Arkansas River, was started in 1868 or 1870 when Charlie Nachtieb, a German immigrant, built an adobe house with walls three feet thick. According to Humbeutel his name was hard to pronounce and to remember so he changed it to Nathrop. Before cattle ranching became prominent in the Arkansas Valley, wheat was the principal crop and Nathrop started a water-powered grist mill. A sawmill, blacksmith shop, other buildings, and a store were added. The stage from Cleora to Buena Vista made Nathrop a regular stop and the railroad arrived in 1880. A depot and hotel were built and the town incorporated October 23, 1880. Population was 200 and the town boasted a newspaper, several stores and other necessary structures.

With one of the earliest settlements in the Arkansas Valley only a half mile west of Ruby Mountain the minerals were probably known in the late 1870s. Garnets, mistakenly thought to be rubies, probably gave the mountain, an otherwise unimportant hill of the area, its name. Sanford listed the area in his compilation of useful minerals of the United States. Van Alstine says garnet and topaz were first reported by the Colorado State geologist in 1883.

This part of the Arkansas Valley is in a graben which is one of several along the upper Arkansas section of the Great American Rift. Ruby Mountain, Dorothy Hill, the only unit west of the Arkansas River, Sugarloaf Mountain, and Ball Mountain, about 1.5 miles northeast of Ruby Mountain, are composed of a volcanic sequence which Van Alstine named the Nathrop volcanics. A small exposure of this formation is in a small graben structure 2–3/4 miles southeast of Ruby Mountain.

The Nathrop volcanics, which are about 500 feet thick, rest directly on Pce gneissic quartz monzonite. This formation is made up of pumiceous tuff and breccia, perlite that contains black obsidian pellets (Apache tears or more correctly marekanites), and a rhyolite flow that contains small crystals of garnet and topaz. This formation is of Oligocene age, dated more closely at 28 to 29 m.y.B.P., and the series is therefore younger than the youngest unit of the Mount Princeton batholith of the Sawatch Range.

On the east side of Ruby Mountain, 20 feet of volcanic breccia overlies 70 feet of light-colored pumiceous tuff. About 110 feet of west-dipping perlite is above this and the formation is capped by 300 feet of gray rhyolite. The perlite is light-gray, brownish gray, or dark gray and contains almost 3 percent water while the marekanites, within the perlite, contain less than 1 percent water.

Van Alstine gives the following information, as assembled from various sources particularly Sinkankas and Rogers and Cann on the minerals of the rhyolite of the Nathrop volcanics.

Garnet (var. spessartine), topaz, sanidine, quartz, minute prismatic crystals with prominent pinacoidal faces (one of the few authentic occurrences of the pinacoid of quartz), tridymite, bluish opal, calcite, magneitie, as tiny octahedrons, chalcedony and hematite, as six-sided flat rhombs, all occur.

Phenocrysts in the rhyolite include double terminated smoky quartz.

Van Alstine also points out that Dana (1932, p. 596) incorrectly attributed large dodecahedral almandine garnets from the Sedalia Copper Mine to the Ruby Mountain area. This has been an unfortunate mistake as this error has been repeated by quotation.

Seaman reported an occurrence of a trace of gold in the rhyolite of Ruby Mountain, Nathrop, Colorado, and also the occurrence of pseudobrookite in the area.

TROUT CREEK PASS AREA

Clara May and Yard Pegmatites

The Clara May and Yard Pegmatite Mines are in the Trout Creek Pass area near U.S. Highway 24. Trout Creek Pass is a low-altitude pass that was the traditional route of explorers and prospectors over the Mosquito Range from South Park into the Arkansas River Valley.

The Clara May Mine is about one half mile south of U.S. Highway 24, and about ten miles east of Buena Vista.

At the surface the pegmatite pod is 175 feet by 70 feet wide but is only about 30 feet thick. The walls are exposed in several places and the deposit is in quartz–mica schist. A cut 100 feet by 40 feet by 30 feet deep was used to mine the deposit. Feldspar reserves were estimated at about 1,000 tons in 1944.

Pegmatites of the Trout Creek area have cores of quartz, microcline, biotite, and muscovite with one to three intermediate zones containing quartz, potassium-feldspar, and albite. The intermediate zone may have niobium-terbium, (rare earth), or thorite minerals and be radioactive.

Minerals of the Clara May pegmatite were: quartz, microcline, altered plagioclase with garnets, euxenite, allanite, biotite, in books up to two feet across, and potassium-feldspar in the core area up to 14 feet across.

About 600 pounds of bismuth minerals were produced prior to 1944, but none were visible when Handley visited the mine in 1944. Euxenite was reported in masses up to 10 inches in size. Much of the euxenite, allanite and bismuth in local collections came from this deposit.

Minerals in the Yard pegmatite were: quartz, pink microcline, seritized plagioclase, biotite, muscovite, monazite, and euxenite.

REFERENCES

B-6, F-2, F-4, F-6, G-1, G-5, G-8, J-1, J-14, J-18, J-28, J-32, J-59, J-62, Q-46, R-18, S-27, S-50, S-52, S-56, S-102, S-108, S-135, S-138.

South Park Alma Mining District, and the Mosquito Range

The early gold seekers in South Park found placer deposits at Tarryall, Como, Fairplay, and Alma along the streams originating in the Mosquito Range. Silver was discovered on Mt. Lincoln at the Leadville dolomite contact with an intrusive porphyry sill in the summer of 1871. Quartzville and Montgomery were established and flourished to a small extent; however by 1886, the pockety nature of the ore and rich strikes at Leadville soon caused the towns to be nearly deserted. The Alma district, as the area became known, survived as a mining district due to the placers and the rich gold and base metal deposits of the London Fault and smaller replacement deposits (Fig. 5-17).

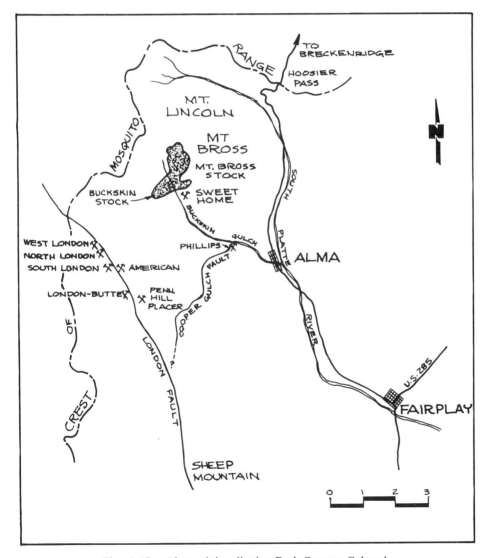

Fig. 5-17. Alma mining district, Park County, Colorado.

Mosquito Range formed the eastern flank of the giant Sawatch Anticline which formed during the Laramide orogeny as did South Park Basin. During late Eocene time South Park was beveled to a relatively flat surface. Oligocene eruptions from the Thirty-Nine Mile volcanic field and material from sources in the Sawatch Range clogged the streams coming off the anticline. Prior to this time streams from the Sawatch Anticline flowed across South Park and to the Denver Basin further east. These streams are preserved today as paleovalleys, segments of stream bed protected by volcanics of the Thirty-Nine Mile volcanics and clogged with ash flow tuff from the Sawatch Range. They are found in the Mosquito Range and in downfaulted blocks along the rift.

Age of the rift in the Upper Arkansas Valley is not known; the rift, however, was active in places 10,000 years ago and may still be active. The start of rifting and formation of the rift has been bracketed between the last Oligocene volcanism and before deposition of the Dry Union formation. Evidence of late Miocene fossils in the Dry Union formation and dating of interbedded volcanics indicate rifting had begun by 18 m.y.B.P. (Chapin).

Bruns and others bracket the rifting between 36 m.y.B.P. (age of ashflow tuff in paleovalleys) and later Miocene (12 to 15 m.y.B.P.).

The valley of what is now the Upper Arkansas River was still high on the east slope of the Sawatch Range until Neocene time. Rifting split the flank of the range and formed a narrow, elongated graben. This left the Mosquito Range isolated from the Sawatch Range. Uplift of the Mosquito Range east of the Mosquito Fault helped increase the distance between similar sediment beds in the rift and in the Mosquito Range. The Antero syncline developed along the inflection line of the Mosquito uplift in South Park at the time of rifting.

Paleozoic sediments that cap part of the Mosquito Range dip under South Park and they are found around the edges of the Sawatch Range dipping away from it. They have been eroded from the top of the Sawatch Range and from part of the Mosquito Range, but are thick in sections near the Gilman-Battle Mountain area on the southwest end of the Gore Range.

Antero Basin

In South Park, the Antero Basin is about ten miles east of the crest of the Mosquito Range, along the inflection line of this uplifted block. Oligocene volcanics of the Thirty-Nine Mile volcanic field are covered by as much as 700 feet of late Miocene–early Pliocene sediments of the Dry Union formation. In early Oligocene time streams flowing into South Park off of the Sawatch Range had steep gradients and deposited boulders 20 to 30 feet in diameter in the Antero Basin.

This is the fourth basin along the eastern inflection line of the rift that was proposed by Chapin to be included with the rift. These basins were formed at the same time that rifting occurred along the Rio Grande and Upper Arkansas River Valleys.

Phillips Mine

The Phillips Mine, one of the earliest mines in the Alma mining district, was discovered by Joseph Higgenbotham, (Buckskin Joe) in 1860. This was the start of quartz mining in the district and a small gold rush started. Buckskin Joe townsite had over 1,000 population within the first year. It was named county seat of Park County, one of the original nine counties of Colorado Territory.

By 1863, the ore had become so low in gold value that the town was almost deserted and the county seat was transferred to Fairplay. Production the first two years from the Phillips Mine was said to have been $300,000 in gold.

Mineralization occurred for about 2,000 feet along Buckskin Gulch at near-stream level where erosion had exposed it. The ore was a gossan over massive pyrite containing about $6 per ton in gold. Placer mining methods were used to recover the rich free gold in the oxidized ore.

The first opening on the deposit was an open pit 20 to 30 feet wide and 15 to 20 feet deep. Arrastras were used to grind the quartz–gossan ore. Chalcopyrite and barite also occurred in the deposit which was made up of lenticular layers.

Russia Mine

The Russia Mine was discovered in 1872. It is about 500 feet below the top of Mt. Lincoln in a south-southeast direction. Quartzville was the nearest camp and Dudley was the main office of the operating company with a small reverbatory furnace, assay office and sampling works.

With elevation of the mine at 13,700 feet the miners couldn't reach the mine from Quartzville until after 10:00 a.m. This made a hard and short workday, however, mining continued until 1893 when the Silver Panic closed the mine. The mine was reopened in 1923 and again during World War II and small productions were made.

Leadville dolomite was the host rock and the deposit was irregular. Sometimes the ore opened out into chambers (solution channels) as much as 25 feet high. This was a replacement deposit.

Although the ore was pockety, a nearby mine, the Sovereign, was said to have made $7,000 in thirty days with use of an inefficient mill. Some ore from the Russia, which was primarily galena and silver, was worth $500 per ton. Production from the mine was said to have been $2 million up to 1893.

The mine was reopened in the 1950s and worked intermittently since then; however, production has been small.

Moose Mine

The Moose Mine is on the northeast slope of Mt. Bross near the summit of the wall overlooking the Cameron Amphitheatre. It is at an elevation of 13,700 feet. This mine was found in 1871, however, the Dwight Mine, which is supposed to be an extension of the same vein, was found about three years earlier.

Leadville dolomite forms a spur between Cameron and Bross Amphitheatres and east of the Moose Mine it is pockmarked with prospects along the contact of the Lincoln porphyry and the Leadville dolomite.

Ore occurred in large irregular shaped masses, probably in large solution cavities in the Leadville dolomite. Much ore was mined from open cuts and there was little, if any, continuity between bunches of high grade silver ore. Lenticular replacement bodies were followed for over a half mile from the outcrop. Many small north-south mineralized faults offset the deposit and raises were required to keep in the ore. Sometimes prospect tunnels were driven close to ore masses and they were not discovered until later by further prospecting. Some chambers were 20 feet high and stood well without timbering.

Horses were used to haul the ore up the inclined shaft. Much sorting and screening of the ore was done underground to avoid the bad weather at the surface. Jack trains (strings of pack animals) were loaded in these stopes before taking the ore to Alma. Ice crystals lined the walls and back of the stopes. Some individual crystals were up to 3½ inches in diameter.

Shipping ore varied from 100 to 700 ounces silver per ton. A single breast of ore averaging 700 ounces of silver per ton had 15 pairs of miners double jacking at the same time. Production to 1879 was about $1 million, mostly in silver. The main mineral was argentite (acanthite). The Moose Mine has been credited with a total production of $5 million, which makes it one of the top producing mines of the Alma district.

A fault cut off all mineralization and the Silver Panic of 1893 evidently closed most of the mines in the Alma district. In 1911, the mine was reopened and exploration work resulted in finding the ore horizon on the other side of the fault. Evidently the Bonanza ore was gone. The mine produced some ore in 1917, but probably not a significant amount. It was reopened during World War II but production was probably small. The exact amount is unknown.

In the Moose Mine, the ore was galena, argentite and chalcopyrite with their oxidation products in the upper part of the mine. Barite and selenite were gangue minerals and rhodochrosite occurred, probably in the vein ores.

On Mount Bross, an unnamed property was reported to have rhodochrosite veinlets cutting a two foot vein of limonite. The rhodochrosite occurred 300 feet from the portal and the vein was lost by faulting 200 feet further along the strike according to Patton.

London Fault and London Mine

At the head of Mosquito Gulch and south through Horseshoe and Sacramento Gulches, Paleozoic sedimentary rocks with intruded prophyry sills have been tightly folded into an asymmetrical anticlinal structure. The west limb of this structure is steep and has been cut by the London Fault zone, whose apparent vertical displacement is about 3,000 feet (Fig. 5-18).

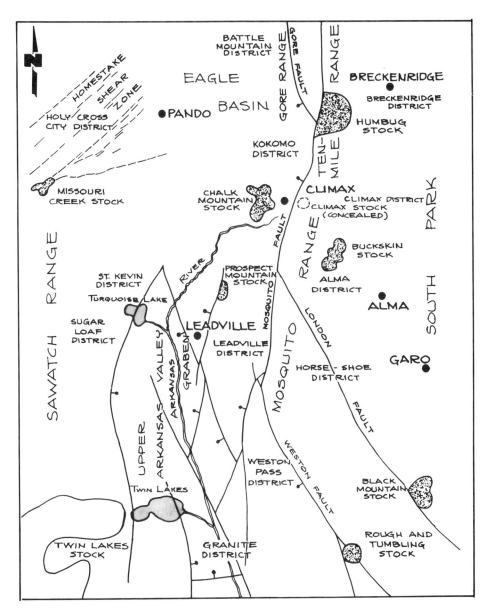

Fig. 5–18. Structural features of central Colorado. Adapted from U.S.G.S. P.P. 726–C, 1972.

On the west side of the Mosquito Range, about half way between Evans Gulch and Climax and north of Mosquito Peak, the London Fault junctions the Mosquito Fault. From this junction it crosses the Mosquito Range in a southeast direction. The London Fault crosses London Mountain about 700 feet from the summit and continues diagonally across the east flank of the Mosquito Range onto the plains of South Park and toward Black Mountain. It is crossed and offset by several short faults and its course is marked in South Park by several intrusive bodies.

The London Fault is a reverse fault and one of the major faults of central

Colorado. Parallel mineral veins developed within the London Fault zone on London Mountain. The hanging wall vein had small replacement deposits in favorable beds with lead-zinc mineralization typical of the Leadville and Alma districts. On the footwall side of the fault a gold-quartz vein was developed. London Mountain divides the head of Mosquito Gulch into two drainages.

London Mine

The London Mine is on London Mountain between two drainages.

An old wagon road goes up the north fork of Mosquito Gulch, passes through a notch between London Mountain and the crest of the Mosquito Range, climbs to the crest at Mosquito Pass and continues downhill to Leadville.

The London Mine was discovered in 1875 by following rich float, which had been found in the area for about two years, before the source uphill was found. Mining was carried on continuously from 1875 to 1944 with few interruptions. Production from 1895 to 1910, after high mining, milling, hauling, and reduction costs were taken out, was over $2 million. Gross production from 1908 to 1931 was $8 million.

Emmons found the property developed by two short tunnels. The lower of the two had been driven into debris containing large blocks of rock cemented by permafrost that had to be blasted.

Ore in the upper tunnel was in the top of a white limestone bed. Parallel veins were about 40 feet across. One was vertical, about four feet wide, and carried values in lead, copper, and gold. The second vein was two feet wide and carried gold in country rock and quartz.

Emmons called attention to a powerful and strongly built windmill that had been constructed as a power source. The wind flattened it the first winter.

By 1882, there were 3,000 feet of levels and raises and five big stopes working. A railroad was built from London Junction, below Alma, to the mill and loading bins were constructed in 1881 and 1882. It was seven miles from London Junction to the mill.

A second stamp mill was constructed at London Junction in 1883 and in seven months produced $124,000 in bullion and 240 tons of concentrates and 15 cars of high grade ore were shipped to the Black Hawk smelter and to the Denver smelter. Litigation closed the mine briefly in 1884 after which the London Mining Company was formed. This company owned four miles along the London vein system. The first adit into the vein was known as the North London. Another adit, the South London, was started to crosscut the vein in 1892. When no vein was cut, a branch drift was driven and it did cut the vein. The first one had hit a place where the vein was pinched and had not been mineralized. Between 1892 and 1912, ore bodies in the area between the North and South London levels were worked. After 1912, a large block of ground above this area was worked. In 1912 another crosscut tunnel had been driven 1,600 feet and had 400 feet to go to cut the vein.

During World War II all gold mines were closed to divert supplies and equipment to strategic mineral production and so the machinery was sold and the mine closed in 1944.

In the London Mine, pyrite, sphalerite, galena, tennantite, argentite, and chalcopyrite occurred in varying proportions in the hanging wall vein, but the main value was in free gold which occurred in slightly glassy milk quartz in the footwall vein. Narrow veinlets of calcite cut the quartz and the sulfides. Free gold occurred in the sulfides to a lesser extent. Accessory minerals were sericite, and small amounts of apatite, barite and manganiferous ankerite. Luzonite (a dimorph with enargite) was reported from the district but was not reported from the London Mine.

American Mine

A small block of vein, completely enclosed by London Mine property, was found and filed on in 1931. This was the American Mine and it was credited with $4.5 million in production during the relatively short time it was worked.

About half the production came from a gold-bearing quartz vein and the other half came from a replacement deposit in limestone that contained lead, zinc, silver and gold. A 5,000 foot aerial tramway connected the mine to the Record (or American) Mill. This mine was allowed to work during World War II because of the lead, zinc, and silver. By the end of the war, or shortly thereafter, the ore was all worked out as mining could only follow the veins downdip to the London Mine lines.

Most mining districts have at least one occurrence of valuable mineral ground that was improperly staked or overlooked, only to be claimed by someone else. They are not always as valuable as the American Mine turned out to be.

Sweet Home Mine

(Home Sweet Home Mine) In the upper part of Buckskin Gulch in the Red Amphitheatre area is the Sweet Home Mine, Patent No. 106. The old patent number suggests its early discovery, probably in early 1872. Emmons, in 1886, records the mine as having been worked but idle at the time of his visit. It was of interest because of the variety of minerals it produced.

Mines in this area are close to the Buckskin Gulch stock and seem to have higher temperature minerals than other mines in the Alma district. Rhodochrosite, tetrahedrite-tennantite, and hubnerite, minerals not generally found in the lead–zinc–silver mines of the area occur. Porphyry associated with the mineralization was found by Emmons to have iron oxide containing arsenic and antimony. The Moose and Russia Mines are also included in this group because the stock is thought to be closer to the surface in their respective areas. Both the Moose and Russia Mines had rhodochrosite in their ore.

Emmons in his famous Mon. 12 spoke of pink and blue fluorite, cuprite, jamesonite, melanterite, rhodochrosite, and zinkenite as among the many minerals found in this mine.

Patton says the Home Sweet Home, Tanner Boy, Queen Mary, Enterprise and other veins in upper Buckskin Gulch contain argentiferous galena, rhodochrosite and often, sphalerite. Gold and fluorite may also be present.

Production of ore has been sparse and the mine was not active the first part of the war years. Shipments were made in 1945 to the Resurrection Mill at Leadville and the mine was worked in 1948, 1955, 1960 and again in 1963.

Most of the interest in this mine was from rhodochrosite mineral specimens. Possibly some of the finest rhodochrosite specimens in the world came from this mine in 1965. It has been mined for specimens intermittently since that time.

The Encyclopedia of Minerals by Roberts, Rapp and Weber, p. 65, shows a superb rhodochrosite with hubnerite from the Sweet Home Mine, Park County, Colorado.

Kosnar and Miller show a specimen of rhodochrosite on needle quartz from the Sweet Home Mine, Alma, Park County, Colorado.

Rhodochrosite from the Sweet Home Mine is found in numerous famous mineral collections. Bancroft classes a specimen of rhodochrosite on needle quartz (from Alma, Park County, Colorado) as one of the world's finest minerals. This specimen was without a doubt from the Sweet Home Mine.

Tanner Boy Mine

The Tanner Boy Mine across the gulch south of the Sweet Home Mine has also produced deep red rhodochrosite. Emmons said this rhodochrosite occurred in well defined rhombic crystals, interchangeable with calcite.

Penn Hill Placer

Pennsylvania Hill is east of Mt. Evans, on the crest of the Mosquito Range, south of Mosquito Gulch, and north of Sacramento Gulch. London Hill is to the northwest. Emmons referred to the top part of Baldhead and described the deposits capping it as moraine material from the ancient Mosquito glacier. Ball Hill is located just east of the Penn Hill placer.

Capps showed the Pleistocene glaciers as joining between Mt. Evans and Pennsylvania Hill and flowing down both Mosquito Gulch to the north and Sacramento Gulch to the south. Ice flowed between London and Pennsylvania Hills but not over Pennsylvania Hill.

This eluvial placer deposit on Pennsylvania Hill is well above timberline and mostly above 12,000 feet in altitude. Work is carried on during a short season, May to September, with late spring and early winter storms limiting the season even more. The gold-bearing material which is in permafrost is ripped with a large bulldozer and allowed to thaw. It is then sluiced in the age-old method of separating the waste from the heavy fraction which is then cleaned and the gold recovered.

The gold is angular, coarse and has not traveled far. Although the upper limit of the deposit is known, the source has not been found. Gold has not been concentrated on bedrock as in a stream deposit but is mixed throughout the deposit. Nuggets over an ounce have been found.

In 1938, H.W.C. Prommel, a placer expert who had sampled platinum placers in Russia and many various types of placer deposits worldwide, sampled the Penn Hill placers. A large nugget was found that weighed nearly a pound. It was displayed in the bank window in Fairplay for a brief period; however, with only an 1/8 inch of old and brittle glass between it and potential unauthorized removal, it did not stay long before it was removed to a safer place.

The Penn Hill placer has been seasonally worked for a long time and is still worked in the short summer season. Production is unknown.

During the early 1930s, as many as several hundred men worked the placers of the Alma area. Some made enough to pay expenses and some did not.

Minerals of the Alma district are: alabandite, anglesite, anhydrite, argentite, azurite, barite, beegerite, (a mixture) bornite, calcite, cerussite, chalcanthite, chalcopyrite, chlorargyrite, chromite, copper, cuprite, dolomite, embolite, enargite, fluorite, gadolinite, galena, gold, gypsum, hematite, hubnerite, jamesonite, kaolinite, limonite, magnetite, malachite, melanterite, mimetite, orthoclase, proustite, psilomelane, pyrargyrite, pyrite, pyrolusite, pyromorphite, quartz, rhodochrosite, serpentine, selenite, siderite, silver, stephanite, stibnite, tennantite, tetrahedrite, and zinkenite.

Hartsel Barite Area

Blue barite occurs in a limestone unit of the Maroon formation near Hartsel, Park County. This limestone unit overlaps Pce granite about a mile to the east toward Hartsel and is interpreted as filling in an old Pce structural basin. Soil in the area is red and could be from the red beds of the Maroon formation, which has been removed by erosion, or from residual weathering of the limestone.

Adams describes the deposit as four miles southwest of Hartsel. A gravel road turns west from Colorado Highway 9 to Guffey and goes into the Agate Creek drainage. Just past the first hills to the right of this road is the deposit which was staked in 1932. The work done on the claims since that time has been done mostly for mineral specimens.

Barite occurs in vertical veins a foot or two thick that cuts across the bedding. It is also in layers six inches to three feet thick. No sulfides occur with the barite which was bluest where exposed to the sun.

Barite crystals are found as singles but more often in clusters, some quite large. Howland gives the dimensions of a crystal 1 1/2 inches along the "C" axis and 5 inches along the "D" axis.

Source of the barite is not known and the color has not been explained. Laboratory tests have shown that colorless barite will change to blue from exposure to radiation. Sunshine in a high altitude could have added to the color of the exposed crystals; however, those found underground are also blue, but not quite as deep blue. Although the hot springs at Hartsel are quite radioactive they contain no barite and this possible source of radiation is discredited.

The limestone in which the crystals are found is at a horizon just below the beds in which the uranium deposits at Garo occur. A source of the radiation could be similar radioactive beds which were eroded from over the limestone. The barite could have been leached from Maroon shales containing gypsum, which acted as a precipitating agent and deposited the barite in the structural basin. This origin is much preferred to other possibilities.

A trachyte body of Oligocene age is present in the area and the possible source could have been solutions rising from the magma chamber. No minerals usually associated with this type of deposit are present.

Shirley May Deposit

About nine miles south of Fairplay, on Colorado Highway 9, and a half mile south of Garo, in the center of South Park, is the Shirley May Uranium Mine. The deposit is on the northeast flank of the Garo Anticline where north to northeast trending faults have displaced sedimentary beds of the Maroon formation of Permian age as much as 1,000 feet horizontally. The local structure is probably due to Tertiary deformation and localization of the uranium deposit is confined to the faults and adjacent porous sandstones.

Mineralization occurs in three porous sandstone beds as disseminations, cementing material and fracture filling.

By 1953, the mine had produced 272 tons of ore, mostly from bed No. 1, which is 50 to 150 feet stratigraphically above the other ore bearing horizons, with an average grade of 0.16 percent uranium and 0.72 percent vanadium. In 1952, a shipment of 24 tons of ore containing 5 percent copper was made.

At the Shirley May deposit commercial uranium minerals are carnotite and tyuyamunite; other minerals of the deposit are: volborthite, calciovolborthite, azurite, malachite, chalcocite, covellite and complex vanadium oxides. Gangue minerals are calcite, magnetite, and hematite (See Fig. 5–18).

REFERENCES

A–5 Ridge, (Tweto), (Sec. 27), (Tweto), (Sec. 32), B–3, C–1, C–13, D–1, (Burbank), (Traver), G–5, G–6, G–8, G–11, H–4, J–1, J–5, J–16, J–48, J–49, J–50, J–55, J–56, J–63, K–3, K–18, L–1, 1948, 1950, 1952, 1955, 1960, 1963, N–18, P–7, James, (Chapin), S–18, S–31, S–52, S–107, and S–136.

LEADVILLE MINING DISTRICT
(NORTH END OF UPPER ARKANSAS GRABEN)

The boundary of the Leadville mining district is informally considered to be that area east of the Arkansas River between Iowa Gulch and Evans Gulch and west of the crest of the Mosquito Range, in Lake County. The district is east of the Sawatch Range (Fig. 5–19).

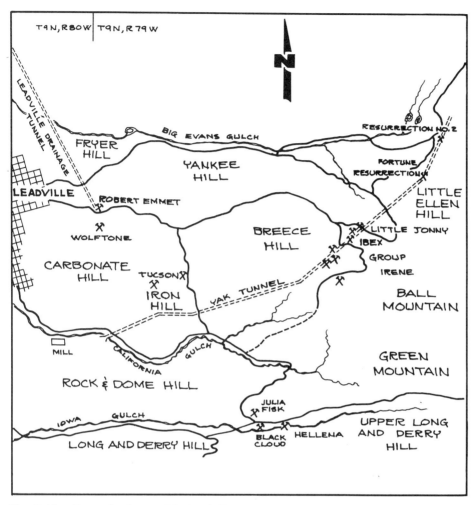

Fig. 5-19. Generalized map of the Leadville mining district showing location of a selected few mines. Adapted from U.S. Bu. M. , I.C. 8464, 1970.

Fremont and his party explored the upper part of the Arkansas River in 1845, coming into the valley from South Park by way of Trout Creek and leaving to the north over Utah Pass, now called Tennessee Pass. The pass between the East Fork of the Arkansas River and Tenmile Creek was named for Fremont.

Placer gold was discovered on Tarryall Creek in South Park in 1859 and prospecting parties crossed into the Arkansas Valley by way of Trout Creek in the spring of 1860. Gold was found where Cache Creek enters the Arkansas River and the town of Granite was established.

S. B. Kellogg and H.A.W. Tabor, later to become one of Leadville's "Silver Kings," were with the first group of prospectors who hand-sawed lumber from local timber and constructed sluice boxes. On April 26, 1860, they were prospecting lower California Gulch when a group of men who had just located 14 claims came down the gulch. Gold had been reported in the lower part of California Gulch in 1859.

Tabor and Kellogg located claims near what was to become Oro City and in sixty days they were said to have recovered $75,000 in gold. A gold nugget weighing 28 ounces was later recovered from the California Gulch placers.

Oro City was established and by the end of 1860 there were 5,000 people in the gulch; in 1861 the population increased to 10,000. A ditch was constructed to bring much needed water from Evans Gulch and placer mining increased. Quantities of heavy rock and black sand were troublesome. This material was later determined to be cerussite containing silver stained with iron and manganese oxides. By 1867, the placers were exhausted and most of the people were gone.

A search for gold in place resulted in the discovery of lode mines on Printer Boy Hill and the Printer Boy, Lower Printer Boy, Five-Twenty and other mines were opened. A stamp mill operated on ore from these mines until 1877.

A. B. Wood identified the heavy rock and black sand and confirmed his finding with assays in 1874. He waited until the early placer claims under the early mining camp laws terminated in 1875 and filed claims under the U.S. Mining Laws on almost a mile of black outcrops from which he had traced the black sand.

These were the replacement ore beds in the Leadville limestone, the blue lime of the miners, which at porphyry contacts contained the Bonanza ore that made Leadville world famous as a mining district. Carbonate ore was first mined in place from the Rock Tunnel on Dome Hill in 1874 and later from the Iron and the Bull's Eye claims in 1876 (Fig. 5-20).

Assays of as high as 800 ounces of silver per ton were recorded and the true value of the carbonate ore was established when an agent of a refinery in St. Louis, Missouri, shipped a small lot to his company.

That fall, a lot of between 200 tons and 300 tons of high grade carbonate ore was hauled by wagon to a Colorado Springs smelter. Although the freight charge was high, a profit was made because lead was selling at 7 cents a pound.

Prospecting for carbonate ore brought another population influx to the district and the 1877 population of about 200 had jumped to 15,000 people by 1879. There were 30 mines producing from 2 1/2 to 150 tons of carbonate ore per day. Sixteen smelters had been built and some had already become obsolete. Two railroads served the district by 1883 and had made the long strings of freight and ore wagons traveling Weston Pass a part of history.

Leadville was well established and had over 28 miles of streets, some of which were lighted by gaslight. Schools, churches, and even opera houses were built. The Leadville Trotting and Running Association, with a half mile race track and good buildings, attested to the affluence of the 1885 population.

Production of metals from 1877 to 1884 was 103,022 ounces of gold, 51,102,396 ounces of silver, and 306,698 tons of lead, the value of which was in excess of $95 million.

In 1886, the Yak Tunnel was started to drain most of the workings above it and for transportation of ore. This tunnel was worked intermittently until 1898, but was then driven continuously to completion by 1910 with a total length of 23,800 feet. Many laterals were also driven to drain and to develop the mines above the tunnel.

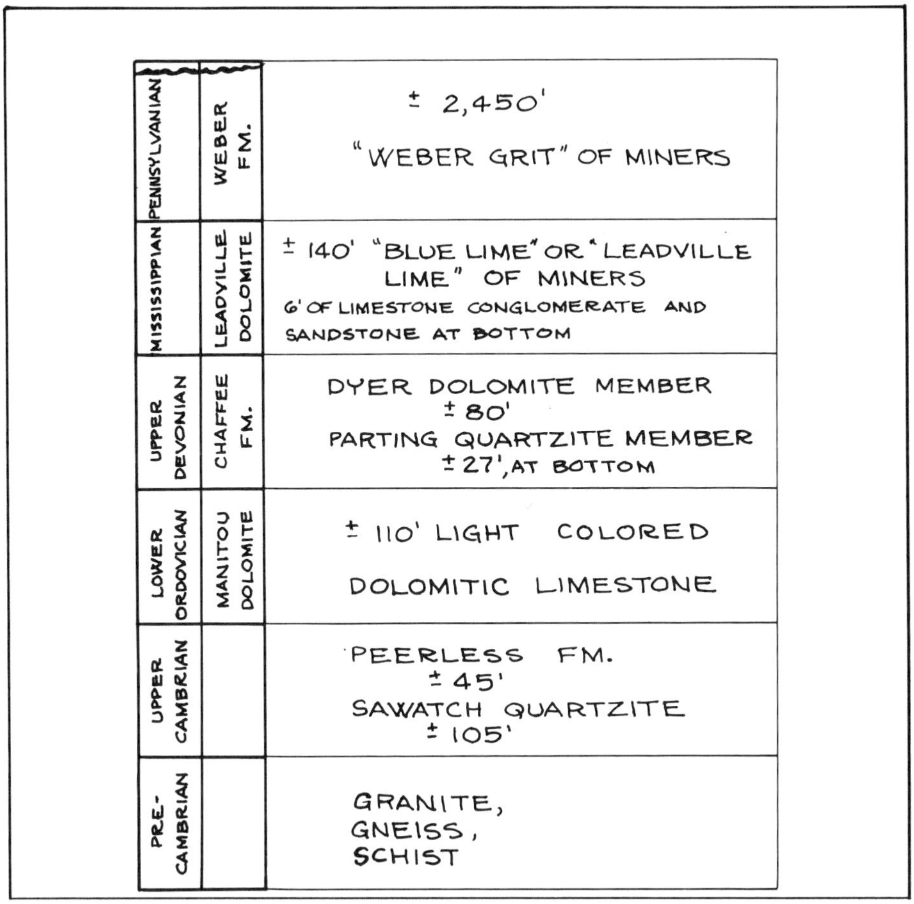

PENNSYLVANIAN	WEBER FM.	± 2,450' "WEBER GRIT" OF MINERS
MISSISSIPPIAN	LEADVILLE DOLOMITE	± 140' "BLUE LIME" OR "LEADVILLE LIME" OF MINERS — 6' OF LIMESTONE CONGLOMERATE AND SANDSTONE AT BOTTOM
UPPER DEVONIAN	CHAFFEE FM.	DYER DOLOMITE MEMBER ± 80' — PARTING QUARTZITE MEMBER ± 27', AT BOTTOM
LOWER ORDOVICIAN	MANITOU DOLOMITE	± 110' LIGHT COLORED DOLOMITIC LIMESTONE
UPPER CAMBRIAN		PEERLESS FM. ± 45' — SAWATCH QUARTZITE ± 105'
PRE-CAMBRIAN		GRANITE, GNEISS, SCHIST

Fig. 5-20. Generalized stratigraphic section at Leadville, Colorado. These formations also occur in the Battle Mountain-Gilman district, Alma district, Monarch-Taylor Gulch district and the upper end of the San Luis Valley. In general around the flanks of the Sawatch Range where exposed by uplift. Local variations in composition and thickness of beds are common. Adapted from U.S.G.S. P.P. 235, 1953.

Large deposits of copper ore were found in the Henrietta and Maid of Erin Mines in 1890. Value of copper produced in 1891 was $220,000, the first important copper production to come from the district which was deficient in copper. Total silver, lead, and copper produced from these mines was $2.3 million in 1891.

Mines on Breece Hill, including the Little Jonny Mine, were producing gold by 1891. In 1892, value of gold produced was $50,000 with combined gold and silver valued at $2.2 million.

Manganese–iron and manganese–silver ores were produced from 1890 to 1892. Bismuth ore was shipped from Leadville in 1899 and zinc ore and concentrates (sulfide) was shipped to Belgium from 1899 to 1903.

By the early 1890s, the Bonanza silver ores were becoming depleted and the Silver Panic of 1893 closed most of the silver mines. Oxidized zinc ores were discovered in 1910, starting a round of new activity.

Diversification into other than silver ores helped to keep the district going until World War I, when demand for all metals brought renewed activity. This was the pattern of slump and boom that brought Leadville up to World War II.

Below the Yak Tunnel, especially in the Downtown Area, water and high pumping costs closed mine after mine. A tunnel from Malta to drain the district was proposed as early as 1892, but was never driven. Other tunnels were proposed, however, the Canterbury Tunnel on Canterbury Hill was the only one actually started. It was started in 1922 and driven 4,000 feet as a community project.

In 1943, the Federal government, through a combination of agencies, proposed a 2½ mile tunnel to drain the district and open large deposits of known lead, zinc, and manganese ores for production. An appropriation of $1.4 million was authorized to construct 17,300 feet of drainage tunnels and laterals, including a 6,000 foot lateral under the Downtown Area. Two periods of activity on this tunnel resulted in the main heading being driven 11,299 feet to the Mikado Shaft.

The first period of activity advanced the tunnel only 6,601 feet because of heavy ground (weight of broken and unstable rock overhead) and water in buried moraines in the Pendry Fault area. Inflows of loose material and water necessitated the driving of a bypass tunnel starting at 1,681 feet.

The main heading had been driven to 2,126 feet when a large inflow of water and mud forced the miners out of the tunnel. After it was cleaned out, another mud rush and a large volume of water collapsed the heading. A mucking machine, locomotive, and four loaded ore cars were rolled 400 feet down the tunnel where they dammed the flow of loose material. Fortunately, no men were lost. A bulkhead was then constructed at 1,795 feet and the tunnel continued with the bypass. This was typical of the conditions found in the tunnel and the cost soared with small headway.

Mining in the district became active again in 1949 because of metal shortages in the Korean War. Large sulfide bodies were discovered by diamond drilling in the Resurrection and Eclipse Mines and in the Irene Shaft. Work was started on the Hayden Shaft and other Fryer Hill Mines where ore bodies were discovered. The Robert Emmet Shaft was rehabilitated and mining continued after the drainage tunnel was completed. The Helena Shaft and Resurrection No. 2 Shafts were also producing ore. By 1948, the decline in base metal prices slowed mining activity in the district and work on the drainage tunnel stopped in 1952. Mining activity was almost at a standstill by 1957. Rising metal prices started a renewed activity in the district and in 1965 the Irene Shaft was dewatered to the 1,750 foot level. Massive sulfide bodies were mined until 1969 in a newly discovered block of down-faulted ore and mining on this ore is continuing through the Black Cloud Shaft. The Hilltop mineral deposit and veins common to Park and Lake Counties are being worked through the Sherman Tunnel. Leadville now serves as a base of support for the Climax Molybdenum Mine, on Fremont Pass, and the old mining camp has stabilized again.

Production of gold, silver, copper, lead, and zinc in the Leadville mining district was valued at over $500 million by 1954. Up to 1939, and with little or no production since then 3.5 million long tons of manganiferous ore was produced. During World War II, several large dumps were milled for their lead, zinc, and silver content but the manganese was not recovered. Iron ore and bismuth were also produced from the Leadville area. Value of these minerals was in addition to the above $500 million; however, their total value is unknown.

Scraps Picked From the Old Leadville Dumps

Four of the eight operating smelters in the Leadville mining district in 1880 produced over a million ounces of silver and one of the eight smelters produced over two million ounces of silver. There were sixteen smelters built by this date but they were not all active as some had already become obsolete. This was largely due to the rapid change of the ores in depth and to inherent inefficiencies of the smelters. The oldest smelter was at Malta at the junction of California Gulch and the Arkansas River. It was built in 1875 to process ore from the Homestake Mine, in the Homestake district, which is over Tennessee Pass in the Homestake Creek drainage.

Production of the Leadville smelters in 1879–80 was given in the 1880 census as 28,000 tons of lead; 8,000,000 ounces of silver; and 3,800,000 ounces of gold. Average price paid for a unit of 20 pounds of lead was $0.25.

Bullion and lead bullion, containing the precious metals, were shipped to the Denver Mint or East for refining.

Average charges of feed for the smelters was 100 parts of ore to 10.88 parts of dolomite, 8.3 parts of hematite, and 32.83 parts of fuel. For each 100 parts of this smelter charge, 24.03 parts of fuel to melt it were required. This contained 1.33 parts of charcoal to 1.00 part of coke.

Coke was shipped by rail from El Moro, near Trinidad, Colorado, or from Como, in South Park. The charcoal was made at Malta from local forest. Hematite came from the Breece Iron Mine, on Breece Hill, and also from the Silver Wave Mine, located in that area. Dolomite was from the Montgomery quarry on Iron Hill.

A large charcoal industry was carried on at Malta to satisfy the demand for charcoal. Burning pits 40 by 12 by 15 feet were excavated in the ground and spruce logs, cut to four foot lengths, were stacked in them. They were set afire and when burning sufficiently were covered with earth and allowed to smolder for about two weeks. Then the charcoal was recovered.

Beehive kilns were also used; they were 21 to 22 feet high and were capable of producing about nine tons of charcoal each in about ten days. Between timber for the mines, the charcoal industry, and domestic firewood, it is little wonder the nearby forest was depleted (Fig. 5–21).

An interesting aspect of the early ore and its smelting was that the rich silver halide ore was responsible for the loss of lead in volatile compounds of chlorine, bromine and iodine. This material was, to some extent, collected in the flue dust and an assay from material collected in dust chambers at eight smelters showed the halide content to have 82.45 percent chlorine, 16.83 per-

Fig. 5–21.   Beehive charcoal kiln at Red Cliff, Battle Mountain area, Colorado. W.H.

cent bromine, and 0.72 percent iodine. Some silver was also lost and assays as high as 36 ounces per ton were obtained from the flue dust.

In the Leadville blast furnaces, it was found that nickel concentrated in the speises (metallic arsenides and antimonides) and cobalt concentrated in the skimmings of the lead pots. Also found in the smelter were the products: molybdenum, titanium, bismuth, cadmium, copper, and tin.

Bonanza ores of the early mining days greatly influenced the development of areas. Several factors contributed to the rapid growth of Leadville as one of the greatest mining districts in the world. First was the occurrences of large bodies of Bonanza-grade replacement ore at or near the surface; second was the repetition of the ore not only in at least two horizons but the repetition of contact zones near the surface. This later condition was caused by a series of step-fault blocks that descended from the crest of the Mosquito Range through the district like a giant staircase. The third, but not the least factor, was the ease with which the ore was smelted.

The Bonanza ore occurred principally at the contact of the Leadville limestone with intruded porphyry sills. The first contact was on top of this blue lime and a contact with a white porphyry sill. The second contact was at the base of this limestone in contact with a gray porphyry sill. The third contact was with white limestone, Manitou dolomite, and the lower quartzite, the Sawatch quartzite.

After the first claims were staked on outcrops, it was only a matter of tracing the blue lime. When the work revealed the bedding and its dip, shafts were sunk ahead of the adits to intersect them. Discoveries came at a rapid pace with so many prospectors in such a small area.

Not all discoveries were made by such carefully laid plans. The famous ore bodies of Fryer Hill were discovered by two prospectors who had been grubstaked by H.A.W. Tabor. Included in their provisions was a jug of whiskey which the men consumed during the course of the investigation not far from town. It seemed a good place to dig was right on the spot where they were. At 25 to 30 feet, they struck the ore body of the afterwards famous Little Pittsburg Mine. The ore body was up to 90 feet thick and 100 feet to 150 feet wide and of Bonanza grade. As the overburden is 100 feet thick or more over the rest of Fryer Hill and this was the only place that the blue lime was within such a short distance of the surface, it could only have been the whiskey. This mine was the real start of Tabor's rise to Silver King status.

Bonanza ore was classed as either hard or sand (soft) carbonate ore. The sand carbonate filled pockets of what was probably an old karst surface in the Leadville limestone and it was composed of argentiferous-cerussite, anglesite, relic galena, and silver combined with chlorine, bromine, and iodine in varying amounts. The ore could be shoveled up as it had the texture of sand. Hard carbonate ore was composed of the same minerals cemented into solid rock. One block of cerussite, weighing several hundred pounds, was found in the Chrysolite Mine. It was nearly transparent.

An analysis of ore from the Adelaide Mine on North Iron Hill showed it to be 85.605 percent cerussite, 9.748 percent pyromorphite, and 4.647 percent carbonates, silicates and oxides.

Amie Mine produced a special lot of ore that contained 1,189.7 ounces of silver per ton and was 31.7 percent lead. One of the most sought after ores was argentiferous galena. Lead occurred as anglesite and pyromorphite as well as litharge or minium. Silver occurred as a chlorobromide or as a chloro-iodide and proportions were not constant.

Specimens of galena were found that had 1,200 ounces of silver per ton. In the Adelaide Mine masses of white sand carbonate contained 95 percent cerussite but were deficient in silver. In the Ward Shaft on the same property red oxide, cuprite and native copper were found. Copper was also found in the Fortune Mine and the Little Jonny Mine, among others, on Breece Hill.

On the line between the Catalpa and Evening Star Mines a carbonate ore body 40 feet thick was found. It extended into both mines.

An ore body in the Vulture No. 1 and Eaton Shafts had a single transparent mass of chloride which weighed several hundred pounds. This was also described as horn silver. We call it chlorargyrite today. The Chrysolite Mine ore body averaged 60 feet to 80 feet thick and the ore bed in the Little Chief extended 90 feet vertically. The iron ore body in this mine varied from six feet to 90 feet.

Ore varied considerably from mine to mine. In the Robert E. Lee, one of the greatest silver producers in the district, the ore was relatively free of lead. The gangue in this mine was silica and clay with enough iron oxide to make it a bright red. There was no manganese oxide and the principal mineral was silver chloride.

In the Little Pittsburg Mine, at the No. 1 shaft, the vein material was hydrated iron and manganese oxides, small irregular masses of barite, and a fine, blue, dolomite sand. The ore minerals were argentiferous galena, cerussite, chloride of silver, (with varying amounts of bromine and iodine), anglesite, pyromorphite, and wulfenite.

Between Ball Mountain and the Weston Fault in the Highland Chief Mine, near the present day Sherman Tunnel, the Leadville limestone was almost entirely replaced by granular, porous quartz impregnated with impure silver chloride, and minor copper carbonates. Red hematite mixed with magnetite occurred in two ore bodies nearly 30 feet thick in the Breece Iron Mine. The ore was at a contact of white and gray porphyry.

Ore minerals on Iron Hill were argentiferous galena, cerussite, anglesite, silver chloride, pyromorphite, minium, sphalerite, calamine (hemimorphite), sulfur, and native silver.

In March, 1880, the *Engineering and Mining Journal* gave an assay of 1,000 tons of Leadville ore representing every producing mine in the district. Percentages agreed with the average smelter charges used in the district of 23 percent lead, 18 percent iron, 22.5 percent silica, and 90.5 ounces of silver per ton. Assays of high-silver lots of ore at the Harrison Reduction Works in 1880 from the Little Pittsburg Mine gave results of 266 ounces of silver per ton and on ore from the Carbonate Mine 218 ounces of silver per ton.

A white sand resembling decomposed porphyry, from the Climax Mine (Leadville) assayed 1,600 ounces of silver per ton and gave mill runs of 300 ounces of silver per ton.

Carbonate ore from three mines averaged 24.77 percent lead oxide, 0.31 percent silver, and a trace of gold. The highest assay for gold from a lot from the Colorado Prince Mine was 17.70 ounces per ton and on ore from the Ready Cash Mine 9.20 ounces per ton.

Before 1910, rich zinc carbonate ore bodies had been bypassed and even thrown over the dumps as useless. In 1909, W. E. Jones found a large body of zinc carbonate ore in the Robert E. Lee Mine and made shipments from it. The dump of the Penrose Mine was shipped for its zinc carbonate, but failed to show a profit. However, in 1910, high grade zinc ore reported to be calamine (hemimorphite) was shipped from the Hayden Shaft of the May Queen Mine.

A search of the old workings in the Wolftone Mine disclosed the largest bodies found in the district. Zinc silicate and zinc carbonate in varying amounts were found throughout the old workings and the oxidized zinc industry of Leadville was founded.

In the early days of the lead smelters, zinc was avoided as it brought penalties. However, markets for zinc ores existed and the minerals were ignored simply because they were not recognized. There were four varieties of zinc deposits:

1. Gray carbonate ore which resembled the limestone.
2. Reddish-brown to brown carbonate ore with silicate pockets. This resembled the oxidized ores but contained no silver, gold or lead.
3. Brownish-black to black carbonate oxide ore which resembled the manganese ore.
4. White to brown, dense silicate ore (zinciferous clay or Chinese talc of the miners).

Numbers 2 and 3 of the above were the most common.

Sulfide ore deposits were the ores mined after the oxidized ores were depleted. They contained pyrite, galena and sphalerite with little silver and generally only trace amounts of gold. Production in the Leadville district in this century has been principally from the sulfide ore bodies.

A layer of ore in the Robert E. Lee Mine consisted of barite impregnated with chlorargyrite. Rich ore sometimes consisted of chert or siliceous iron whose joints and cracks were lined with chlorargyrite.

East of Yankee Hill, in the Great Hope Mine, five to six feet of galena passed through quartzite impregnated with gold and a shipment of 1 1/2 tons of this material yielded 31 ounces of gold per ton.

In the Printer Boy Mine, gold occurred in both pyrite and galena. A specimen of galena crystals connected by a filament of wire gold was the pride and showpiece of the mine. Leaf gold was found in cerussite in the oxidized ore.

Cerussite pseudomorphs of cubic galena were found in the mines of Fryer Hill and sulfate of baryta (barite) was a gangue mineral.

On the eighth level of the North Incline fine, silky, white crystals of hemimorphite were found in joint planes in the limestone.

Descloizite was found in the Evening Star, Aetna, and Morning Star Mines.

Native sulfur was found in a mass two feet in diameter in the North Incline. Pyromorphite and wulfenite were minerals found in the Little Chief Mine. Anglesite and chlorargyrite were common to most mines. The Florence Mine produced minerals of bismuth and silicates of lead in reddish crystals.

An ore deposit in the Evening Star Mine was in a porphyry breccia and was largely pyromorphite and cerussite with some galena.

In the Carbonate Incline the ore body was said to be about 15 feet high and spreading out northward in a thin and continuous sheet of sand carbonates.

On the hill above the Fortune Shaft, in Evans Gulch, a body of slightly decomposed Lincoln porphyry outcrops and extends under a light organic soil covering. Bipyramidal quartz crystals weather out and have been found along the drainage ditches of old roads in the area. No quartz crystals with prism planes were found (Fig. 5–22).

Emmons says the Lincoln porphyry has orthoclase crystals, frequently Carlsbad twins, up to two inches in length, fresh and glassy, so as to resemble sanidine; inclusions of biotite are common. Plagioclase crystals are abundant and are usually white. Quartz shows development of pyramidal planes added. He says that on a ridge east of Hoosier Pass, outcrops of a porphyry sheet have quartz crystals showing both pyramid and prism planes.

Matildite occurs in the Yak Tunnel and with hessite in the Tucson Shaft. Native arsenic, mimetite, bismuthinite and hetaerolite were reported in the Wolftone Mine.

Lindgren found the fine-grained siderite replacing limestone in large masses to contain:

Siderite, 40–65 percent; rhodochrosite, 20–40 percent; and magnesite, 7–13 percent.

Only a few specimens of rhodochrosite had been found at Leadville up to that time, 1933.

Tucson Shaft

The Tucson was staked in 1881 by W. H. Stevens and was worked by two inclines. Later a shaft was sunk to a depth of 1,100 feet. High grade silver with gold was mined from the Sawatch quartzite. Assays of up to 2,000 ounces silver per ton were recorded. Lead–zinc sulfides were mined from 1912 to 1918. The

Fig. 5–22. Bipyramidal quartz with limonite filling solution pits, Leadville, Colorado.

mine was flooded although a few attempts by leasees were made to mine it in the 1918 to 1926 period. It was 1940 before it was opened and five cars of zinc carbonate ore shipped. By 1944 it was again closed. The Leadville Drainage Tunnel was projected to end at the Tucson Shaft. It caved at the top while work on this tunnel was in progress and the tunnel was ended at the Mikado Shaft.

Old reports tell of open cavities in the Tucson Shaft up to 10 feet wide and 4 feet high lined with argentiferous galena, sphalerite, pyrite, and chalcopyrite crystals. Crystals of galena, up to one inch cube, were coated with a silver-bismuth overgrowth. Silver minerals lined pockets; arsenopyrite was found on the sixth level; and sphalerite crystals up to 1/4 inch in size enclosed pyrite crystals. An octahedral pyrite specimen in the Colorado School of Mines Museum came from the Tucson Shaft.

Hessite and wolframite were two unlikely minerals from the Tucson Shaft. Pseudo-rhombohedrons of arsenopyrite with manganosiderite and pyrite-hedrons of pyrite along their twinning plane were reported. Jackstraw cerussite occurred in the oxidized ore zone (Fig. 5–23).

Leadville Drainage Tunnel and the Blonger-Ponsardine Workings

The Leadville Drainage Tunnel was started in 1943, under supervision of the U.S. Bureau of Mines, with the purpose of draining many of the old mine workings for production of metals needed in World War II. Pumping costs were responsible for the closing of many of the older mines. After driving 6,600 feet through wet and difficult ground the work was recessed in 1945.

Fig. 5–23.   Jackstraw cerussite, Tucson Shaft (PR–17).

When metal demands increased during the Korean Conflict in 1950, work was resumed again and in 1951, lateral connections were made with the Hayden and Robert Emmet Shafts. In February, 1952, after a lateral to the New Mikado Shaft cut the Mikado Fault and went into Precambrian rock, the tunnel was considered completed.

A small amount of ore was produced in the Hayden Shaft area and in the nearby Blonger–Ponsardine property. This work was short-lived and the tunnel was abandoned. Decline in metal prices in 1952 sealed the fate of this development. By 1968, the tunnel was caved.

In driving the Leadville Drainage Tunnel, the U.S. Bureau of Mines had to take extraordinary precautions as water from old workings posed an ever present threat. Accuracy of old surveys of the Blonger Mine was in question as it was known by surface surveys that the caved Blonger Shaft was 50 feet southwest of the tunnel center line. The depth of the shaft and position of the bottom level were in doubt. It was thought from available data that this level was 15 feet above and crossed over the tunnel center line. Workings were in the soft Peerless shale above the drainage tunnel level which was in quartzite. A small opening would erode rapidly and cause a breakout if the shaft was flooded, which was almost certainly the case.

When the drainage tunnel reached 8,450 feet from the portal, about 200 feet short of the Blonger Shaft, tunnel sets were started with 10 by 10 inch timbers. At each five foot advance of the tunnel, drill holes 30 to 40 feet deep were drilled. After the tunnel had advanced beyond 8,650 feet, normal driving resumed. A station was cut at the supposed position of the Blonger Shaft and four 50 foot holes drilled in an effort to find the shaft. Probably the sump was packed with decomposed shale that could not be differentiated by drilling.

In 1952, a contractor working for ASARCO drove a raise from a new crosscut southeast of the Downtown lateral of the drainage tunnel and made a connection to the bottom level of the Blonger Shaft. Position of the bottom level plotted from the old surveys was accurate but the floor of the level was five feet higher than the supposed elevation. The old drift was completely filled with shale and old timbers.

A small amount of ore was mined in this general area. It was oxidized and enriched ore and most probably of high grade. Some specimens of massive silver and acanthite were saved by local collectors.

Sherman Tunnel and Hilltop Mine

Sherman Tunnel.   The Sherman Tunnel is at the head of Iowa Gulch in Iowa Amphitheatre, Lake County. Mt. Sherman and Mt. Sheridan form part of the crest of the Mosquito Range east of the Sherman Tunnel and the old workings of the Hilltop Mine are in the saddle between these two peaks. Sherman Tunnel was projected to go under the old Hilltop workings and prospect the veins at a lower level. It was also to serve as a transportation tunnel to bring the ore from under the crest of the Mosquito Range to Leadville for processing (Figs. 5–24 and 5–25).

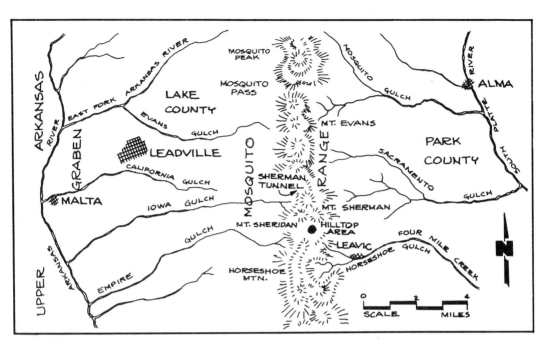

Fig. 5-24.   Location of Hilltop area and Sherman Tunnel in Lake and Park Counties, Colorado. Adapted from U.S.G.S. P.P. 235, 1953.

Horseshoe Zinc Company and Leadville Lead Company started a tunnel, Sherman Tunnel in 1946 and continued to consolidate mining claims in the Iowa Gulch and Hilltop areas through 1947. Day Mines Inc. is the present operator.

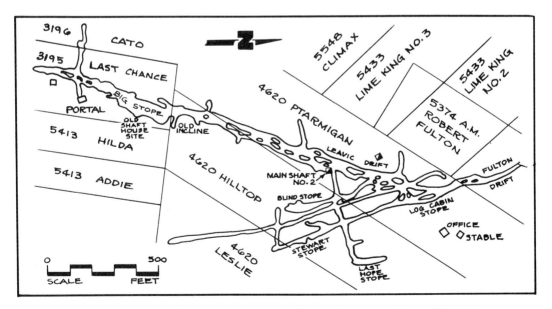

Fig. 5-25.   Claim map and underground workings of Hilltop Mine. Adapted from U.S.G.S. P.P. 235, 1953.

Transportation from one side of the Mosquito Range to the other by tunnel was not new. In 1903, a Mr. James Shinn proposed the Shinn Tunnel through the Mosquito Range at about the same location as the Sherman Tunnel. The purpose was to cut the travel time to Denver from Leadville as distance from Leadville to Leavick was 13 miles. Leavick was the headquarters of the Hilltop Mine and was four miles down the gulch where a stream from the Horseshoe Amphitheatre formed the headwaters of Four Mile Creek. After much promotion and publicity the project was forgotten.

Work had started on the Sherman Tunnel while surface exploration was being done on the Hilltop Mine. By 1969, a 450 foot raise was started and 3,500 feet of haulage tunnel had been completed. Shops and storage areas had been constructed at the tunnel portal.

A contract for engineering and design of a half-million dollar chemical refining plant to treat oxide and sulfide ores was let. This plant was on stream by 1973 and development ore from the Sherman Tunnel was being processed at a rate of 150 tpd. In 1973, the Sherman Tunnel was fifth highest in silver production of mines in Colorado that produced over 2,000,000 ounces of silver in that year.

Hilltop Mine.   The Hilltop Mine is at the head of Horseshoe Gulch, a tributary of Four Mile Creek which flows eastward into South Park as part of the South Platte River drainage. Horseshoe Gulch gets its name from Horseshoe Amphitheatre (Fig. 4–2) which has the shape of a horseshoe. This is caused by bedded sedimentary deposits of the same formations found at Leadville dipping in a rather tight fold down under South Park as a part of the South Park syncline. Alpine glaciation has cut away the center of the amphitheatre leaving the walls in the form of a horseshoe.

Claims were located on the Last Chance and the Hilltop group in 1875. The Hilltop Mine was established in 1882, but most of the early work up to 1883 was on the outcropping ore on the Last Chance claim. The mine worked intermittently until 1888 when a large production, reaching into 1889, was made. Production from 1888 to 1890 was $1.1 million in silver and lead. These were the Bonanza years of the mine.

A large stope on the north end of the Last Chance claim was worked in 1892.

Production from 1901 to 1923 was $0.8 million in gold, silver, lead, zinc, and copper. About $212,000 of this amount was made in the period 1920–3. In 1906, the first carbonate and silicate zinc ore in commercial quantities in the Leadville area was shipped from the Hilltop Mine. From 1901 to 1923, this mine produced 2.5 million pounds of zinc. The year 1910 had a production of $81,556 in metals. Fire destroyed the No. 1 shaft house in 1910 and the mine was closed for a while in 1913. In the early period of activity, an aerial tramway over three miles long connected the workings in the saddle with the mill and offices at Leavick. Two shafts, No. 1 at 70 feet deep, and No. 2, a 4 feet by 4 feet shaft 540 feet deep, gave access to the workings which were mainly large stopes. In about 1928, a tunnel was driven from the Park County side to cut the old workings. This tunnel was in 766 feet in 1930 when the mine was closed again. Fighting with ice was costly and this, plus administrative difficulties, caused the closing.

The Last Chance claim was first worked on the surface where the Leadville dolomite outcropped. Later, a large stope developed that was 1,300 feet long, 80 feet wide, and 100 feet high. This was called the Ice Palace Stope and it was famous for the large frost crystals that lined it. Some were up to four inches in diameter and glittering in the miners' lights made a spectacular exhibit. This stope was last worked in 1923. Ice is common underground and in the Hilltop it was a real problem; however, ventilation conditions that would permit such large frost crystals to form are not common. Patton found such frost crystals in a stope on the Moose Mine on Mt. Bross in the Alma mining district.

When the shaft on the Last Chance claim, which was filled with ice, was reopened for inspection in 1947, blasting, drilling, and lots of calcium chloride was used.

Prospecting around the surface in 1947–8 disclosed an abandoned ore stockpile of 300 tons at the Hilltop. It was abandoned in 1923 when the Pittman Silver Act was repealed. Shipped to the mill this material ran 15 ounces silver, 20 percent lead, and 5 percent zinc. The company thought the old timers had miscalculated the direction of the vein and they hoped to cut it with the new Sherman Tunnel and stope up to the old workings.

In 1950, a lessee uncovered a vein 40 feet wide on the surface of the Last Chance that contained cerussite and ran 15 ounces of silver to the ton. He mined this ore with a bulldozer after blasting it.

Heyl has described the Hilltop ore body as an oxidized zinc replacement shell, of supergene origin, around a pipe or manto.

In the Hilltop Mine, other than the common minerals of the Leadville district, rosettes of barite and a spongy textured, olive-green to grayish smithsonite (var. monheimite) were found. Recrystalized calcite (resorbed) in curved-faced rhombs, some with acanthite specks included, was a collector's item from this mine.

Sherman Tunnel was home to probably the finest golden barite from Colorado. Floaters up to an inch on an edge were found. Crystals this large in matrix were also found as were parallel twins 2½ by 2 by 6 inches thick. Rosasite and malachite, monheimite, (gray smithsonite), cuprite and wire silver also occurred.

Resurrection No. 2 Shaft

Resurrection No. 2 Shaft is in Evans Gulch north of Little Ellen Hill. Blanket replacement bodies had been mined in the Resurrection No. 1 and Fortune Shafts since the early 1880s. In February, 1889, a big strike was made in Resurrection ground and the No. 2 Shaft may date from this period of activity. A mill of 150 tpd capacity was built in 1902 and large ore bodies were opened up in 1903. The Fortune was also working large ore bodies, presumably the same as Resurrection was working in 1899.

By 1909, the Yak Tunnel was projected to reach the Resurrection No. 2 Shaft at a distance of 3½ miles, and drain all workings above it. There is a record of the mine reopening in 1915 and working until 1918, so it must have been closed some time between 1909 and 1915. Work done in Resurrection No. 1 Shaft was on the 9th level at a depth of 1,098 feet in 1918.

Nine veins were known in the Resurrection workings. Most terminated in the Weber formation. The No. 7 vein had a large tonnage of siliceous gold ore with subordinate galena, sphalerite, and silver. This vein had a fault displacement of about 40 feet. A siliceous gold ore vein was cut in the Resurrection No. 2 Shaft, but its value as ore was disappointing.

In 1932, all pumping below the Yak Tunnel level was stopped. Emmons showed five levels in the Resurrection workings, but little work was being done from the No. 2 Shaft. Newmont Mining Co. became interested in the Resurrection prior to 1938 and later purchased the Yak Tunnel to which it was connected by a drift.

During World War II, the lower workings were dewatered and in 1942, a 250 tpd mill was being planned. Mining continued through the war years. Most of this work was through the Resurrection No. 2 Shaft and the Yak Tunnel. In 1956, fire destroyed the surface plant and the mine was closed. Exploration work was done sporadically and in 1969 the mine reopened and production began in 1971.

Sphalerite and galena specimens from this mine showed cube, octahedron, and combinations and modifications of these forms.

Irene Shaft

The Irene Shaft is on Breece Hill with the Ibex group of mines. It was also known as the Hawkeye Shaft. In 1957, the headframe and the headframes of Ibex Shafts Nos. 2, 3 and 5, were torn down and the areas barricaded as a safety measure as most of these shafts are now caved at the collars.

Irene No. 2 Shaft was sunk in 1951 in the area between Breece Hill and Ball Mountain to develop mineral bodies discovered from the old Ibex and other working by drilling. This shaft is simply called the Irene today by common usage and the Irene No. 2 designation has been dropped.

A connection to the Yak Tunnel was started, possibly in 1955 and the Irene Shaft was completed to a depth of 1,750 feet. This makes the Irene Shaft one of the deepest in the Leadville area. The connecting level to the Yak Tunnel is at approximately the 13th level of the Ibex group. A lateral on the 1,750 foot level goes under Iowa Gulch and connects with the Black Cloud Shaft, a distance of about 8,000 feet.

Water was pumped up to the Yak Tunnel level during construction of the crosscut drift but now it is pumped at the Black Cloud Shaft for use in the mill.

A drop in metal prices in 1957 caused the Irene Shaft to close until 1965. Levels below the Yak Tunnel filled with water but were cleared and exploration work under Iowa Gulch, in the Sunday–Hellena–Julia Fisk area, was continued in 1965. A heavy inflow of water in 1967 caused the operation to close until sufficient pump capacity could be installed.

In general, the area explored was a down-faulted block of ground 400 to 500 feet below the Yak Tunnel level which had been recommended as a possible ore horizon by Emmons, Laughlin, and Behre. This area was between the Weston and Ball Mountain Faults. Resurrection Mining Co. (a Newmont Mining Co. subsidiary) and ASARCO are mining this block as a joint venture.

Some idea of the extent of the exploration program can be gained by statistics for 1967, which listed 600 feet of drifting, 1,500 feet of long hole drilling and 2,000 feet of diamond drilling.

Meeves and Darnell estimated that ore reserves were a million tons between the Irene Shaft and Printer Boy Hill, *The Minerals Yearbook* for 1972 gave ore reserves at 2.6 million tons (Irene-Black Cloud Shafts) averaging 15 percent combined lead–zinc and 2.5 ounces silver per ton.

A 700 tpd mill has been built at the Black Cloud Shaft and most of the activity has been transferred to this shaft with the Irene Shaft as an auxiliary.

Vermiform zinc ore, similar to that of the Eagle Mine at Gilman and of the Ten Mile district, occurred. Thin plates of pyrite in a matrix of black marmatite gave the impression of worm tracks. Floaters of thumbnail-size pyrite crystals occurred. These crystals were distorted forms, elongated and with curved faces. Some were striated and some not; some were heavily etched (Fig. 5–26).

Black Cloud Shaft

On the north side of Iowa Gulch between the Julia Fisk and Hellena Shafts, work was started in 1968-9, on the new Black Cloud Shaft and Mill. This shaft was bottomed out at 1,654 feet in mid-1970. There were five levels at that time and the 700 tpd mill was under construction. It was completed in 1971. Project cost to 1971 was given as $15 million.

In 1886, Emmons stated the Black Cloud Shaft went through the Weber formation and cut the underlying porphyry. No other information was given. The target horizon for the present development is probably the Leadville dolomite and lower possible ore contacts, in a down-faulted block roughly outlined by the Resurrection No. 2 on the north, the Hellena, Irene, and Sunday on the east, and the Julia Fisk and Black Cloud Shafts on the west.

A production of 208,000 tons of ore was made in 1972, the first full year of operating. Underground, the development work was completed on the No. 5 ore body and capacity production was expected in 1973.

In 1973, the Black Cloud Shaft produced 11,350 ounces of gold, ranking third in the state for gold production. It was second in lead production, and sixth in silver production. The mine is still active and work is progressing in the 1,800 foot shaft on the 1,500 foot and 1,800 foot levels.

Creamy to white dolomite on black shiny marmatitic sphalerite and clusters of green-amber sphalerite crystals occurred in the Black Cloud Mine. Wurtzite on stalactitic dolomite also occurred (Fig. 5–27).

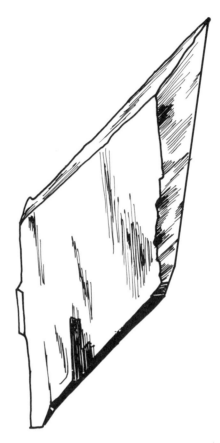

Fig. 5–26.   Distorted pyrite floater, Irene Shaft, Leadville, Colorado.

Golden barite and galena crystals both occurred. A quartz crystal on sulfide matrix that was twinned by the Japan Law was seen in a private collection.

Thumbnail-sized pyrites with cathedral-type striations came from the mine in 1976–77. The crystals were complex and distorted forms.

Hellena Shaft

In the early 1880s, a shaft, the Hellena, was sunk on the mineralized Hellena Fault, one of two major mineralized faults crossing the Iowa Gulch area. The Sunday Fault is the other one. This shaft is between Long and Derry Hills on the south and Printer Boy Hill on the north and is in Iowa Gulch. Ore generally occurred cementing breccia and fault material up to 19 feet wide. However, on the 195 foot and the 290 foot levels, open cavities occurred. Several geologic phenomena were observed in the Hellena Fault. Mud dikes occurred as small faults parallel to the Hellena vein in white porphyry. A black shale from the Weber formation was the probable source of the mud and represented gouge torn from the wall when the porphyry on one side was in contact with the Weber formation. A reversal of fault direction caused the white porphyry to be

Fig. 5-27. Wurtzite on stalactitic dolomite, Black Cloud Mine (JM#915).

in contact with white porphyry, and hence, the black mud dike (Figs. 5-28 and 5-29). A large block of Precambrian rock was found up in the sedimentary rocks, where repeated faulting had left it out of place.

Two new boilers were installed in the surface plant in 1907 in an effort to keep up with the inflow of water. A good body of sulfide ore was said to have been cut on the 500 foot level.

Excessive water and the high cost of pumping closed the Hellena in 1912 and it remained closed until 1928. Ore shipped to the smelter in 1929-30 averaged 0.165 ounces gold, 9.64 ounces silver, 28.6 percent lead, and 9.48 percent zinc, with minor copper, during this period of activity.

The zinc penalty was too much to make it a profitable operation at that time; however, the shaft was extended to 766 feet. Five churn drill holes drilled in 1930 located ore in two of the holes west of the shaft. This probably indicated replacement ore bodies in this area and was probably responsible for the renewed activity since then in the Iowa Gulch area.

During World War II, the mine was dewatered and milling ore shipped to a local mill which recovered the zinc as a separate concentrate. In 1953, the shaft was pumped dry to the 500 foot level and track relaid on that level.

Production fluctuated with metal prices. Another period of activity in 1956-7 produced 45,000 tons which averaged 0.77 ounces gold, 4.56 ounces silver, 4 percent lead, 6.5 percent zinc and 0.16 percent copper.

Reserves were estimated in 1968, by the U.S. Bureau of Mines, to be 200,000 to 250,000 tons of ore, based on old records as the shaft was filled with water to within 60 feet of the collar at that time. It is probable that these reserves will be worked through the Black Cloud Shaft. The Black Cloud Mill is a short distance down the gulch.

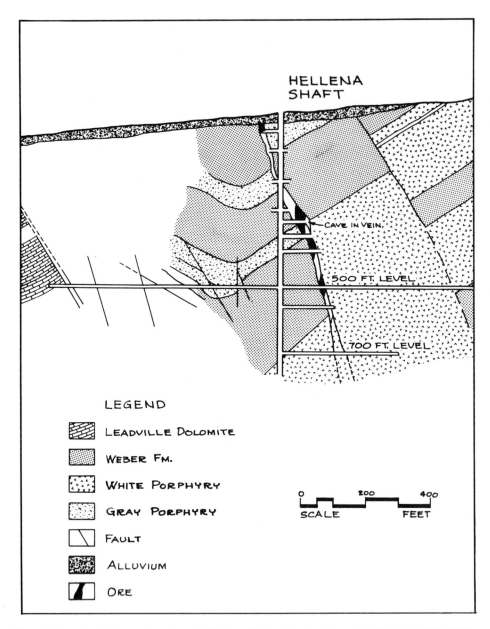

Fig. 5-28.   East-West section through Hellena Shaft. Adapted from U.S.G.S. P.P. 235, 1953.

As early as 1939, Behre called attention to the possibility of ore deposits in the area bounded by the Mosquito and the Weston Faults on the east and west respectively, Long and Derry Hill on the south, and Ball Mountain on the north. Activity in this area from the Irene, Julia Fisk, and Black Cloud Mines and construction of the Black Cloud Mill nearby proved his predictions to be correct.

In the Hellena Shaft oxidized ore rich in gold and silver was found to the 300

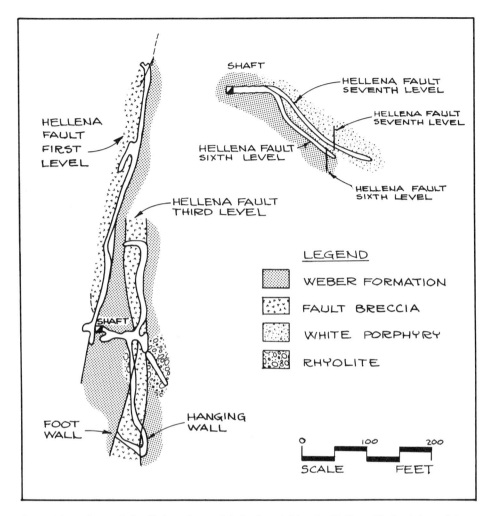

Fig. 5-29. Plan and detailed geology of 1, 3, 6, and 7 levels, Hellena Shaft. Adapted from U.S.G.S. P.P. 235, 1953.

foot level. Work on the 500 foot level in 1906 was in both oxidized and sulfide ore. By 1909, production was $100,000.

Visible gold occurred in the oxidized ore with cerussite, smithsonite and silver halides. Galena, sphalerite, chalcopyrite, and silver sulfide (acanthite) occurred with rhodochrosite and dolomite gangue. Enargite was reported.

Chalcopyrite occurred as inclusions in sphalerite crystals. Resurgence is sometimes used to define a process whereby a new influx of solution, sometimes at a different temperature, repeats all or part of a mineralizing sequence, similar or different from the original one.

Steel–galena, much in demand in the days of crystal radio sets, was found. This fine-grained galena represents a relatively faster state of formation than larger crystals of galena. It was rare at Leadville.

Replacement ore bodies were small and few. They were only found on the 195 foot and 500 foot levels, with higher temperature minerals such as rhodochrosite and chalcopyrite present. This is unusual. It may be that the fault gouge sealed off the attacking solutions.

The Green Mountain Shaft, a little to the northeast of the Hellena, made a Bonanza shipment in 1884. Five tons averaged 456 ounces gold and 42 ounces silver per ton and eight tons averaged 266 ounces gold and 90 ounces silver per ton. In a camp where Bonanzas were frequently found this did not compare with the strike made on January 14, 1880, on the Robert E. Lee when $118,500 in ore was taken out in 17 hours work, but it did spur activity on the Hellena Shaft.

Julia Fisk Shaft

About 3,000 feet west of the Hellena Shaft down Iowa Gulch, a modern enclosed headframe and surface buildings mark the Julia Fisk Shaft. Mining was carried on in 1900–10 and the shaft was down to the 600 foot level at that time. White porphyry, Leadville dolomite, and the Sawatch quartzite were penetrated. Small deposits of argentiferous galena were mined at this time on the 410 foot level at the contact between the Dyer dolomite and the Parting quartzite. Near the bottom of the shaft, a vein was mined that had ore containing 1 ounce of gold, and 40 to 50 ounces silver per ton. Organizational problems and the high cost of pumping water caused the operating company to close down. Exploration work at the Irene Shaft, which was recessed in 1957, was continued in the Julia Fisk Shaft, which had been rehabilitated in 1957. However, a decline in metal prices curtailed most activity at this time.

In 1965, the Irene Shaft was dewatered and exploration work from the 1,750 foot level was continued from a lateral, said to have reached the Iowa Gulch area.

In 1968, the U.S. Bureau of Mines estimated a block of ore 350 to 425 feet long below Iowa Gulch contained 200,000 tons of ore.

Exploration continued in the Irene Shaft through 1968 and into the early 1970s. Present activity is centered in the Black Cloud Shaft.

Aurichalcite was found by Behre on the dump of the Julia Fisk Mine. He also found brown sphalerite. Most of the sphalerite of the Leadville district is black marmatitic sphalerite.

Pale pink to violet-pink, saddle-shaped crystals of rhodochrosite (or oligonite) were reported from the Julia Fisk and three other Leadville Mines and illustrated by Miller and Kosnar and Miller.

Possibly the last of this material, oligon spar of the European mines, came out of the Julia Fisk Mine in the 1956–7 season. The early mined oxidized ore in the Julia Fisk Mine was said to be argentiferous cerussite and at depth, argentiferous galena.

The First National Shaft, which is only 400 feet southwest of the Julia Fisk Shaft reached the Leadville dolomite at 198 feet and had the same geologic conditions as the Julia Fisk. This shaft was 256 feet deep. In 1932, the dump had considerable manganosiderite, some of which was rhombohedral in form with curved crystal faces. Some very thin rhombohedrons formed rosettes under which short prisms (1.22 mm in length) of arsenopyrite occurred.

These high temperature minerals and the rhodochrosite in the Hellena Shaft led Behre to call attention to the possibility of an igneous center and associated substantial ore deposits in the part of Iowa Gulch north of Iowa Fault and between the Weston and Ball Mountain Faults.

Little Jonny-Ibex Group of Mines

The Little Jonny (also Johnny) Mine was discovered in 1879 on vein material at the contact of Leadville dolomite and Gray porphyry. By 1884, the shaft was 197 feet deep with levels at 82, 112 (115), and 166 feet. Drifts had been run southward 187 feet on the 112 foot level and 201 feet on the 166 foot level (Fig. 5–30).

John Campion (Leadville Johnny) owned the Little Jonny and became a

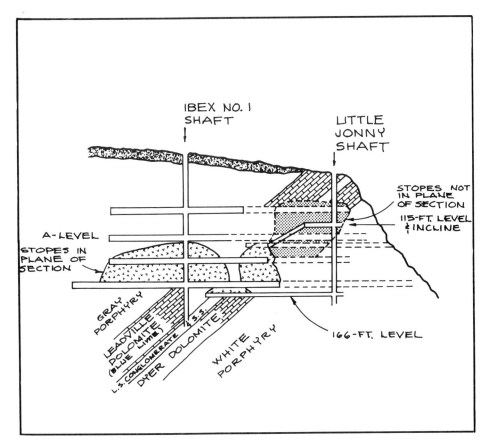

Fig. 5–30. Cross section of Little Jonny—Ibex No. 1 workings. Adapted from U.S. Bu. M., I.C. 8464, 1970.

millionaire. James Joseph Brown (Leadville Johnny Brown of fiction) was one of the seven original stockholders and became a very rich man also.

Ore in the Little Jonny was similar to the ore found in the Highland Chief Mine on Ball Mountain. This mine was one of the first in the gold belt and the ore was primarily a gold, not a silver ore. In the Little Jonny sand carbonate replacement ore 1 to 3 feet thick containing 30 ounces of silver and 40 to 50 perent lead per ton, with copper mineralization carrying gold, was found. Copper ore was shipped prior to 1886. The gold was too fine to be panned and was in a gray quartz.

A. V. Hunter was said to have supplied the last $5,000 for developing the Little Jonny. The ore body extended 300 to 350 feet below the surface and into the Ibex No. 1 and Ibex No. 3 Shafts, which had been sunk to the south of the Little Jonny on the continuation of the ore horizon. In 1891, new machinery was installed on the Ibex No. 1 Shaft and the Little Jonny Shaft was abandoned. The Little Jonny was worked from this shaft and below the 300 foot level the ore deposit changed from replacement-type to a siliceous gold vein that stopped in the Weber formation above the blue lime and did not go to the surface.

By 1898, the Ibex Group was working six shafts and 500 men were employed. About 1900 the company started leasing small blocks of ore to various individuals. A copper strike was reported in shaft No. 3 in March, 1907. No. 4 shaft had already produced a fair amount of copper ore. Gold pockets found on the 13th level ran $100 per pound and shipments of a quantity of ore to the smelter had a net return of over $100 per ton.

By May, 1907, the Ibex group had 150 sets of lessees and 450 men working. Ore was being shipped to the smelters at the rate of 400 tpd. One lessee reported ore as rich as any produced from this famously rich mine.

The Yak Tunnel was extended to the No. 4 shaft which was 10,813 feet from the portal. A lateral was also extended 750 feet to the Little Vinnie Shaft.

Below 350 feet, sulfide ore was found in veins and blanket deposits that ran 0.5 ounces in gold, 40 ounces in silver, and 8 to 15 percent copper per ton. This type of ore continued down to the seventh level, but from the seventh to thirteenth level vein type ore deposits were predominant. The Ibex No. 4 vein was the largest producer and produced high grade ore from the third to the thirteenth level. On the third level, it flattened out into a blanket-type deposit, which contained values in gold, silver, and copper throughout its extent. The Ibex No. 1 vein extended through blanket deposits nearly to the surface (a later mineralization) and from the first level up it had high grade gold in oxidized porphyry. There were 72 faults found in the Ibex group.

As the deposit was found to be larger in size than it was first thought to be when worked in the Little Jonny, other shafts were sunk to allow better and quicker extraction of the ore. There were seven Ibex Shafts, the Little Vinnie, and the Garbut, which was a famous mine in its own right, on the vein system and bedded deposits.

Gold-bearing quartz–pyrite veins containing wolframite and scheelite were being mined in 1914 from the St. Paul group of claims; Nonie, Ontario, and Capitol claims in the Ibex group of mines. The ore occurred east of the Weston

Fault in what was considered to be high temperature veins, according to Fitch and Loughlin (1916).

A stockwork was discovered on the Garbut second level, 25 feet west of the Ibex No. 4 vein, that extended down to the seventh level and was 330 feet along its strike length, 550 feet in dip length, and 60 to 120 feet thick. It was worked from 1915 to 1919 and produced 200 to 250 tons per day, which averaged 0.21 ounces gold per ton with some shipments averaging 1 ounce gold per ton. The rock was broken into a breccia with quartz, pyrite, scheelite, and wolframite mineralization cementing the fragments.

The Ibex group has produced for almost a century. In 1935, rich gold ore was being mined north of the Ibex No. 2 Shaft in the upper levels, but prospecting work below the seventh level for replacement bodies of ore in down-faulted blocks was receiving the most attention. These workings are dry as they are drained by the Yak Tunnel.

Resurrection Mining Company explored large blocks of down-faulted ground between the Weston and Ball Mountain faults, 400 to 500 feet below the Yak Tunnel level from 1952 to 1959 and again in 1965 to 1968. Some of this work was done from the Irene Shaft. A large block of ore has been developed between the Ibex group-Irene-Printer Boy Hill area it is said.

Few mines have produced the large quantity of mineral specimens that have been credited to the Little Johnny. It is estimated that if these specimens were crammed back into the mine they would extend out the shaft collar.

Probably the one single factor that caused this phenomenon was the appeal of the Little Jonny Mine.

It is reasonable to speculate that the Ibex management went into small block leases in the early 1890s to prevent massive high grading, unauthorized removal of ore. Although this has not been said publicly, it has been said among the miners.

Many specimens of free gold came from these leases in the Little Jonny–Ibex workings.

Wire and leaf gold occurred in a seam of sulfides in black shale on the sixth level. A stope above the third level had seams of leaf gold and wire gold in decomposed porphyry and it also lined cracks and joints in jasperoid.

Quartz stained by oxidation and with many solution-type pits had gold in these pits as wire and leaf deposits. Gold occurred as leaf gold on porphyry in the Ibex No. 7 on the tenth level.

Siliceous oxidized ore and magnetite and hematite in serpentine were found cut by siliceous gold ore veins. Mixed sulfides occurred as blanket deposits at gray porphyry-Leadville dolomite contacts, as replacement bodies in limestone, and as veins in deeper prophyritic bodies.

Gold occurred in ore containing sphalerite and a company specimen was of sphalerite crystals coated with gold.

Logan Hawkins and Robert Walker, lessees, made one of the most exciting finds in the district in 1902. A streak of ore five feet high, two feet wide and one inch thick yielded 110 pounds of ore which brought $250,000. A short time before this, 57 pounds of ore was sold to Eastern banks as gold specimens for

$13,680. The area between Ball Mountain Fault and Weston Fault was known as the gold belt and a new era of production was started for the old silver camp.

In the late 1960s, a quantity of pyrite crystals, mostly single crystals, came on the market. These were the cube-pyritohedron and octahedron combination faces attributed to the South Ibex stockwork by Emmons and others. These were said to have come from the Little Jonny. It is more probable they came from the South Ibex stockwork by way of the Yak Tunnel or the Irene Shaft (Fig. 5-31).

In the stockwork of the Ibex group some open spaces allowed crystals to form and pyrite up to five inches on cube edge were found. The prevailing form of the pyrite was octahedron, cube, and pyritohedron combinations, but several less common forms were also present. Trapezohedral and diploid combinations were represented in small faces on the pyrite crystals. Octahedral beveling of edges and corners also occurred. Another form has been the repetition of Gothic window markings. This was probably the start of the term, cathedral pyrite.

Quartz crystals up to two inches long were found in vugs, in parallel growth with pyrite crystals, and penetrating pyrite crystals. Pyrite showed a marked intergrowth with wolframite and parallel growth with scheelite and with quartz. Sericite was found in parallel growth in quartz, as inclusions.

As a rule, the tungsten minerals lined cavities with small crystals, but some larger ones were also found. Scheelite was generally massive but some crystals grew on quartz or pyrite. They were doubly terminated pyramids of the tetragonal system truncated by narrow pyramid faces of second order.

Wolframite was intergrown with pyrite. The brownish-black crystals generally terminated against quartz or scheelite. One crystal over half an inch long projecting into a vug was rhombic or wedge-shaped in outline.

Three large pyrite cubes, under five inches on a side, were seen in three different old collections marked Little Jonny Mine. This size of cube was also

Fig. 5-31.   Pyrite, Little Jonny-Ibex group (#3-244). T.E.C.

Minerals in Leadville Area
Classified by Zone and Formation Temperature
(See also Fig. 5–32)

	ORE MINERAL		GANGUE MINERAL	
Oxidized Zone:	Anglesite	Limonite	Aragonite	
	Aurichalcite	Melanterite	Calcite	
	Calamine	Molybdite	Chalcedony	
	(Hemimorphite)	Psilomelane	Gypsum	
	Chlorargyrite	Pyrolusite	Kaolinite	
	Cerussite	Sauconite	Quartz	
	Chalcanthite	Zinciferous-clay		
	Chrysocolla	Silver		
	Goethite	Smithsonite		
	Gold	Turgite		
	Hetaerolite	Wad		
	Hydrozincite			
	Jarosite			
Sulfide Zone:	Argentite			
	Chalcocite			
	Covellite			
	Silver (?)			
Lowest Temperature	Galena		Calcite	
Veins and	Pyrite		Dolomite	
Replacements:	Sphalerite		Jasperoid	
			Quartz	
Low Temperature	Argentite		Ankerite	
Veins and	Chalcopyrite		Barite	
Replacements	Galena		Calcite	
	Gold		Dolomite	
	Pyrite		Fluorite	
	Silver		Quartz	
	Sphalerite		Siderite	
Moderate Temperature	Argentite	Lillianite	Albite	Quartz
Veins and	Arsenopyrite	Proustite	Ankerite	Rhodo-
Replacements	Bismuthinite	Pyrite	Barite	chrosite
	Chalcopyrite	Silver	Calcite	Serpentine
	Enargite	Sphalerite	Chalce-	Siderite
	Galena	Tennantite	dony	Talc
	Gold	Tetrahedrite	Dolomite	
	Hematite		Manganosiderite	
			Muscovite (or	
			Sericite)	

(Adapted from Behre, 1953, U.S.G.S. P.P. 235, p. 88)

documented by Emmons and others as coming from the South Ibex stock-work.

According to some older residents of Leadville the largest pyrite cubes came from the Old Cord Incline and were up to 12 inches on an edge. Some of these probably exist in museums.

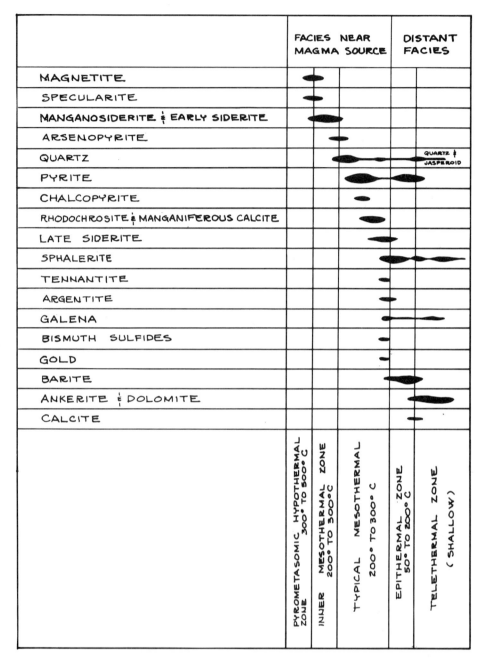

Fig. 5–32. Paragenesis of ores in Leadville district, Colorado. Adapted from U.S.G.S. P.P. 235, 1953.

Wolftone Mine

East 5th street in Leadville runs into Stray Horse Gulch and the Wolftone Mine is on the south side of this gulch, north of Carbonate Hill. Many of the most successful carbonate mines of the early days of the camp came from an area described as the Little Stray Horse syncline.

Minerals of the Leadville
Mining District

Allanite
Alunite
Anglesite
Ankerite
Apatite
Aragonite
Argentite (dimorphous with Acanthite)
Arsenic
Arsenopyrite
Augite
Aurichalcite
Azurite
Barite
Beidelite
Biotite
Bismuthinite
Bismutite
Bornite
Bromyrite
Calamine (Hemimorphite)
Calcite
Caledonite
Cerargyrite
Cerussite
Chalcanthite
Chalcedony
Chalcocite
Iodyrite
Jarosite
Kaoline
Kobellite
Lanarkite
Lillianite
Limonite
Magnetite
Malachite
Manganosiderite
Marmatite
Massicot
Melanterite
Microcline
Minium
Muscovite
Nicholsonite (zincian aragonite)
Opal
Orthoclase
Paragonite
Plagioclase
Plumbojarosite
Psilomelane
Pyrite

Chalcophanite
Chalcopyrite
"Chinese Talc"
Chlorite
Chrysocolla
Clay (zinciferous)
Copper
Dechenite (natural lead vanadate)
Descloizite
Diopside
Dolomite
Embolite
Epidote
Ferric sulfate
Friebergite
Galena
Gold
Goethite
Goslarite
Tetrahedrite
Hedenbergite
Hetaerolite
Hematite
Hornblende
Hydrozincite
Hypersthene
Matildite
Pyrolusite
Pyromorphite
Quartz
Rhodochrosite
Rhodonite
Rutile
Sericite
Serpentine
Siderite
Silver
Smithsonite
Sphalerite
Sulfur
Titanite
Topaz
Turgite
Vanadinite
Vivianite
Wad
Wollastonite
Wulfenite
Wurtzite
Zircon

Adapted from Emmons & Others (1927) p. 145–146.

Emmons first records that the Wolftone Mine had penetrated 500 feet of white porphyry without a contact and he later footnotes that, since the field work, the Wolftone had reached a contact with the Leadville Limestone at 633 feet and had 40 feet of carbonate and sulphurete ore.

Ore was found at more horizons, or contacts of the miners, in the Little Stray Horse syncline than at any place west of the Iron Fault. The Wolftone had six. One ore shoot extended for 1,200 feet from the Wolftone, through the Maid of Erin and on to the Seneca Shaft. The ore body on the sixth contact was on and extended into the Cambrian quartzite. This was one of the most highly mineralized areas in the camp.

The Wolftone must have had a large and long production record as the *Leadville Republican* of January 1, 1907 states that a 500 foot tunnel would connect the shaft with a 250 ton mill, at a point 100 feet below the collar of the shaft. This was also to relieve the pumps of the extra 100 foot lift.

The A.M.W. combination was made up of the Adams, Maid of Erin, and Wolftone Mines, and by 1892, this combination had produced $20 million from an area of four blocks. These mines were in the Downtown area.

Emmons found the workings inaccessible. It is known that all the mines were flooded in the miner's strike of 1896–7, and the work of dewatering them did not start until 1898 and was not completed until 1899.

In 1899, work was seriously curtailed at Leadville due to a timber famine; with all the wood burned for charcoal for the smelters and to hold up the mountains it is small wonder.

There was a financial panic that allowed the mines to again fill with water in 1907 and it was 1916 before they were dewatered again. It is not known if the Silver Panic of 1893 closed the Downtown Mines or not, or if pumping was continued until they reopened. One dump of the Wolftone Mine was milled in 1942–3 for its metal content.

REFERENCES

A–4 Lindgren Volume, (Burbank) (Ch. VI), (Knope), (McKnight), (Burbank) (Ch. XI), (Hewitt), (Henderson), A–5 Ridge (Tweto) (Sec. 27), (Tweto) (Sec. 32), B–5, C–11, C–13, D–1, (Burbank), (Traver), D–3, E–1, E–2, F–1, F–2, G–5, G–8, H–6, I–17, I–18, J–14, J–18, J–58, J–68, J–74, J–75, K–2, K–3, K–12, K–16, L–1, 1940–1974, N–1 through 13, N–14, N–19, Q–10, Q–12, Q–13, Q–17, Q–35, Q–36, Q–37, Q–38, Q–40, Q–41, Q–42, Q–43, Q–54, Q–59, Q–60, Q–61, Q–62, Q–63, Q–64, R–6, R–8, R–11, R–20, R–22, S–7, S–18, S–30, S–31, S–33, S–36, S–52, S–55, S–79, S–80, S–126, S–127, S–132.

BATTLE MOUNTAIN DISTRICT

Eagle Mine

The Eagle Mine, at Gilman, and adjacent mines at Redcliff form the Battle Mountain mining district, Eagle County.

Blanket ore deposits in the Leadville limestone were discovered in late 1878 or early 1879 and the word soon brought a rush to the district, (Fig. 5-33). The Belden lode was discovered in 1879 on Battle Mountain, which was named from a battle purportedly having taken place between the Utes and Arapahoes, and many other claims were soon staked. By 1883, the district, which had been named Battle Mountain to separate it from the Gold Park and Holy Cross areas with which it was grouped at first, had a production of over $1 million in gold, silver and lead. The Belden was the largest producing mine. In 1884, gold was found in the quartzite beds and the Ground Hog group, Combined Discovery, Uncle Sam, Horn Silver, Highland Many and other mines were opened.

The Mable, Tip Top, and Ben Butler Mines had veins in the Precambrian rocks which were opened contemporaneously with the mining of the replacement beds; however, they were never of as great importance as the other deposits.

A two-stack smelter was built at Red Cliff in 1881 but arrival of the railroad and access to the Leadville and other smelters soon forced it to close.

Mining soon depleted the rich oxidized ores and the sulfide ores contained too much zinc and were too complex for profitable smelting.

A roaster and magnetic separator were constructed in 1905 and zinc production soon became important. From 1912 to 1917, the Black Iron and Iron Mask Mines produced between 6,000 to 10,000 tons of oxidized zinc ores, which were largely smithsonite and hemimorphite replacing dolomite and manganosiderite. Iron-manganese ores were shipped to the Pueblo steel mill of C F & I in 1905 and 1907.

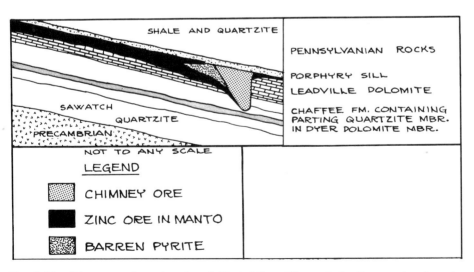

Fig. 5-33. Diagrammatic section though Eagle Mine, Gilman, Lake County, showing relationship of chimney ore body to manto ore body replacing Leadville dolomite. Adapted from Vanderwilt (1947).

New Jersey Zinc Company, the principal operator for many years, entered the district in 1912 and consolidated the mines into the Eagle Mine. A banner production year was achieved in 1916 when zinc valued at over $3.8 million was produced out of a total production of $4.1 million for the district. Production of Eagle County between 1864 and 1880, most of which was estimated to have come from the Eagle Mine, was over $254.6 million in gold, silver, copper, lead, and zinc.

By 1917, the Eagle Mine was working 225 men to produce 6,000 tons of ore per month, of which 10 percent went direct to the smelter and the rest was milled at the mine with concentrates going to the company's magnetic separation plant at Canon City, Colorado. The main workings were through the No. 1 Incline, 1,800 feet, and No. 2 Incline, 1,400 feet, in length.

In 1920, a modern zinc oxide plant was completed in Canon City to treat Eagle Mine ore; however, it was not operated until 1922. The magnetic separation plant, which had been in operation since 1902, was closed in 1920.

In 1928, an underground mill, 47 tons per hour capacity, shops and utility rooms were constructed in an area excavated on the 16th level. This level, also known as the Tunnel Level, was just above the Eagle River in the canyon below Gilman, the company-owned town. An opening 330 feet long by 52 feet wide by 22 to 56 feet high was cut underground. The old Wilkesbarre Shaft, Eagle No. 1, bottoms out at the Tunnel Level and serves for lowering and hoisting men and supplies. A series of incline shafts serve the lower mine, one bottoms on the 20th level and one on the 24th level.

In general, the iron, copper, silver, and gold ore went to the smelter and the lead–zinc ore to the mill. Capacity of the mill was increased to 1,000 tpd in 1951 and to 1,200 tpd later. Only copper–silver (chimney) ore was produced in the period 1932–40 but zinc production was resumed in 1941.

New areas opened in 1960 did not have copper–silver shipping ore; however, some was mined in 1961. Gold production increased in the early 1960s and over 1,000 ounces of gold were produced in 1965 and over 100,000 ounces of silver in 1968.

The Canon City plant was closed in 1969 and a new fluid column roasting plant, invented by the company and built at De Pue, Illinois, was used. A sulfide fire occurred on the Tunnel Level in 1973 and the area was sealed off to contain it.

Sulfide fires are caused in underground mines when the heat of oxidation becomes so great that a fire starts and the sulfide ore actually burns.

The Company had closed the DePue plant and for the preceeding two years had stockpiled ore at Leadville in anticipation of a new smelter opening there. When this did not materialize, the ore was shipped to their new smelter in Acquashiocola, Pennsylvania. This glorious old mine on the Eagle River could not go on forever and on January 1, 1978, after 100 years of production the mine was said to be closed. Some minor clean up work and mining of small pockets of high-grade silver ore continues.

Tweto and Lovering and Heyl, describe the ore bodies in limestone as shaped like a trident pointing southwest or updip of the bedding. These sediments dip 10° northeast off the northeast flank of the Sawatch Range. Tines of the trident are three long mantos of zinc–lead–iron sulfides in manganosiderite casings. These tines turn downward into chimneys containing pyrite–copper–silver ore. The chimneys are themselves connected by zinc mantos that are nearly parallel to the strike of the beds. The tines are about 4,000 feet long and about 4,000 feet apart at the upper end. Gold deposits in the Sawatch quartzite were under the trident and approximately in line with the upper ends of the zinc mantos.

Ground Hog Mine

The Ground Hog Mine, which later became part of the Eagle Mine, developed vein and replacement ore bodies in the Sawatch quartzite beds in the early days of mining at Gilman. An adit extended about 1,400 feet down the dip of the NE-dipping quartzite bed and about 1,500 feet along the strike. Ore was oxidized iron minerals with pockets of free gold in the form of large wires or nuggets. In many places the side drifts were from 2.5 to 3.0 feet high and extended several hundred feet along the bedding. Such small workings were often made because the thrifty Cornish miners, Cousin Jacks, would not remove any more rock than was needed to uncover the ore.

Much of the production from the Ground Hog Mine came from pockets or bullion holes. Individual pockets were credited with $37,000, a small winze with $50,000 and the No. 5 South Drift with $47,000, mostly in gold. The early workings in oxide ore are credited with $660,000 production.

Any discussion of the Eagle Mine and the Battle Mountain district would be incomplete without a word about the Bonanza gold specimens found in the Rocky point horizon, at the top of the Sawatch quartzite, in the Ground Hog Mine.

Guiterman describes the ore as occurring in two chimneys 600 feet apart which were four and six feet in diameter. At the time of his visit, the pay ore averaged 7 ounces gold and 50 ounces silver per ton. In one ore deposit, the gold nuggets were isolated and had a peculiar spiral twisted appearance, often taking the shape of bent horns. A beautiful specimen of this description from the Ground Hog Mine was on display at the Denver Museum of Natural History in Denver, Colorado. This specimen is also shown on page 284, of the Mineralogical Record, Vol. 7, No. 6 (Kosnar and Miller). Similar gold specimens were seen in a private collection, passed down through a mining family involved in early-day mining in the Ground Hog Mine.

On another lease the gold occurred as nuggets composed of crystalline pieces cemented together by chlorargyrite. The gold was also found in troughs in the quartzite floor, imbedded in clay and closely associated with very rich silver ore, which proved on examination to be horn-silver. Guiterman also identified crystalline copiapite, triclinic, as occurring in the Ground Hog Mine.

Ore in the Eagle Mine has been classified by Radabaugh, by mineral content, as: pyrite-zinc, siderite-zinc and copper-silver ore. Pyrite forms about three quarters of the sulfide minerals, marmatitic sphalerite and siderite make up 20 percent of the ore, and other minerals form only 5 percent.

Age of the mineralization is thought to be late Laramide. The source of the mineralization is not known but study of lead isotopes indicate that all ores of the district had a common source.

Sand carbonate ore, similar to that found at Leadville, is one type of ore of the Eagle Mine. At Eagle, however, it may be made up of sulfide mineral grains and minor siderite grains. This material can be shoveled like sand.

Massive replacement ore and rubble ore are other more common forms. Crude banding has been observed in the sand ore. Ore minerals cement the rubble pieces together.

In an envelope of manganiferous siderite around a pipe of sulfide ore, in the Battle Mountain district, it was found by analysis that the content of the manganiferous siderite was: 40 to 50 percent siderite, 20 percent rhodochrosite and 20 to 30 percent magnesite.

Siderite and mangano-siderite occurs in what has been described as flattened rhombohedrons, or as hexagonal pinacoids. However, the description of similar siderite from Portugal by Gains and Thadeau, (Mineralogical Record), seems to be more fitting: crystals of a rounded discus-like habit. Probably all members of the siderite–poinite–manganosiderite–oligonite–rhodochrosite series (Deer, Howie, Zussman, Vol. 5) are present in the Eagle Mine. At Leadville, the series only seemed to go to oligonite, oligon spar, and the rhodochrosite member was rare if found at all. Analysis of the Leadville mineral are not available but it is probably as close to manganosiderite as it is to rhodochrosite. At Eagle, if color is a field guide, the color range is from light cream to deepest red, and all members are present in the ore. In the manganosiderite range, manganese equals iron content. The manganese content is from 6.5 to 16.5 percent (Radabaugh), in the Eagle Mine ore.

Dolomite, usually coated with ankerite of a yellowish cast has been reported in rhombohedrons up to two inches long. It also occurs as white rhombs coated with a sprinkling of pyrite. It has been found with tetrahedrite and pyrite sprinkled over the ankerite coating. Most of the dolomite in the lower part of the mine came from 2,300 and 2,400 levels. Siderite casts, pseudomorphs of dolomite and pyrite pseudomorphs of dolomite occur but are rare.

Sphalerite was almost all the black shiny marmatitic variety. Wurtzite, hexagonal trimorph with sphalerite (Michael Fleisher), occurred. Iron content of the sphalerite ranged from 6.5 to 11.8 percent. A botryoidal, massive form of sphalerite, sphalenblende, occurred in the Rocky Point claim ore horizon. Dana (4th ed. p. 427) says this form is a mixture of sphalerite and wurtzite (Fig. 5–34).

Barite occurs in clear and in golden varieties. A large blade of blue barite from the Eagle Mine was seen in the collection of F.A. Cajori, at the Denver Museum of National History, on temporary display in February, 1977.

Grybeck in examining specimens of stephanite in the collection of the Colorado School of Mines Museum found most to be tennantite or tetrahedrite; however, one from the Eagle Mine was, in fact, stephanite.

Fig. 5–34.   Sphalenblende, Eagle Mine, Gilman, Colorado (JM#30).

Pyrite, the most common mineral at the Eagle Mine, occurs in vugs as large groups of small to medium-sized crystals usually cubic in habit. Crystals over two inches are rare at this time. Octahedral and pyritohedron forms are less common to rare. Floaters occur in mud pockets; most of those seen were pyritohedrons in various sizes to one inch (Fig. 5–35). Reported from the Ground Hog Mine were pyritohedrons up to two inches in size. Cathedral pyrite, with convex or concave striations, that resemble gothic arches, was found. Reportedly the 2,300 level produced the most, but much of the pyrite pseudomorphic material was said to have occurred on the 1,800 level.

Pseudomorphs of scalenohedral calcite and rhombohedral dolomite have

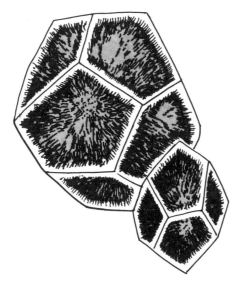

Fig. 5–35.   Pyritohedron floater of pyrite, whiskered, or velvet appearance (whiskers are more numerous and smaller than those of the Climax deposit), Eagle Mine, Gilman.

been found. The most prized pyrite pseudomorphs are probably the pseudohexagonal prism and pinacoids of pyrrhotite. Similar pseudomorphs were reported by Grice and Gault, from the Blue Bell Mine.

Pyrite pseudomorphs of apatite are said to occur and wafer-thin pyrite-coated casts of some unknown mineral, said by one collector to possibly be covellite, are found.

Vermiformed ore similar to that found at Leadville and Kokomo occurred (Fig. 5–36).

Minerals of the Eagle Mine are: alunite, arsenopyrite, apatite, acanthite, anglesite, bornite, barite, bournoite, beegerite (a mixture), boulangerite, chalcanthite, chalcocite, chalcopyrite, copiapite, covellite, cerussite, chlorargyrite, coquimbite, calcite, copper, cubanite, calaverite, dolomite, dyscrasite, digenite, epsomite, freibergite, gypsum, gold galena, goslarite, hessite, hydrozincite, hematite, kaolin, limonite, matildite, massicot, manganosiderite, magnetite, marble, oligonite, pyrite, pyrrhotite, pyrolusite, psilomelane, petzite, plattnerite, pyrargyrite, proustite, polybasite, pearceite, quartz, rhodochrosite, siderite, silver, sulfur, sphalerite, stephanite, smithsonite, stromeyerite, tetrahedrite, tennantite, turgite, and wurtzite.

It was noticed from earliest mining days that the Leadville limestone in the Mineral Belt, at Battle Mountain, Leadville, and Alma, was dolomitized. Recrystallization formed the zebra rock of the miners, which was usually an indication of ore.

Tweto and Lovering developed a geologic model to explain why this dolomitization occurred in a special area. The Leadville limestone is not

Fig. 5–36. Vermiform pyrite ore, Eagle Mine, Gilman, Colorado (JM#299).

dolomitized in other areas. The process was as follows: (1) moderate heating occurred above a batholith that was beginning to rise beneath the Mineral Belt, and (2) the first rise of the huge Sawatch Range Anticline. This process began in earliest Laramide (late Cretaceous) time.

Tilting of rocks in the anticline caused ground water carrying magnesium, from evaporite-rich Pennsylvanian rocks, to circulate into the Leadville limestone on the flank of the anticline. Elevated temperatures caused these ground waters to dolomitize the limestone. Areas above swells in the batholith were heated so that the dolomite recrystallized. Solutions from these swells or cupolas formed ore deposits in parts of some recrystallized areas.

REFERENCES

A–5 Ridge, (Radabaugh), C–1, C–6, C–12, D–1 Burbank, (Tweto), E–9, G–1, G–5, G–6, I–21, J–41, J–51, K–3, K–16, K–18, K–20, L–1, 1940–1973, Q–14, S–52, S–55, S–83, S–89, S–103.

CLIMAX

Climax Molybdenum Mine

Climax was the name of a station house, on the South Park branch of the Colorado and Southern Railroad, which was on the divide between the Arkansas River and Tenmile Creek, at the head of Tenmile Gulch. This point was the climax, for the narrow gauge engines, of a long uphill pull from Breckenridge and the helper engines were uncoupled and sent back to Breckenridge while the train continued on down the Arkansas Valley to Leadville. The name, Climax, has become synonymous with one of the largest molybdenum mines in the world and today it includes the large open pit, the underground workings, mills, surface workshops, and the tailings pond complex (Fig. 5–37).

The open pit mine includes the area above the old Phillipson Tunnel level and that part of Tenmile Amphitheatre between Bartlett Mountain and Ceresco Ridge. This area is roughly a mile square and is in Lake County. Underground workings now active are in the valley of the East Fork of the Arkansas River southwest of the mill and the Fremont Pass complex of workshops. They are known as the Storke workings. A conveyor belt almost a mile long conveys ore uphill from the Storke crushing plant to the mill.

The Storke Level is the main working level; it is 300 feet below the old Phillipson Tunnel level. A shaft from the Storke Level services the 600 and 900 levels, each 300 feet apart vertically. The 600 and 900 levels are the main haulage levels other than the Storke Level and all ore and materials are moved to and from the work areas along these levels.

Tailings ponds extend down Tenmile Creek, in Summit County, to and over the old mining camp of Kokomo. A gravel plant is operated on the East Fork of the Arkansas River below the Storke Level complex. All this is Climax, sitting

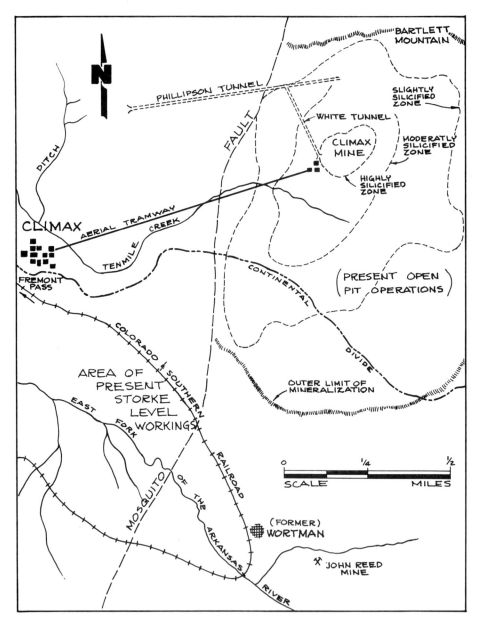

Fig. 5–37. Climax Mine workings in 1933. Adapted from U.S.G.S. Bull. 846–C, 1933.

astride the Continental Divide, producer of a billion pounds of molybdenum by 1966.

In his visit to the Tenmile district, S.F. Emmons was aware of molybdenum in the area and in 1886, he wrote, "In addition to this, copper, bismuth, molybdenum, and vanadium have been locally observed in mineral combination."

In 1890, claims were staked on Bartlett Mountain by Sam and John Webber and E. G. Heckendorf, on a deposit thought to be galena. Later, it was thought to be graphite until the Colorado School of Mines correctly identified the mineral as molybdenum.

In 1902, M. Leal drove an adit into the deposit to explore for gold. Heckendorf started a number of short adits into large blocks of loose rock, float, in the Chalk Mountain area. He continued this work for three years but each outcrop proved to be not in place but float and to have been moved across the Continental Divide by glacial action. Following the glacial debris back to Bartlett Mountain and his old claims, he found other prospectors had staked the area. One of these prospectors, C. J. Senter, had also spent some time driving adits in float and in talus blocks on Chalk Mountain.

Prospecting and limited mining continued in the Leal and White Tunnels but a demand for molybdenum did not develop until World War I when it was discovered that the Germans were bombarding Paris with Big Bertha, a cannon whose barrel was made of molybdenum steel in order to withstand the high pressure developed in hurling missiles a hundred miles or more. Molybdenum which has a melting point of 4,730° F, 2,000° higher than steel, was first added to steel to make armor plate by the French in 1894. It was said that one inch of molybdenum steel would stop as much of a direct hit as four inches of ordinary armor plate steel.

In 1916, the Pengrey Mines and Ore Reduction Co. treated 1,000 tons of Climax ore in their Leadville Mill with apparent success. Claims were consolidated and the Climax Molybdenum Co. became the principal owner of the deposit. By 1918, ore from the White Tunnel was being sent by aerial tramway to a 250 tpd mill in the Fremont Pass area.

After World War I, demand for molybdenum soon faded and by 1919, the mine closed. New uses and new technology, by 1924, allowed the mine to reopen and it has continued in operation up to the present. Today, production is in excess of 48,000 tpd.

By 1931, the Philipson Tunnel, which is 500 feet below the White Tunnel and 300 feet above the Storke Level, had penetrated 500 feet of ore assaying 0.80 percent molybdenite. Drawing ore from this deposit created the Glory Hole. Pressure was a continuing problem and closed concrete-lined drifts shut. This was caused by about 1,000 feet of broken rock, half ore and half from a waste capping, pressing downward. Yieldable steel arches were used to combat this problem.

The Storke Level was developed 300 feet below the Phillipson Level and production started in 1952. By 1955, there were 29,300 feet of haulage drifts. Today, future development is being carried on from the 900 level of the Storke workings.

Open pit mining in the Glory Hole, above the Phillipson Level, was begun in 1964. On May 23, 1963, 417,216 pounds of explosives were loaded into 4 foot square drifts which totaled 600 feet in length. Several months of work went into preparation of one of the largest blasts in U.S. mining history. When the blast occurred it broke 1.5 million tons of ore. In 1973, large scale open pit mining was begun and the open pit produced about 20,000 tons per day for the mill feed.

Tin was recovered from the mill in 1949 and a plant to recover tungsten was being built. A new plant to recover tin, tungsten, and pyrite, for making sulfuric acid, was built in 1959. Of the 33,000 tpd milled in 1960, 150 tons of pyrite, 225,000 pounds of molybdenite, 3,500 pounds of tungsten, in hubnerite concentrates, and 70 pounds of cassiterite concentrates were obtained.

The Mosquito Fault, of which Behre once said "it was known for 33 miles and traceable for not less than 50 miles," goes through the Climax ore body. This fault, one of the major faults in Colorado, divides Precambrian rocks on the east from Pennsylvania-Permian sedimentary formations of the Minturn formation on the west. The ore body is in Pce rocks of the Tenmile Range which have moved up in relation to the west side of the Mosquito Fault. Both sides have been intruded by Tertiary porphyries as dikes, sills, and stocks. An Oligocene stock, the Climax stock, is concealed below the Pce rocks. The ore body has been dated as 30 m.y.B.P.

In the Kokomo–Tenmile district just north of Climax, Bergendahl and Koschmann give the displacement of the Mosquito Fault as probably 8,000 feet. Wallace places the displacement at Climax as 9,000 feet. Tweto says that deep drilling on the west side of the Mosquito Fault has established the Pce as 6,500 feet below the surface and on the basis of the faulted ore body this would make 9,000 feet of post ore displacement. Slices of Dry Union (Miocene) formation are found in the fault zone, which in places is several hundred feet wide.

The Climax stock is wholly within the Precambrian rocks east of the Mosquito Fault. It is a complex stock and was emplaced by four major surges of material rising from a single vent, about 30 million years age. Each surge fractured the previous one and prepared the way for a period of mineralization. The Ceresco ore body followed the first surge of igneous activity; a second surge formed the central mass of the stock and the subsequent upper ore body; the third formed radial dikes and the folowing lower ore body; and the fourth stage emplaced porphyritic granite and rhyolite porphyry. It did not produce any commercial mineralization.

Most of the Ceresco ore body was eroded by glacial action and only the roots remain. Some big blocks that were moved over the divide into the Chalk Mountain area were the ones Heckendorf and later, Senter, prospected with adits thinking they were outcrops and not float.

Molybdenum, as molybdenite and ferrimolybdite, is the most important product at Climax; byproducts tin, tungsten and pyrite are insignificant in comparison. Monazite has been produced as a concentrate, as the market demanded, and topaz was considered for use in the ceramic industry; however, a demand or market didn't develop. The monazite is not a mineral of the Climax stock but comes from adjacent granitic rocks.

Cassiterite has been found as small crystals in vugs but is generally not recognizable in the ore. Hubnerite and wolframite both occur but the tungsten mineral is referred to as hubnerite in everyday usage.

Two curving faults cut the Climax stock without any serious displacement. They are called the East Fault and the South Fault. The East Fault has coarse fluorite, pyrite, and rhodochrosite. It also has fine-grained galena, sphalerite, and chalcopyrite. According to Wallace, this mineralization belongs to the last stage of noneconomic mineralization. The South Fault has coarse fluorite and quartz crystals in small vugs.

Fluorite has been found in pale green crystalline masses and crystals as deep green cubes, some flaoters, as bicolored crystals, usually cubes, and as small blue dodecahedral crystals, as well as in octahedral form (Fig. 5–38).

On the Storke level bicolored and dodecahedral fluorite was associated with quartz, topaz and xanthophyllite (= clintonite, monoclinic, of the mica group).

Pyrite, which is sold for making sulfuric acid and sponge iron, is ever present and is distributed in many small veinlets and cracks quite uniformly throughout the deposit. It has been found in larger veins and vugs as bright and large crystals, sometimes with included fluorite and as floaters in mud pockets. Much of the larger pyrite is flat and rectangular in habit with one axis much smaller than the other two; cathedral striations are found on some crystals (Figs. 5–39 and 5–40).

Miners tell of seeing pyrite crystals with slivers or small, pointed, needle-like spikes developed along edges of cubes or protruding from them in various directions. These slivers (Fig. 5–41) have been recovered from the water ditches; however, blasting usually clears them from the parent crystal. They often leave solution-pit-type holes where they formerly were.

During World War II, underground work was suspended until 1946, and the

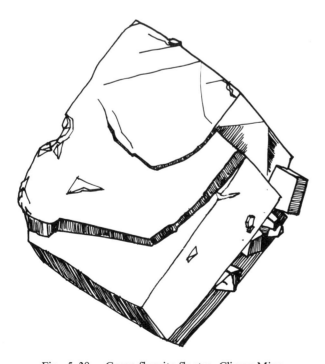

Fig. 5–38.   Green fluorite floater, Climax Mine.

Fig. 5-39. Pyrite showing cathedral striations, Climax Molybdenum Mine (H-83) T.E.C.

mill feed was taken from stockpiles of ore. It was said that large pyrite cubes were seen in some of this ore; however few were saved from the mill. Recent reports of pyrite cubes one foot on an edge have been circulated, but only one near that size has been seen. Possibly others went into museum or private collections.

Brannerite and ilmenorutile have been found in the tin and tungsten concentrates. Smoky quartz has been found in a few vugs and it is possible that the brannerite could be the source of radiation that caused the change in color.

Rhodochrosite occurs as deep red rhombs in the Ceresco 414 south section

Fig. 5-40. Pyrite showing parallel twinning, Climax Molybdenum Mine (JM#940).

of the Storke Level and is found as light pink crystalline matrix in the north 6170 drift.

Locations of minerals from underground in the larger mines are often incorrect and purposely misleading as the miners often do not disclose the true working place from which specimens were obtained. To do so might put them in jeopardy with management, which usually discourages specimen hunting by its employees. A location given may, however, be one from which similar specimens might have been found.

Wallace says veins of coarse rhodochrosite and fluorite are found in the rocks surrounding the mine. This, of course, is in reference to the rhodochrosite from the John Reed Mine in the old Alicante mining district, which is in the headwaters of the East Fork of the Arkansas River. This mine, which is now a part of the Climax Mine property, is up the gulch from the Storke workings.

A large mass of cordierite was reported in 1976. This mass, 8 feet by 2 feet, was said to be the largest on record.

Powellite, aikinite and alaskaite, a mixture of sulfosalts and not a specific mineral, have been reported.

Blue apatite crystals were reported by Kosnar and Miller.

Frondel in writing about mineral incrustations upon the edges and corners of crystals, describes two specimens of rhodochrosite with dolomite in parallel growth from the John Reed Mine, Alicante Gulch.

These specimens of pale rose-red rhodochrosite rhombohedrons, up to 1 cm. on an edge, are incrusted by minute dolomite rhombohedrons with a vitreous appearance, which are aligned in parallel position along the edges of the crystals. One specimen had these dolomite crystals at the corners only, while the other specimen had the dolomite crystals forming a continuous ridge along the edges of the rhodochrosite crystals. Oriented overgrowth of dolomite upon rhodochrosite had not been previously described at that time.

Orthoclase crystals have been found in the Lincoln porphyry at Climax.

John Reed Mine and the Alicante District

It is anticipated that work on the Storke Level may some day (if it does not now) extend under the old workings on the John Reed and other mines in the Alicante district. This will indeed be of interest to mineral collectors as the rhodochrosite that has come from the John Reed and from the Climax Mine ranks with the finest ever found in Colorado.

Mines which were developed in the Summit or Alicante district in the 1880s were the Alicante, John Reed, Gold Field, Walter Scott, Miners College and others. The Alicante, U.S. Survey No. 948 was one of the oldest patents: the John Reed was U.S. Survey No. 11,682. A 2,000 foot aerial tramway connected the Walter Scott with a 20 stamp mill. Alicante, the town, was said to have been destroyed by 1888.

According to an old report by Schwartz, the Alicante Mine and John Reed claims Nos. 1-5, which adjoined the mine on the south claim endline, were

Fig. 5-41. Pyrite sliver (whisker), Climax Mine.

within 1,000 feet of the tracks of the Denver, Leadville, and Gunnison Railroad (Colorado and Southern Railroad) at Wortman Siding, which was 1½ miles from Climax Station.

The Alicante vein was east of a strong porphyry dike, eight to ten feet wide, and at one place it cut through this dike. It could be traced on the surface by pits and excavations which strike N 14 degrees E; the vein dips 45 to 52 degrees from horizontal, making it a rather flat vein. It was cut 164 feet from the portal of the tunnel and from this point it was 238 feet to the working face. Mineralization, which varied from 0 to 33 inches and averaged 22 inches wide, consisted of pyrite, zinc and lead sulfides, chalcopyrite, quartz and manganese spar, (rhodochrosite). The ore streak was massive sulfides with but little quartz and spar mixed in.

The John Reed incline shaft was 354 feet south of the Alicante claim end-line, in the bottom of the valley. It was timbered to the 70 foot level and full of water below this point. North of the incline shaft the ore was 6 inches to 15 inches wide in the face and it consisted of spar. The dump was made up of this material and crosscut rock and contained about 250 tons. A sample of pyrite from the north face assayed 2.00 ounces gold and 4.00 ounces silver per ton. Surface buildings at the mine at the time Schwartz examined it included the 60 foot by 30 foot John Reed shaft house, 48 foot by 20 foot boarding house two stories high, and a 36 foot by 16 foot bunk house. There was a No. 5 Cameron pump, a hoist, and a boiler, all in good condition. On a list of needed supplies in case the owner decided to reactivate the mine, was timber squared at $13.00/1,000 feet, powder at 15 cents per pound, and candles (Goodwin) at $3.75 per box. The report was not favorable and it is questionable if the mine was reopened at that time. It is not known if the John Reed Mine was worked at a later date.

NORTH OF CLIMAX

Kokomo–Tenmile Mining District

Kokomo–Tenmile mining district extends northward from Fremont Pass in Lake County down the headwaters of Tenmile Creek for approximately fifteen miles into Summit County. The western edge of the district is in Eagle County and the crest of the Tenmile Range marks the eastern boundary. Tenmile Creek and the old mining community of Kokomo center this district (Fig. 5–42).

In 1860, prospectors coming up the Arkansas River drainage crossed the Divide, now Fremont Pass, into the upper reaches of Tenmile Creek and discovered gold in the upper part of McNulty Gulch. Placer miners from Breckenridge were familiar with the lower part of Tenmile Creek and had given it this name as it was ten miles down the Blue River Valley from Breckenridge. Although spotty, the placers of McNulty Gulch were rich and some areas of no more than twenty square feet produced from $10,000 to $20,000 in mineral value. Native silver in masses weighing up to a pound and gold nuggets up to two and a half ounces were found. Veins of argentiferous galena in the cirques of the Tenmile Range, east of the Mosquito Fault, were worked in the early 1860s and were probably the source of the rich placers. The adits and pits on these veins were so difficult to reach and to work that they were soon abandoned and tunnels, mostly unsuccessful, were started from lower elevations to intersect the veins. Early production is not known. Old workings can be seen

Fig. 5–42.   The old mining camp of Kokomo, Colorado. This area is now covered by a thick deposit of tailings. W.H.

from the Tenmile Valley and in their positions high in the amphitheatre walls they seem impossible places to mine. As late as World War II, a few remaining old time miners in the district were holding the interest of newcomers with tales of 1,500 ounce silver ore from the Tenmile Range.

West of the Mosquito Fault along Tenmile Creek and the Tenmile Fault, which parallels the Mosquito Fault, Bonanza silver ore was found in 1878. The ore was at the contact of limestones of the Minturn formation with porphyry intrusions. The most productive beds were the Robinson limestone, middle bed of the White Quail limestone, and to a lesser extent the Jacque Mountain limestone.

Two to three thousand people rushed to the district and the towns of Robinson, Kokomo, and Recen were established. Kokomo burned in 1882, whereupon, everyone moved to Recen and renamed that town Kokomo.

By 1879 fifty mines on Sheep Mountain reported ore from 3 to 34 feet thick, some of which averaged up to 280 ounces of silver per ton.

A toll road over Argentine Pass from Georgetown was completed and the first stagecoach arrived August 9, 1879. Railroads reached the district, first from Leadville over Fremont Pass in 1881 and then from Breckenridge, up Tenmile Creek in 1883. Three smelters were constructed and ore was processed for shipment by railroad.

The largest mine of the district was the Robinson. It was named for G. B. Robinson, a Leadville merchant who was Lieutenant Governor of Colorado at that time. A year after discovery of the mine Robinson was fatally shot by a guard hired to keep adverse claimants off the property. The No. 1 ore shoot in the Robinson was said to have produced about six million dollars worth of ore; however, by 1881, the enriched oxidized ore was gone and the mine could not fulfill its contracts with the smelters. Population fluctuated with metal prices in the Kokomo–Tenmile district and after the Silver Panic of 1893, Kokomo was almost a ghost town. Both wars brought renewed activity.

Surface ores were easy to smelt to obtain the enriched metal values, but this ore was soon gone. This was a familiar story to the early mining camps of the west. The sulfide primary ore was difficult to treat and a great deal of interest and effort was expended in roasting plants and other ways of trying to get rid of the zinc in the ore. The lead smelters penalized sphalerite ores as the zinc would freeze (solidify) the melted smelter charge. The only way to clear such a furnace was to cool it and then drill and blast it out. This was quite a costly and time consuming undertaking, so it is not surprising they exacted a zinc penalty.

In 1895, A. R. Wilfley invented a concentrating table that separated the sphalerite from the other mineral grains. This type of table still bears his name and is in universal use in some mills. Development of this table helped to keep the district alive to a limited extent by separating the zinc from the other concentrates.

A. H. Rine reopened some of the old mines in 1934 and started the period of greatest activity for the district. Production from 1942 to 1950 was $13.8 million in zinc, lead, silver, gold, and copper.

The Lucky Strike Mine was the largest producing mine in this period. Other mines producing were the Wilfley, Victory, McKinley, Wilson, Michigan-Snowbank group, Colonel Sellers, Silver Cloud and Queen of the West. In the Lucky Strike Mine solid sulfide ore occurred 12 to 35 feet thick in beds between walls of Robinson limestone and White Quail porphyry.

Interest in molybdenum in 1917 caused some activity in the tactite zones of the district. Two miles north of Kokomo, at the level of the old wagon road, a tunnel was driven 540 feet into a breccia zone in which molybdenum, calcite, and garnet occurred. Assays of 1 percent molybdenum were obtained; however, the Pengrey Mill at Leadville failed to make a good recovery on 500 tons and the venture failed.

By 1950, the tailings ponds of the Climax Mine were beginning to advance over the old Kokomo townsite. Today Kokomo is a memory.

Three types of mineral deposits were found in the Kokomo–Tenmile mining district, most important of which were the massive sulfide replacement bodies. Two types of vein deposits, one in which pyrite, sphalerite, and galena were found and which usually led to replacement bodies in the limestone, and one in which coarse calcite and minor quartz was found. High temperature veins, disseminations, and replacement bodies in epidote and garnet tactite zones were the third type. Magnetite and molybdenite occurred in the garnet.

At Kokomo, the Bonanza surface ores were soon mined out. Oxidized minerals were similar to those found at Leadville.

Replacement sulfide ore bodies occurred in the Robinson, White Quail, and Jacque Mountain limestone beds of the Minturn formation of Pennsylvanian age. These ore bodies were 100 feet to 2,000 feet in length, a few inches to 100 feet in thickness, and up to 35 feet wide. The principal primary ore minerals were pyrite, marcasite, pyrrhotite, minor arsenopyrite, sphalerite, galena, and chalcopyrite. Gangue minerals were fine grained quartz, phases in the calcite–rhodochrosite–siderite series, and phases in the dolomite–ankerite–kutnahorite series.

Banded ore, possibly traceable to the original banding in the limestone, was found in the Lucky Strike Mine. Some of this ore displayed a graphic texture that was formed by large tabular crystals of pyrite, possibly pseudomorphs of pyrrhotite intergrown with sphalerite and, to a lesser extent, with galena. The common name of vermiform was given to ore of this structure. This type of ore was also found in the Eagle Mine at Gilman, and at Leadville.

Large irregular-shaped masses of pyrrhotite with minor pyrite and marcasite were found in the replacement beds. Arsenopyrite crystals were present but due to the fine-grained size of the ore, they could not be detected with a hand lens. Marcasite and pyrite replaced pyrrhotite in many places. Galena was sometimes encased in jasperoid and crystals were few. Marmatitic sphalerite was found throughout the district; however, amber-colored sphalerite occurred in the Free America Mine on Jacques Peak where crystals up to eight inches in longest dimension were found.

High temperature vein and metamorphic deposits occurred on Copper and Tucker Mountains. Garnet, epidote, calcite, wollastonite, chlorite, sericite, biotite, magnetite, and molybdenite were the minerals of these deposited.

The Denver and Rio Grande Tunnel explored a 2½ to 5 feet bed of garnet impregnated with molybdenite. The Boston Cooney vein was all crystalline calcite with much zoning of the individual crystals. This vein was 12 to 20 feet wide and could be traced on Tucker Mountain for about 2,000 feet. Future study of this vein may prove it to be a carbonatite deposit.

In high temperature veins of this district, magnetite, molybdenite and hematite were deposited near the source and further away along the veins pyrite, pyrrhotite, sphalerite, and galena were deposited.

Minerals of the replacement deposits and veins near the Ten Mile Fault, which was parallel to the Mosquito Fault, but in the center of Ten Mile Gulch were: pyrite, pyrrhotite, marcasite, arsenopyrite, galena, sphalerite, chalcopyrite, molybdenite, pearceite, enargite, gold, fluorite, hematite, magnetite, rhodochrosite, siderite, covellite, silver, cerussite, smithsonite, malachite, azurite, anglesite, goethite, limonite, pyrolusite, psilomelane, and pyromorphite.

Kutnohorite which forms a series with dolomite and ankerite was reported from the Kokomo district. This mineral has been mistaken for rhodochrosite and for rhodonite, to the degree that in the fine-grained gangue it is not easily identified. Barite, rhodonite, and rhodochrosite were reported from the White Quail Mine by Emmons and later by Vanderwilt.

Tetradymite was reported by Eckel. Joseite was reported by Grybec from specimens in the Colorado School of Mines collection. The bismuth minerals occurred with galena. Although this joseite specimen was marked only Summit County, Colorado, on the label, it probably was from the Kokomo area.

Nickel and chrome were trace elements found in the ore.

Euhedral phenocrysts of orthoclase, tending toward the adularia variety, were found in and weathered from the Lincoln porphyry at Kokomo and at Robinson. These crystals were up to three inches long. This was a Dana location, but is now under the tailings from the Climax mine. (Fig. 5–43)

Big Four Mine, Summit County

The Big Four Mine is above the north bank of Green Mountain Reservoir, in Summit County. Colorado Highway No. 9 passes 75 feet below the portal and dump. The mine was located in 1937 by Walter McDaniel and his wife, Frances, and worked by the family for some years. The area had not been considered a likely place for mineralization, however, the McDaniels had prospected the area since 1933 and finally located the source of float mineralization. The find caused some local excitement and mining started in 1937 with only modest production.

Production for the period 1941 to 1944 was about 1,650 tons of ore with a grade of 30 to 35 percent zinc.

The ore was trucked to Kremmling and shipped by rail to the International Smelting Company at Tooele, Utah or to Combined Metals at Bauer, Utah.

Minerals Yearbooks show the mine working in 1950, 1959, and again in

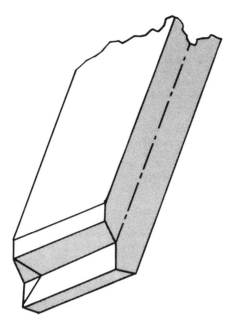

Fig. 5–43. Orthoclase, Manebach twin, Kokomo, Dana location.

1964. The Bureau of Reclamation grouted the area heavily to prevent leakage from Green Mountain Reservoir and closed the old portal.

Mrs. McDaniel continued to prospect the area above the reservoir level, and as late as the 1970s hoped to find other deposits of sphalerite.

The ore deposit of the Big Four Mine is in the Dakota sandstone which has been intruded by porphyry dikes. Green Mountain, on which the property is located, is formed by a series of domed sills in the form of a crude laccolith. Cretaceous shales through which this mass intruded have been squeezed and badly broken. The ore deposit was confined to the underlying Dakota sandstone which was metamorphosed to a quartzite.

In the center of the laccolith a plug of similar porphyry may occupy a vent. Deposits of scoria are found within a two to three mile radius of this vent, which the plug now occupies. Dikes radiate from Green Mountain. This igneous activity is dated as Pliocene by Tweto. The Pliocene occurred from 3 to 12 m.y.B.P.

The ore was a high grade sphalerite which was partly oxidized to a depth of 150 feet. It occurs along a fault that has the Dakota quartzite on one side and the porphyry on the other. Mineralization occurs in open spaces along the fault and extends into the fractured and broken quartzite for fifteen to twenty feet. A second fracture zone was encountered about 400 feet from the portal. It follows a fold in the quartzite. This second zone was cut in a branching drift by a postmineral fault about three hundred feet from the main drift. This same postmineral fault cut the main drift at about six hundred feet from the portal. A large body of sphalerite was mined at this point and evidently was all the ore found in the mine.

Sphalerite occurred in the Big Four Mine in crystals up to four inches across. They contained minor amounts of galena and chalcopyrite and some were coated with a thin layer of quartz. Silver averaged between 10 and 20 ounces per ton and gold from 0.02 to 0.05 ounces per ton. Shipments of oxidized ore were said to have run as hgh as 150 to 200 ounces silver per ton and one shipment contained 8 ounces gold per ton.

Northgate Mines

Northgate Mines is a name that is in common usage for a group of fluorspar mines on the southwest side of Pinkham Mountain, North Park. These are about 2½ air miles northeast of the Northgate Station on the Union Pacific Railroad and about a mile east of the junction of Colorado Routes 125 and 127 (Fig. 5–44). The Pinkham Mountain access road leaves Route 127 and goes north, east of Dean Peak, a half mile to the Pember Shaft and incline, which are the southerly workings of the group. Garo Open Cut and Tunnel are adjacent and just below Ozark–Mahoning Company's townsite for employees. The Fluorspar Mine and numerous open cuts and tunnels are above the mill and Springer Open Pit is further up on the mountain. The road continues uphill to the Fluorine Mine and the Camp Creek Mine. These mines were worked by various owners and lessees over the years but most of them were consolidated as a group by Ozark–Mahoning Company, the last operator and present owner.

Prospectors looking for copper deposits in 1900 probably first found the fluorspar veins on Pinkham Mountain. In 1918, the material was identified after Frank Heaton and Charles Baker filed on the Feldspar claim. In 1921, they filed on four more claims and changed the name of the first one to Fluorspar. It became the Fluorspar Mine.

Colorado Fluorspar Company bought the claims and mined them from 1922 to 1926 when the price of fluorspar dropped. During this period the 90 level and 200 level tunnels were started on the original Feldspar claim which became the Fluorspar No. 2 claim. Garo Tunnel, on Fluorspar No. 1 claim, was started and about 15,000 tons of metallurgical grade fluorspar, for use as a flux in the steel mills, was produced in this period. The mines on this vein system were mostly idle from 1927 to 1941.

The Pember property was leased from the State of Colorado's school land in 1937, and a 90 foot shaft produced a small tonnage of fluorspar before it was closed.

Fluorine-Camp Creek vein was staked by Fred Baker and others in 1924 and relocated by Baker in 1928; Baker Open Pit was started and a 40 foot shaft sunk. In 1941, the old mill was rehabilitated only to burn in December, 1942, after only five months production. A new 450 tpd sink-float plant was built only to be replaced by a new flotation mill in 1952 after Ozark–Mahoning Company acquired the mines in 1951.

In the Garo Tunnel there were three roughly parallel veins, one vein was massive green and green-yellow botryoidal fluorite. Quartz monzonite in a

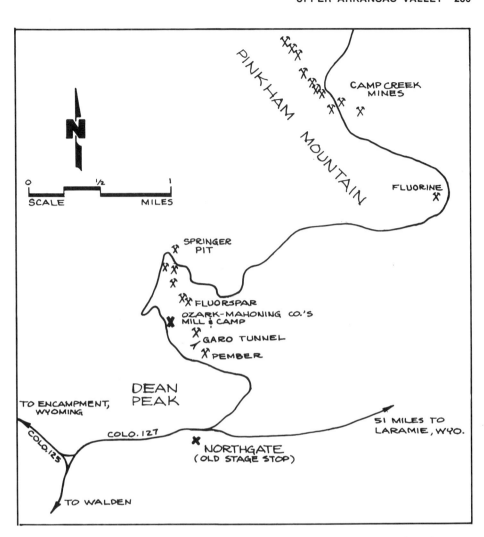

Fig. 5-44.   Northgate fluorspar location map. Adapted from U.S.G.S. 7½ Quadrangle Maps: Northgate and Kings Canyon.

mass 400 to 500 feet wide was cut in these workings; however, granite was the most persistent wall rock of the Garo Tunnel and in the 200 level tunnel of the Fluorspar Mine on the same vein system. Two roughly parallel fissures were worked in the 200 level tunnel. They were from 50 to 150 feet apart on the south end, above the Garo Tunnel, but were 250 to 300 feet apart on the north end. By 1955, a heading had been advanced 340 feet on the west vein and the east vein heading was in 2,200 feet. Short drifts connected the two workings at frequent intervals. By 1943, the Fluorspar No. 2 workings through the 200 level tunnel had produced over 10,000 tons of ore. Production was greatly increased after 1951 when Ozark–Mahoning Company started operation of the group.

Baker Open Pit was mined by dragline excavator in 1943 and about 30,000 tons of fluorspar produced. This production was increased to 34,000 tons in 1944.

The 90 foot tunnel on the Fluorspar No. 2 was converted to an open cut mine in 1944 and produced about 20,000 tons. Pember Incline was down to 200 feet, however, the old Pember Shaft was not worked.

On the northwest-trending fluorite vein a continuation called the Camp Creek vein was discovered in 1943. By 1956, the Fluorine-Camp Creek vein had been opened for a length of 4,400 feet and large tonnages of ore were produced by use of power shovels. Ore of economic interest was found for up to 200 feet away from the vein in the hanging-wall block. The Aluminum Company of America bought the Camp Creek deposit in 1950 and spent six years exploring the large deposit but did not produce any ore.

Ozark–Mahoning Company worked the mines on a large scale after 1951 and into the middle 1970s when economic conditions were unfavorable and the mines were put on standby status (see Fig. 5–45).

Steven (1960) estimated the area capable of producing several million tons of concentrates and the Northgate group was considered to be the largest deposit of fluorspar in the western United States.

Pinkham Mountain is a spur of the Medicine Bow Mountains of Wyoming and is made up of Precambrian rocks which includes quartz monzonite and granite–intruded metamorphic rocks. A large stock of quartz monzonite with associated dikes forms much of the mountain.

Independence Mountain thrust fault closes off the north end of North Park Basin,which formerly extended much further north. This fault has thrust Precambrian rocks and Jurassic and younger rocks over younger sedimentary

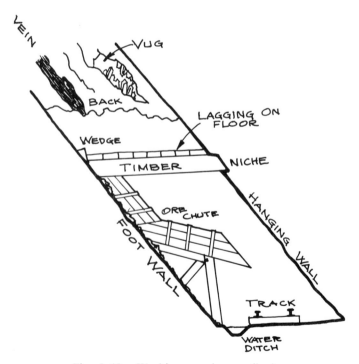

Fig. 5–45.   Working areas in a small mine.

rocks of the North Park Basin. The Independence Mountain thrust fault and other Laramide-age faults of the North Park Basin are mineralized by siliceous fluorspar, which is purple, green or white and is coarse-grained, has much silica as chalcedony, and white comb quartz. These deposits are not of economic grade at this time.

The principal fluorspar deposits of the North Park Basin are in Tertiary age faults of the northeast trending Pember–Garo–Fluorspar vein system and the northwest trending Fluorite Camp Creek vein system. The Pember–Garo–Fluorspar vein extends into the center of the Pinkham Mountain quartz monzonite stock. There has been much crushing and magmatic stoping of the earlier Precambrian rocks in this area and the material has been described as a gross breccia. Magmatic stoping occurs when rocks above a magma chamber drop down into the melt and leave a space for the magma to rise into.

In late Oligocene and Miocene time, between the time of deposition of the Tertiary White River formation and development of a surface upon which the North Park formation was deposited, direction of stream flow in the North Park Basin was reversed from south to north. Old paleovalleys containing White River tuffaceous clays and silts were cut by the Fluorine-Camp Creek vein. Fluorspar replaced and impregnated some of the White River formation at these old paleovalley crossings. Fluorspar forms boxwork ore in which angular fragments of a white clay, which was determined by x-ray studies to be composed of montmorillonite and fine-grained fluorite, was encased. Fluorite-Camp Creek vein system is traceable for 2½ miles and dies out in the White River formation. It is the larger of the two most prominent vein systems.

These deposits were worked through a vertical range of only 600 feet in the Pember–Garo–Fluorspar vein and 370 feet in the Fluorine-Camp Creek vein. They are thought to have been deposited at a temperature of 100 to 150° C., and an igneous source is most probable.

Fluorspar deposits at Brown's Canyon and Poncha Springs seem to be related to the Upper Arkansas Graben. North-trending vein-faults on the west side of North Park are on the line of projection of the Upper Arkansas Graben faults. The Crystal Mine is the largest development along these faults.

In the Fluorine-Camp Creek vein, crystals of fluorite up to two inches, showing color banding, were found. Boxwork ore was composed of fluorspar and not as siliceous as ore in the Crystal Mine. The montmorillonite and granular fluorite encased in this ore was still present in most specimens; however, some had been washed out and green and deep purple botryoidal fluorite coated the walls of the boxwork structure.

Calcite occurs at one place along the Independence Mountain Fault zone, on Pinkham Mountain.

In the Northgate Fluorspar Mines open cavities and water courses occur along the veins. In the Pember Incline an open cavity 20 feet long, and 100 feet high occurred. Crystals are rare as the fluorite occurs in mammillary, botryoidal and stalactitic forms. Breccia of wall rock and of earlier fluorspar, sealed by later fluorspar, is common and much reopening and resealing of the veins is evident. The fluorspar contains fine granular silica and chalcedony occurs in some of the ore. In some cavities, crystal terminations showing three cubic faces were found, but mostly these terminations were not recognizable. Concentric fluorite shells of different colors and inclusions surrounded by concentric rings of pyrite-marcasite banding, called cockade ore by the miners, occurred.

Minerals of the Northgate and Crystal fluorspar deposits are: fluorite, quartz, chalcedony, feldspar, chlorite, iron sulfides (pyrite or marcasite or a combination of both), gypsum, montmorillonite, melanterite, as greenish-yellow incrustations, and ilsemanite, molybdenum bloom, which is thought to have been derived from jordisite, which occurs as a black amorphous mineral. Gearksutite is also thought to occur but like jordisite has not been confirmed by laboratory study.

Crystal Mine

North-trending fluorspar veins of the Crystal Mine and the adjacent area are on the east side of the Park Range on the west side of North Park. The mine is about 18 miles west of Walden. Pitchpine Mountain access road skirts Delaney Buttes to the south and climbs from North Park onto the Park Range passing the Crystal Mine on the way uphill.

An early period of mining resulted in extensive trenching and numerous open cuts along the veins. One small prospect pit was entirely in earthy-red hematite and relic marcasite. This material occurred in the dump.

Ozark–Mahoning Company was the last operator of this mine, in the middle 1970s, and ore was trucked to their mill at Northgate for processing. The mine is developed by two adits, one 150 feet above the other. The upper adit was the principal working, as much of the lower adit is caved. Production was not large enough to distinguish from the other mines worked by Ozark–Mahoning Company and was probably totaled with other mill feed.

Pce rocks of the Park Range have been intruded by granite and quartz monzonites. Faults, some of which are mineralized with siliceous fluorspar, iron sulfides and uranium in minor amounts, are assumed to be of three distinct ages; Precambrian, Laramide, and Tertiary. At the Crystal Mine a vein system, containing fluorspar from 0 to 12 feet wide, was followed for several thousand feet northward. Gray, white (milky), purple, green, banded fluorspar occurred. Several periods of mineralization were recognized; however, the deposit more closely fits the Laramide mineralization as described at Northgate and elsewhere in the North Park area by Steven.

A number of veins that parallel the vein exposed in the Crystal Mine workings were located from aerial surveys made in 1972; some of these had widths up to 50 feet. When the North Park fluorspar mines were closed for economic reasons in the mid 1970s, development of these veins was also stopped.

The Crystal Mine ore is more siliceous than ore from the Northgate workings. In the oxidized ore, pyrite and marcasite were altered to massive hematite and limonite-goethite. Some marcasite is in near-cockscomb-type habit. Quartz forms boxwork structures and banded fluorite occurs in a breccia zone.

Mine water is depositing an unidentified uranium mineral from this deposit. Fluorite extensively replaced pyrite.

A fluorite vein 3½ miles north of the Crystal Mine (Pedal claims) had a radioactive black chalcedony associated with dark purple fluorite. Samples ran as high as 0.34 percent uranium on the black chalcedony. The radioactive mineral has not been identified; however urananite is suspected to be responsible. The fluorspar was slightly radioactive.

Delaney Buttes

About ten miles west of Walden, Delaney Buttes rise as a prominent landmark above surrounding North Park. These buttes are just east of the Park Range, and they are a mass of Precambrian granitic rock in fault contact with sedimentary rocks ranging in age from Tertiary to Holocene. Small and economically unimportant fluorspar veins occur near the top of the buttes. They contain colorless to light green fluorite in octahedral crystals. Pyrite is disseminated in the host rock but does not seem to be in the fluorspar. Most of the fluorspar found in North Park does not occur as fluorite crystals and these small deposits are of interest because they contain octahedral fluorite.

Mount Ethel Pluton

In their study of the Mount Ethel pluton, an oval-shaped intrusive body about 7 by 40 miles in axial dimensions in the Park Range east of Steamboat Springs and west of Walden, Colorado, Snyder and Hedge determined that it contained fluorite as a common accessory mineral. The 1.4 b.y.B.P. Mount Ethel rocks belong to a group of Precambrian intrusives which have been dated by numerous workers as having been emplaced between what is now the Great Plains and the Colorado Plateau in the interval of 1,000 to 2,000 m.y.B.P. This group includes the Pikes Peak batholith and other batholiths of the Colorado Front Range; of the Medicine Bow and Laramie Mountains of Wyoming; the Sawatch Range of central Colorado; and the Needle Mountains, Black Canyon area, and Uncompahgre Uplift area of western and southwestern Colorado.

Of this grouping the St. Kevin granite, west of the Leadville mining district in the Sawatch Range; members of the Sherman granite bodies including Sheep Mountain quartz monzonite at the head of North Park; and the Mount Ethel pluton, and including the quartz monzonite at Northgate which is considered to be part of this pluton, were all found to contain interstitial fluorite.

Fluorite was found in 70 percent of the 149 thin sections of the Roxy Ann Lake quartz monzonite member of the Mount Ethel pluton which were examined petrographically. (Roxy Ann Lake quartz monzonite extends southwest from the vicinity of the Crystal Mine.) This Precambrian fluorite is considered magmatic in origin and was formed by some process of magmatic differentiation about 1.4 b.y.B.P. Three kinds of fluorite, possibly representing three different ages, have been recognized. Evidence of an ancient age for the fluorite is confirmed by petrographic studies which show the usually colorless fluorite to be pink, purple, or deep purple next to zircon or allanite, due to radiation damage over a long period of time.

The Precambrian fluorite was possibly mobile in Laramide or in Tertiary time and was concentrated in quartz monzonite breccia reefs near the Crystal Mine. All true fluorite vein zones in the North Park area that have been worked recently are in rocks equivalent to or are in Roxy Ann Lake quartz monzonites. These fluorite vein zones strike generally northward except the one on Delaney Butte.

There is more silica in the fluorite from the Park Range veins than in the Northgate fluorspar. A white, siliceous fluorspar, that was not seen in the Northgate deposits, occurs in the Park Range deposits.

Recent reports indicate the Crystal Mine is badly caving on the surface and the area is posted as a dangerous caving area.

A shaft was sunk on the Northgate workings, above No. 2 tunnel, but work was discontinued due to economic conditions. This area is also posted.

REFERENCES

A–4 Lindgren Volume, (Vanderwilt), (Burbank), A–5 Ridge, (Wallace), B–2, C–18, D–1, D–3, E–1, E–11, E–13, G–1, G–5, G–8, J–1, J–18, J–20, J–24, J–39, J–48, J–65, J–68, J–71, J–72, K–3, K–16, K–18, L–1, 1948–1964, N–8, N–19, N–20, O–14 Hawley (Tweto), Guide 1, Q–66, R–10, R–16, S–7, S–8, S–9, S–10, S–17, S–31, S–32, S–49, S–52, S–60, S–81, S–110, S–129, S–148.

BIBLIOGRAPHY

American Institute of Mining, Metallurgy and Petroleum Engineers

A-1   Bird, W.H., 1975, Geology and the economic potential of the Platoro caldera, southeast San Juan mountains, Colorado: Paper presented at 18th annual mineral symposium of Colorado plateau section, A.I.M.E., Grand Junction, Colorado, May 30–31.

A-2   Comstock, T.B., 1889, Hot springs formations in Red Mountain district, Colorado, A.I.M.E. Trans. v. 17, pp. 261–264.

A-3   Cook, D.R., 1961, Bonanza project, Bear Creek Mining Company, A.I.M.M. & P.E., Trans. 1960, v. 217, pp. 285–295.

A-4   Committee on the Lindgren Volume, 1933, Ore deposits of the western states, Lindgren volume, A.I.M.M.E., New York,

      Burbank, W.S. and Lovering, T. S., Relation to stratigraphy, structure, and igneous activity to ore deposition of Colorado and southern Wyoming, chapter VI, part 5, p.p. 272–316.

      Schmitt, H., Summary of the geologic and metallogenic history of Arizona and New Mexico, chapter VI, part 6, pp. 324–325.

      Singewald, J.T., Jr., Genetic groups of hypogene deposits and their occurrence in the western United States, chapter XI.

      ——, Magmatic segregations, chapter XI, part 1, pp. 520–521.

      Hess, F.L., The pegmatites of the western states, chapter XI, part 2, pp. 526–536.

      Knope, A., Pyrometasomatic deposits, chapter XI, part 3, pp. 542, 547–548, 552–554.

      McLaughlin, D.H., Hypothermal deposits, chapter XI, part 4.

      Vanderwilt, J.W., Molybdenite deposits, chapter XI, part 4, pp. 572–573.

      McKnight, E.T., Mesothermal silver–lead–zinc deposits, chapter XI, part 5, pp. 589, 599, 601.

      Nolan, T.B., Epithermal deposits, chapter XI, part 6.

      Burbank, W.S., Base metals, chapter XI, part 6, pp. 645–649.

      Hewitt, D.F. and Pardee, J.T., Manganese, chapter XI, part 6, pp. 675–681.

      Henderson, C.W., The history and influence of mining in the western United States, chapter XIII, pp. 730–770, 773–777.

A-5   Ridge, J.D., Ed., 1968, Ore deposits of the United States, 1933–1967, Graton-Sales Volume, A.I.M.M. & P.E., New York, v. 1, part V, Colorado Rockies

      Tweto, O., Geologic setting and interrelationships of mineral deposits in the mountain province of Colorado and south-central Wyoming, sec. 27, pp. 551–588.

      Wallace, S.R. and others, Multiple intrusion and mineralization at Climax, Colorado, sec. 29, pp. 605–640.

      Radabaugh, R.E., Merchant, J.S. and Brown, J.M., Geology and ore deposits of The Gilman (Redcliff, Battle Mountain) district, Eagle County, Colorado, sec. 30, pp. 641–665.

Tweto, O., Leadville district, Colorado, sec. 32, pp. 681–705.

Steven, T.A., Ore deposits in the central San Juan mountains, Colorado, sec. 33, pp. 706–713.

Burbank, W.S. and Luedke, R. G., Geology and ore deposits of the western San Juan mountains, Colorado, sec. 34, pp. 714–733.

    v. I, part VI, Colorado Plateau Uranium Deposits

Fischer, R.P., The uranium and vanadium deposits of the Colorado Plateau region, sec. 35, pp. 735–747.

Kelley, V.C., Kittel, D.F. and Melancon, P.E., Uranium deposits of the Grants region, sec. 36, pp. 752–769.

    v. II, part IX, Arizona and Adjacent Areas

Anderson, C.A., Arizona and adjacent New Mexico, sec. 56, pp. 1172–1177.

Hernon, R.M. and Jones, W.R., Ore deposits of the central mining district, Grant County, New Mexico, sec. 58, pp. 1211–1237.

Carpenter, R.H., Geology and ore deposits of the Questa molybdenum mine area, Taos County, New Mexico, sec. 63, pp. 1328–1350.

    v. II, part XII, General

Graton, L.C., Lindgren's ore classifiction after fifty years, sec. 81, pp. 1703–1712.

Ridge, J.D., Changes and developments in concepts of ore genesis—1933–1967, pp. 1813–1834.

A-6   Somers, R.E., 1915, Geology of the Burro mountains copper district, New Mexico, doctoral thesis, Cornell Univ. and Reprinted Bull. 101, A.I.M.E., Sept., 1915, pp. 957–996.

American Mineralogist

B-1   Burbank, W.S., 1933, The Manganese minerals of the Sunnyside veins, Eureka Gulch, Colorado, Am. Min. v. 18, no. 12, 1933, pp. 513–527.

B-2   Goldring, E.D., 1942, An occurrence of ilsemanite, Am. Min. v. 27, pp. 707–719.

B-3   Howland, Arthur L., 1936, An occurrence of barite in the red beds of Colorado, Am. Min. v. 21, pp. 584–588.

B-4   Kelley, V.C., 1940, Iceland spar in New Mexico, Am. Min. v. 25, pp. 357–367.

B-5   Mayo, E.B., and O'Leary, J.W., 1934, Oligonite, a manganosiderite from Leadville, Colorado, Am. Min. v. 19, p. 304.

B-6   Rogers, A.F., and Cahn, Lazard, 1937, Quartz with pinacoid faces from Nathrop, Chaffee County, Colorado (abs.): Am. Min. v. 22, no. 12, pt. 2, pp. 13–14.

Colorado Geological Survey Bulletin and Colorado Bureau of Mines

C-1   Colorado Bureau of Mines, 15th Biennial Report, (1919) for 1917–1918, pp. 64, 66, 94.

C-2   Colorado Bureau of Mines, Annual Report (1958).

C-3   Colorado Bureau of Mines, Annual Report (1960).

C-4   Colorado Bureau of Mines, Annual Report (1972).

C-5   Colorado Bureau of Mines, Annual Report (1976).

C-6   Aurand, H.A., 1920, Mineral deposits of the Western Slope, Colorado Geol. Survey, Bull. 22, pp. 30

C-7   ——— 1920, Fluorspar deposits of Colorado, Colorado Geol. Survey, Bull. 18, pp. 61–67.

C-8   Crawford, R.D. and Gibson, R., 1925, Geology and ore deposits of the Red Cliff district, Colorado, Colorado Geol. Survey, Bull 30, 86p.

C-9   Grose, L.T., 1974, Summary of geology of Colorado related to geothermal energy potential: in Proceedings of a symposium on geothermal energy and Colorado, Pearl, R.H., Ed., Colorado Geol. Survey, Bull, 35, pp. 11–31.

C-10 Hayden, F.V., 1876, Annual Report of the United States Geological and Geographic

Survey of the Territories, p. 103 in (also) Crawford, R.D., 1913, Colorado Geol. Survey, Bull. 4, 317p.

C–11 Howell, J.V., 1919, Twin Lakes district of Colorado, Colorado Geol. Survey, Bull. 17, pp. 12–13.

C–12 Muilenburg, G.A., 1919, Manganese deposits of Colorado, Colorado Geol. Survey, Bull. 15, pp. 44–45.

C–13 Patton, *et al.,* 1912, Geology and ore deposits of the Alma district, Park County, Colorado, Colorado Geol. Survey, Bull. 3, pp. 151, 163, 175–181, 284.

C–14 Patton, H.B., 1916, Geology and ore deposits of the Bonanza district, Saguache County, Colorado, Colorado Geol. Survey, Bull. 9, 136p.

C–15 ——— 1917, Geology and ore deposits of the Platoro Summitville mining district, Colorado, Colorado Geol. Survey, Bull. 13, pp. 65–66.

C–16 Pearl, R.H., 1972, Geothermal resources of Colorado, Colorado Geol. Survey, spec. publ. 2, 54p.

C–17 Worcester, P.G., Coffin, R.C., Butters, R.M. and Warner, G.B., 1909–1910, Colorado state geologic survey map, Monarch–Tomichi special map, Bull. IV, pl. V, (map), horiz. scale: 1:25,000, vert. scale: 2 $\frac{1}{2}$ inches = 1 mile.

C–18 Worcester, P.G., 1919, Molybdenum deposits of Colorado, Colorado Geol. Survey, Bull. 14, pp. 34–38, 87–96.

State of Colorado Mineral Resources Board

D–1 Vanderwilt, J.W., editor, 1947, Mineral Resources of Colorado, Colorado Min. Res. Board, Denver, Colo., 547p.

      Including: Part I, Metals, nonmetals and fuels by Vanderwilt, J.W.

                  Part II, Summaries of mining districts and mineral deposits by Burbank, W.S. with contributions from: Koschman, A.H., Goddard, E.N., Singewald, Q.D., Loughlin, G.F., Behre, C.H., Jr., Tweto, O., Lovering, T.S., Eckel, E.B., Varnes, D.J., Fischer, R.P., and Van Alstine, R.E. and Hanley, J.B.

                  Part III, Investigation of strategic mineral resources by Traver, W.M., Jr.

D–2 DelRio, S.M., 1960, Mineral resources of Colorado, First Sequel, Colorado Min. Res. Board, Denver, Colo., pp. 206–207.

D–3 George, R.D., 1927, Geology and natural resources of Colorado, Univ. of Colorado, Boulder, Colo., pp. 113, 121, 174, 175, 233.

Colorado Scientific Society Proceedings

E–1 Behre, C.H., Jr., 1929, Revision of structure and stratigraphy in the Mosquito Range and the Leadville district, Colorado, Colorado Sci. Soc. Proc., v. 14, no. 2, p. 54.

E–2 ——— 1939, Preliminary geological report on the west slope of the Mosquito Range in the vicinity of Leadville, Colorado, Colorado Sci. Soc. Proc., v. 14, no. 2, pp. 54, 77.

E–3 Burbank, W.S., 1930, Revision of geologic structure and stratigraphy in the Ouray district and its bearing on ore deposition, Colorado Sci. Soc. Proc., v. 12, no. 6, pp. 151–232.

E–4 ——— 1933, Vein systems of the Arrastra Basin and regional geologic structure in the Silverton and Telluride quadrangles, Colorado, Colorado Sci. Soc. Proc., v. 13, no. 5, p. 171.

E–5 ——— 1941, Structural control of ore deposition in the Red Mountain, Sneffels, Telluride districts of the San Juan mountains, Colorado, Colorado Sci. Soc. Proc., v. 14, no. 5, pp. 141–262.

E–6 ——— 1951, The Sunnyside, Ross Basin, and Bonita fault systems and their associated ore deposits, San Juan County, Colorado, Colorado Sci. Soc. Proc., v. 15, no. 7, pp. 296–297.

E-7   Chapman, E.P., 1931, The quartz monzonite batholithic intrusion of Twin Lakes and Clear Creek districts, Lake and Chaffee Counties, Colorado, Colorado Sci. Soc. Proc., v. 13, no. 8, pp. 432–439.

E-8   Eckel, E.B., 1938, Copper ores of the LaPlata district, Colorado, and their platinum content, Colorado Sci. Soc. Proc., v. 13, no. 13, pp. 647–664.

E-9   Guiterman, F., 1890, Gold deposits in the quartzite formation of Battle Mountain, Colorado, Colorado Sci. Soc. Proc., v. 3, pt 3, pp. 264–268.

E-10   Kelley, V.C., 1946, Geology, ore deposits and mines of the Mineral Point, Poughkeepsie, and Upper Uncompahgre districts, Ouray, San Juan and Hinsdale Counties, Colorado, Colorado Sci. Soc. Proc., v. 14, no. 7.

E-11   Koschmann, A.H. and Wells, F.G., 1946, Preliminary report on the Kokomo-Tenmile district, Colorado, Colorado Sci. Soc. Proc., v. 15, no. 2, pp. 51–57, 81, 96–112.

E-12   Stark, J.T., and Barnes, F.F., 1935, Geology of the Sawatch Range, Colorado, Colorado Sci. Soc. Proc., v. 13, no. 8, pp. 468–479.

E-13   Tweto, O., 1949, Stratigraphy of the Pando area, Eagle County, Colorado, Colorado Sci. Soc. Proc. v. 15, no. 4, pp. 149–235.

E-14. Vanderwilt, J.W., 1938, Geology of the "Questa" molybdenite deposit, Taos County, New Mexico, Colorado Sci. Soc. Proc., v. 13, no. 11, pp. 599–643.

Director of the Mint Reports

F-1   Report of the Director of the Mint upon the production of precious metals in the United States, during the calendar year of 1891, 1892, pp. 178–185.

F-2   ———— 1892, 1893, pp. 121–131.

F-3   Report of the Director of the Mint for the calendar yar of 1884, Treasury Department, 1885, pp. 126–127, 189–190, 233, 237, 240–241, 245, 387, 393–394.

F-4   Report of the Director of the Mint for the calendar year of 1885, Production of precious metals in the United States in 1884, pp. 186–187, 232, 240–243, 388–389, 393–394.

F-5   Report of the Director of the Mint for the calendar year of 1898, Treasury Department, pp. 80–81, 90, 98.

F-6   Report of the Director of the Mint for the calendar year of 1900, Treasury Department, 1901, pp. 102–103, 126–128.

F-7   Report of the Director of the Mint for the calendar year of 1901, Treasury Department, p. 112.

Dictionary, Glossary, and Systems of Mineralogy References (Special)

G-1   Dana, Edward Salisbury, and Ford, William E., 1932, A Textbook of mineralogy, 4th ed., John Wiley and Sons, Inc., New York, N.Y., p. 539; 851p.

G-2   Dana, James Dwight, and Dana, Edward Salisbury, The system of mineralogy, 7th ed., v. 1, Palache, Charles; Berman, Harry and Frondel, Clifford, 1944, 834p.

G-3   ———— v. 2, 1951, 1124p.

G-4   ———— v. 3, Frondel, Charles, 1962, 334p.

G-5   Eckel, E.B., 1916, Minerals of Colorado, a 100-year record, U.S. Geol. Surv. Bull. 1114, 531p.

G-6   Fleischer, Michael, 1975, Glossary of mineral species, Mineralogical Record, Bowie, Md., 145p.

G-7   Fleischer, Michael, 1980, Glossary of Mineral species, 1980, Mineralogical Record, Bowie, Md., 192p.

G-8 George, R.D., 1913, Common minerals and rocks, Colo. State Geol. Survey, Bull. 6, 406p. (Reprinted as Bull. 12, 1917, 463p.)

G-9 Hurlbut, C.S., Jr., 1971, Dana's manual of mineralogy, 18th ed., John Wiley and Sons, Inc., New York, N.Y., p. 394.

G-10 Northrup, S.A., 1959, Minerals of New Mexico, University of New Mexico Press, Albuquerque, N.M., 665p.

G-11 Robert, W.L., Rapp, G.F., Jr. and Weber, J., 1974, Encyclopedia of minerals, Van Nostrand Reinhold Co., New York, N.Y., 693p.

G-12 Thrush, Paul W., Ed., 1968, A dictionary of mining, mineral and related terms, Bur. of Mines Special Pub., Dept. of the Int., Washington, D.C.

Economic Geology

H-1 Barton, P.B., Jr., Bethke, P.M., and Roedder, E., 1977, Environment of ore deposition in the Creede mining district, San Juan mountains, Colorado, Part III–Progress toward interpretation of the chemistry of the ore-forming fluids for the OH-vein, Econ. Geology, No. 1, pp. 1-24.

H-2 Behre, C.H., et. al., 1936, Contact ore deposits at the Calumet Iron mine, Colorado, Econ. Geology, v. 31, no. 8, pp. 781-804.

H-3 Bethke, P.M., Barton, P.B., Lanphere, M.A. and Steven, T.A., 1976, Environment of ore deposition in the Creede mining district, San Juan mountains, Colorado, Part II—Age of mineralization, Econ. Geology, v. 71, pp. 584, 1006-1011.

H-4 Butler, R.D., and Singewald, Q.D., 1940, Zonal mineralization in the Horseshoe and Sacramento districts, Colorado, Econ, Geology, v. 35, pp. 793-838.

H-5 Casadevall, T. and Ohmoto, H., 1977, Sunnyside mine, Eureka mining district, San Juan Country, Colorado, Geochemistry of gold and base metal ore deposition in a volcanic environment, Econ. Geology, v. 72, pp. 1285-1320.

H-6 Fitch, R.S., and Loughlin, G.F., 1916, Wolframite and scheelite at Leadville, Colorado, Econ. Geology, v. 11, pp. 30-36.

H-7 Hulin, C.D., 1929, Structural control of ore deposition, Econ. Geology, v. 24, pp. 15-49.

H-8 Lipman, P.W., Fisher, F.S., Mehnert, H.H., Naeser, C.W., Luedke, R.G., and Steven, T.A., 1976, Multiple ages of mid-Tertiary mineralization and alteration of the western San Juan mountains, Colorado, Econ. Geology, v. 71, no. 3, pp. 571-588.

H-9 Nash, J.T., 1975, Fluid inclusion studies of vein, pipe and replacement deposits, northwestern San Juan mountains, Colorado, Econ. Geology, v. 70, no. 8, pp. 1448-1462.

H-10 Roedder, E., Heyl, A.V., and Creel, J.P., 1968, Environment of ore deposition at the Mextex deposits, Hansonburg district, new Mexico, from studies of fluid inclusions, Econ. Geology, v. 63, pp. 336-348.

H-11 Spurr, J.E., 1925, The Camp Bird compound vein-dike, Econ. Geology, v. 22, p. 126.

H-12 Stevens, T.A., and Eaton, G.P., 1975, Environment of ore deposition in the Creede mining district, San Juan mountains, Colorado, Geologic, hydrologic and geochemical setting, Econ. Geology, v. 70, no. 6, pp. 1023-1037.

H-13 Stone, J.B., 1934, Limonite deposits at the Orient mine, Colorado, Econ. Geology, v. 29, no. 4, pp. 314-329.

H-14 Tweto, Ogden, 1960, Scheelite in Precambrian gneisses of Colorado, Econ. Geology, v. 55, no. 7, pp. 1420-1428.

H-15 Van Alstine, R.E., 1975, Continental rifts and lineaments associated with major fluorspar districts, Econ. Geology, v. 71, no. 6, pp. 977-987.

Engineering & Mining Journal

I-1 Chase, C.A., 1929, A geological gamble in Colorado meets with success, Eng. & Mining Journ., v. 128, pp. 202-205.

I-2 Denver correspondence, The true story of the Camp Bird discovery, Eng. & Mining Journ., v. 89, June 18, 1910, p. 1266.
I-3 Engineering & Mining Journal, May, 1964, p. 157.
I-4 —— July, 1964.
I-5 —— Oct., 1964.
I-6 —— Dec., 1964, p. 133.
I-7 —— Jan., 1965, p. 95.
I-8 —— Feb., 1965, p. 193.
I-9 —— Feb., 1966, pp. 166, 184, 187.
I-10 —— April, 1966, p. 142.
I-11 —— Aug., 1966, p. 135.
I-12 —— Sept., 1966.
I-13 —— Oct., 1966, pp. 117–118.
I-14 —— Feb., 1967, p. 229.
I-15 —— July, 1967, p. 131.
I-16 —— Dec., 1967.
I-17 —— Feb., 1968, p. 161.
I-18 —— May, 1968, p. 101.
I-19 —— Sept., 1968, pp. 180, 184.
I-20 —— Nov., 1968, pp. 152–154.
I-21 —— Jan., 1969, p. 104.
I-22 —— Mar., 1969, p. 199.
I-23 —— June, 1969, p. 284.
I-24 Larsh, P.A., 1911, Caballo mountain vanadium mine, Eng. & Mining Journ., July 15, 1911, p. 118.
I-25 Root, A.P. and Simmons, J.E., 1934, The Red Arrow discovery, Eng. & Mining Journ., v. 135, no. 6, pp. 260–261.

General References

J-1 Argall, G.O., Jr., 1949, Industrial minerals of Colorado, Colorado School of Mines Quarterly, v. 44, no. 2, p. 34.
J-2 Badgley, P.C., 1965, Structural and tectonic principals, Harper and Row Publ., N.Y., N.Y., 521p.
J-3 Baker, B.H., Mohr, P.A., and Willimas, L.A.J., 1976, Geology of the eastern rift system of Africa; Geol. Soc. of Am., special paper 136, 67p.
J-4 Baltz, E.H., 1965, Stratigraphy and history of Raton Basin and notes on San Luis Basin, Colorado-New Mexico, Am. Assoc. Pet. Geol., Bull., v. 49, no. 22, pp. 2040–2075.
J-5 Bancroft, Peter, 1973, The world's finest minerals and crystals, Viking Press, New York, pp. 108, 160.
J-6 Barnett, R.M., 1980, Mount Emmons—A mine for the 80s; in Min. Yearbook 1980, papers presented at the 83rd Ann. Nat. West. Min. Conf., Colo. Mining Assn., Denver, Colo.
J-7 Barton, P.B., Jr., and others, 1963, Equilibrium in ore deposits, Mineralogy Society of America, Sp. Papers 1, pp. 171–185.
J-8 Bates, Margaret, 1973, A quick history of Lake City, Colorado, Little London Press, Colorado Springs, Colo., 34p.
J-9 Benham, Jack, 1976, Ouray, Bear Creek Publishing Co., Ouray, Colo., 64p.
J-10 —— 1977, Silverton and neighboring ghost towns, Bear Creek Publishing Co., Ouray, Colo., 64p.
J-11 Bird, W.H., 1973, Mineral deposits of the southern portion of the Platoro caldera complex, southeast San Juan mountains, Colorado, The Mountain Geologist, v. 9, no. 4, pp. 379–387.
J-12 Chapin, C.E. and Epis, R.C., 1964, Some stratigraphic and structural featuers of the

Thirty-nine Mile volcanic field, central Colorado, The Mountain Geologist, v. 1, pp. 117–126, 145–160.

J-13 Chester, A.H., 1894, Acanthite from Colorado, Colorado School of Mines Quarterly, v. 15, pp. 103–104.

J-14 Crofutt, George A., 1885, Crofutt's grip-pack guide of Colorado, a complete encyclopedia of the state, Overland Publishing Co., Omaha, Nebr., CUBAR Reprint of 1966, pp. 114–115, 145.

J-15 Deer, W.A., Howie, R.A., and Zussman, J., Rock forming minerals, John Wiley and Sons, New York, N.Y., v. 4, pp. 321–327 and v. 5, p. 265.

J-16 DeVoto, R.H., 1971, Geologic history of South Park and geology of the Antero Reservoir quadrangle, Colorado, Colorado School of Mines Quarterly, v. 66, no. 3, 90p.

J-17 ——— 1972, Cenozoic geologic history of South Park, The Mountain Geologist, v. 9, nos. 2–3, p. 218.

J-18 Eberhart, Perry, 1959, Guide to the Colorado ghost towns and mining camps, 3rd Edition, Sage Books, Denver, Colo., pp. 193, 249, 393–394.

J-19 Epis, R.C. and others, 1967, Geologic history of the Thirty-nine Mile volcanic field, central Colorado, Geol. Soc. America, Rky. Mtn. Sect., Proj. 1967, An. Mtg., 34–35.

J-20 Fairbanks, E.E., 1976, Largest known crystals and masses, Gems and Minerals, Nov., 1976, p. 54.

J-21 Feitz, L., 1969, A quick history of Creede, Colorado boom town, Golden Bell Press, Denver, Colo., 48p.

J-22 ——— 1969, Platoro, Colorado, mining camp and resort town, Graphic Services, Colorado Springs, Colo., 32p.

J-23 Findlay, J.R., 1922, Report of appraisal of mining properties of New Mexico for years 1921–1922, New Mexico Tax Commission, Santa Fe, N.M., pp. 26, 81–82.

J-24 Frondel, Clifford, 1934, Mineral incrustations upon the edges and corners of crystals, American Museum Novitiates, no. 759, Dec. 20, 1934, American Museum of Natural History, New York, N.Y.

J-25 ——— 1934, Origin of the segmental coloration of amethyst and smoky quartz, American Museum Novitiates, No. 758, Dec. 20, 1934, American Museum of Natural History, New York, N.Y.

J-26 Gibbons, J.J., 1898, In the San Juan, sketches, St. Patrick's Parish, Telluride, Colo., 1972, pp. 41–49.

J-27 Grout, F.F., 1932, Petrography and Petrology, McGraw-Hill Book Co., Inc., New York, 522p.

J-28 Hague, James D., 1871, Mining industry, with geological contributions by Clarence King, 1870, report of the geological exploration of the fortieth parallel, professional paper of the engineering department, United States Army no. 18, v. III, pp. 577–586.

J-29 Heinrich, E. Wm., 1966, The Geology of carbonatites, Rand McNally & Co., 555p.

J-30 Henderson Project, Public Relations Brochures Amax Inc., Empire, Colo.

J-31 Hilander, A.C., 1961, Mining complex ore at Idarado, Explosive Engineer, Nov.–Dec., 1961, pp. 183–187.

J-32 Humbeutel, L., 1975, Nuggets from Chalk Creek, Century One Press, Colorado Springs, Colo., 96p. pp. 11–14.

J-33 Hurlbut, C.S., Jr., 1968, Minerals and Man, Random House, New York, pp. 208–216.

J-34 Johnson, J.H., 1944, Paleozoic stratigraphy of the Sawatch Range, Colorado, Geol. Soc. America, Bull. v. 55, no. 3, pp. 303–378.

J-35 Johnson, R.B., 1960, Brief description of the igneous bodies of the Raton Mesa regions, south central Colorado, Geol. Soc. America, Rky, Mtn. Assoc. of Geol. and Colo. Sci. Soc. Proc., pp. 117–120.

J-36 Kelley, V.C., and Silver, C., 1952, Geology of the Caballo mountains with special reference to regional stratigraphy and structure and to mineral resources, including oil and gas, University of New Mexico Publications in Geol. no. 4, 286p.

J-37 Kelley, V.C., 1955, Regional tectonics of the Colorado plateau and relationship to the origin and distribution of uranium, University of New Mexico, Publications in Geol., no. 5, fig. 2.

J-38 Kempner, H.A.A., 1978, Bonanza, a pictorial history of Colorado's Kerber Creek country, Little London Press, Colordo Springs, Colo., 48p.

J-39 Koschman, A.H., 1963, The historical pattern of mineral exploration in Colorado, Colorado School of Mines Quarterly, v. 57, no. 4, pp. 7–25.

J-40 Kushner, E.F., 1972, A guide to mineral collecting at Ouray, Colorado, Central Letter Shop, Little Falls, N.J., pp. 18, 20.

J-41 Lakes, A., 1905, Geology of western ore deposits, Kendrick Book and Stationary Co., Denver, Co., pp. 242–244.

J-42 Levings, W.S., 1951, Late Cenozoic erosional history of the Raton Mesa region, Colorado School of Mines Quarterly, v. 46, no. 3, p. 87.

J-43 Lindquist, W.F., 1980, The exploration of the Ortiz gold deposit, New Mexico, geology and exploration; in mining year book 1980, papers presented at the 83rd Ann. Nat. West. Min. Conf., Colo. Mining Assn., Denver, Colo.

J-44 Lipman, P.W., 1969, Alkalic and tholeiitic basalt volcanism related to the Rio Grande depression, southern Colorado and northern New Mexico, Geol. Soc. America, Bull. v. 80, no. 7, pp. 1343–1354.

J-45 Litsey, L.R., 1960, Geology near Orient mine, Sangre de Cristo mountains, Colorado, in Guide to the geology of Colorado, Weimer, R.J., and Haun, J.D., editors, Geol. Soc. America, Rky. Mtn. Assoc. of Geol., and Colorado Sci, Soc., pp. 129–131.

J-46 Lindgren, Waldemar, 1933, Mineral deposits, 4th Edition, McGraw-Hill Book Co., Inc., New York, 930p.

J-47 Mains, C.J., 1980, Dawsonite and nahcolite—an overview, in Min. Yearbook 1980, papers presented at the 83rd Ann. Nat. West. Min. Conf., Colo. Mining Assn., Denver, Colo.

J-48 Malan, R.C., 1957, Geology of uranium occurrences in North and Middle Parks, Colorado, in Rocky Mountain Association of Geology, Guidebook to the Geology of North and Middle Park Basins, Colorado, pp. 126–136.

J-49 ——— 1968, Uranium in the Tertiary intermontane basins of Colorado, The Mountain Geologist, v. 6, no. 1, pp. 41–51.

J-50 ——— 1969, Uranium in the Tertiary intermontane basins of Colorado, The Mountain Geologist, v. 6, no. 5, pp. 44–46.

J-51 McGuire, J., 1974, The treasure of Battle mountain, Colorado Magazine, Sept.–Oct., 1974, pp. 51–54.

J-52 McLemore, V.T., 1980, Carbonatites in the Lemitar mountains, Socorro County, New Mexico; N. Mex. Geol., v. 2, no. 4, Nov. 1980, pp. 49–52.

J-53 Nordyke, L., 1955, The Idarado mine, The Explosives Engineer, May–June, pp. 71–83.

J-54 Northrup, S.A., 1975, Turquoise and Spanish mines in New Mexico, University of New Mexico Press, Albuquerque, N.M., pp. 44, 66–73.

J-55 Parker, B., Jr., 1960, Placers of Summit and Park Counties, Colorado, in Guide to the geology of Colorado, Weimer, R. J., and Haun, J.D., editors, Geol, Soc. America, Rky. Mtn. Assoc. of Geol., and Colo. Sci. Soc. Proc., p. 199.

J-56 Pearl, R.M., 1958, Colorado gem trails and mineral guide, Sage Books, Denver, Colo., pp. 73–86, 100–103.

J-57 Pogue, J.E., 1915, The turquoise, National Academy of Science Memoirs, 3rd Memoir 12 (part 2) 3–136, sixth printing, 1914, Rio Grande Press, Inc., Glorieta, N.M., pp. 55–56.

J-58 Ramsey, R.H., 1973, Men and mines of Newmont, Octagon Books, division of Farrar, Straus and Giroux, New York, N.Y., 344p.

J-59 Seaman, D.E., 1979, Gold in rhyolite at Nathrop, Colorado, Rocks & Minerals, v. 54, no. 3, May–June, 1979, pp. 108–109.

J-60 Simpson, B.W., (1970), New Mexico gem trails, 2nd edition, Gem Trails Publications Company, Bowie, Texas, 88p.

J-61 Sims, P.K., 1960, Geology of the Central City—Idaho Springs area, front range Colorado, in Guide to the geology of Colorado, Weimer, R.J., and Haun, J.D., editors, Geol. Soc. America, Rky. Mtn. Assoc. of Geol., and Colo. Sci. Soc., pp. 279–283.

J-62 Sinkankas, J., 1959, Gemstones of North America, Van Nostrand Co., Princeton, N.J., p. 284.

J-63 Sloane, H.N. and L.L., 1970, A pictorial history of American mining, Crown Publishers, Inc., New York, p. 318.

J-64 Stewart, J.H. and others, 1960, Road log Cortez to Whitewater, via Telluride and Naturita, sidelog to Telluride and Pandora, in Geological road logs of Colorado, Rky, Mtn. Assoc. of Geol., J.R. Donnell, ed., 1960, pp. 27–28.

J-65 This is Climax, A division of Amax, Inc. (company public relations brochure).

J-66 Thompson, T.B. and Pulfrey, R.J., 1973, The Mount Antero granite, Sawatch Range, Colorado, The Mountain Geologist, v. 10, no. 4 (Oct., 1973), pp. 117–122.

J-67 Tweto, O., 1957, Geologic sketch of southern Middle Park, Colorado, in guide book to the geology of North and Middle Parks basin, Colorado, 1957, Rky. Mtn. Assoc. of Geol., p. 24.

J-68 ——— 1960, Road log, Fremont Pass to Leadville to Wolcott via Colo. Hwy. 91 and U.S. Hwys. 24 and 6, in Guide to the geology of Colorado, Weimer, R.J., and Haun, J. D., editors, Geol. Soc. America, Rky. Mtn. Assoc. of Geol., and Colo. Sci. Soc. Proc., pp. 71–73.

J-69 Tweto, O. and Sims, P.K., 1963, Precambrian ancestry of the Colorado mineral belt, Geol. Soc. America, Bull. v. 74, no. 8, pp. 991–1014.

J-70 Varnes, D.J., 1948, Geology and ore deposits of the south Silverton area, San Juan County, Colorado, address delivered at annual meeting of Colorado Mining Assn., Feb. 7, 1948, Denver, Colo., 12p.

J-71 Walker, M.S. and Ludwig, J.J., 1964, Climax fights heavy ground and wins., Metal Mining and Processing, Oct., 1964, pp. 27–29.

J-72 Wallace, S. R. and others, 1960, Geology of the Climax molybdenite deposit: A progress report, in Weimer, R.J. and Haun, J.D., Editors, Guide to the geology of Colorado: Geol. Soc. America, Rky, Mtn. Assoc. of Geol. and Colo. Sci. Soc. Proc., pp. 238–252.

J-73 Weber, Rose, 1974, A quick history of Telluride, Little London Press, Colorado Springs, Colo., 52p.

J-74 Wolle, M.S., 1949, Stampede to timberline, Sage Books, Denver, Colo., pp. 358–362.

J-57 ——— 1949, The ghost towns and mining camps of Colorado, Sage Books, Denver, Colo., pp. 48–68.

J-76 Wood, B., 1964, Ghost towns and how to get to them, Press of the Territories, no. 4 of a series of western Americana, Santa Fe, N.M., pp. 5, 12, 21, 31.

J-77 Woodward, L.A. and others, 1975, Tectonic Map of the Rio Grande Rift, New Mexico, Geol. Soc. Am., MC-11, Scale 1:500,000.

Mineralogical Record, affiliated with The Friends of Mineralogy, P.O. Box 783, Bowie, Maryland 20715

K-1 Mineralogical Record, v. 1, no. 1, Spring (1970) Bideaux, R.A., 1970, A multiple Japan Law quartz twin, p. 33.

K-2 ——— v. 2, no. 2, Mar.–Apr., 1971, Gains, R.V. and Thadeau, D., 1971, The minerals of Panasqueira, Portugal, p. 76.

K-3 ——— v. 2, no. 3, May–June, 1971, Miller, H.W., 1971, Rhodochrosite crystal localities in the west, pp. 105–110.

K-4 ——— v. 2, no. 3, May–June 1971, Mrose, M., 1971, Specimen requests, p. 123.

K-5 ——— v. 2, no. 3, May–June, 1971, Yedlin, N., 1971, Yedlin on micromounting, p. 101.

K-6 ——— v. 2, no 4, July–Aug., 1971, Bideaux, R.A., 1971, The collector, p. 185.

K-7 —— v. 3, no. 4, July–Aug., 1972, Bideaux, R.A., 1972, The collector (wulfenites), p. 50.

K-8 —— v. 3, no. 5, Sept.–Oct., 1972, Rosenzweig, A., 1972, What's new in minerals? (blanchardite), pp. 229–230.

K-9 —— v. 4, no. 1, Jan.–Feb., 1973, Bideaux, R.A., 1973, The collector, p. 5.

K-10 —— v. 4, no. 1, Jan.–Feb., 1973, Hammond, J., 1973, The Stevinson-Bennett mine, New Mexico, pp. 31–34.

K-11 —— v. 4, no. 1, Jan.–Feb., 1973, Wilkinson, W.H., 1973, QA column, p. 42.

K-12 —— v. 4, no. 3, May–June, 1973, Bideaux, R.A., 1973, The collector, "pyrite from Leadville", p. 140.

K-13 —— v. 5, no. 5, Sept.–Oct. 1974, p. 235.

K-14 —— v. 5, no. 5, Sept.–Oct. 1974, The occurrence of alstonite at Cave-in-Rock, Illinois, pp. 266–269.

K-15 —— v. 7, no. 1, Jan.–Feb., 1976, Taggart, J.E., and Grigsby, C.O., 1976, An occurrence of multiple Japan Law quartz twins, pp. 34–35.

K-16 —— v. 7, no. 6, Nov.–Dec., 1976, Grybeck, D., 1976, Some additions to the ore mineralogy of Colorado, pp. 274–276.

K-17 —— v. 7, no. 6, Nov.–Dec., 1976, Groben, M.N., 1976, Zuni mine, p. 270.

K-18 —— v. 7, no. 6, Nov.–Dec., 1976, Kosnar, R.A. and Miller, H.W., 1976, Crystallized minerals of the Colorado mineral belt, pp. 278–309.

K-19 —— v. 7, no. 6. Nov.–Dec., 1976, Modreski, P.J., 1976, The Harding mine, Dixon, Taos County, N.M., pp. 270–271.

K-20 —— v. 8, no. 1, Jan.–Feb., 1977, Grice, J.D. and Gault, R.A., 1977, The Bluebell mine, Riodell, British Columbia, Canada, pp. 33–35.

K-21 —— v. 8, no. 2, Mar.–Apr., 1977, Jahns, R.H. and Ewing, R.C., 1977, The Harding mine, Taos County, N.M., pp. 115–126, (also in Guidebook of New Mexico Geological Society, 1976, Vermejo Park, N.M., 300p).

Minerals Yearbooks of the United States

L-1 Minerals Yearbooks of the United States, U.S. Bureau of Mines, (1940–1974), Washington, D.C.

Mining Engineer

M-1 Beall, J.V., 1965, Southwest copper, Mining Engineer, Oct., 1965, pp. 87–90.

M-2 Gibson, W.A. and Trujillo, A.D., 1966, From Indian scrapings to 85-ton trucks, the development of Chino, Mining Engineer, Jan., 1966, pp. 54–60.

M-3 Silman, J.F.B., 1965, Longhole drilling, vital in proving up molybdenum corps. Questa orebody, Mining Engineer, May, 1965, pp. 54–58.

Mining World

N-1 Mining World, June, 1941 through December, 1946.

N-2 —— Dec. 1941, pp. 15–18.

N-3 —— Jan. 1942, pp. 15–21.

N-4 —— April, 1942, pt. 1, pp. 3–4.

N-5 —— June, 1942, pt. II, pp. 10–11.

N-6 —— Aug., 1942, p. 23.

N-7 —— July, 1943, p. 27.

N-8 —— Sept., 1943, pp. 16–18.

N-9 —— Dec., 1943, p. 32.

N-10 —— Aug., 1944, p. 44.

N-11 —— Oct., 1944, p. 40.
N-12 —— Mar., 1945, pp. 42, 56–57.
N-13 —— April, 1946, pp. 69–71.
N-14 —— May, 1946, p. 57.
N-15 —— June, 1946, p. 61.
N-16 —— July, 1946, p. 21.
N-17 —— Aug., 1946, p. 28.
N-18 —— Sept., 1946, pp. 25, 26, 29.
N-19 Sibel, M.V., 1946, Leadville: Camp of the carbonates, Mining World, Sept., 1946, pp. 69–71.
N-20 Mining World, Nov., 1959, pp. 38–43.

New Mexico Bureau of Mines and Mineral Resources, New Mexico Institute of Mining and Technology and other New Mexico publications

O-1 Atkinson, W.W., Jr., 1961, Geology of the San Pedro mountains, Santa Fe County, New Mexico, New Mexico Bur. Mines and Mineral Resources, New Mexico Inst. Mining and Technology, Bull. 77, 50p, (maps).

O-2 Bertholf, W.E., II, 1960, Magnetite taconite rock in precambrian formations in Rio Arriba County, New Mexico, New Mexico Bur. Mines and Mineral Resources, New Mexico Inst. Mining and Technology Circ. 54, 24p.

O-3 Bingler, E.C., 1968, Geologic map of the Valle Grande Peak quadrangle, Rio Arriba County, New Mexico, New Mexico Bur. Mines and Mineral Resources, New Mexico Inst. Mining and Technology, scale: 1:24,000 (map).

O-4 Broderick, G.N., 1965, Sulfur; in Mineral and water resources of New Mexico, U.S. Geological Survey, for U.S. Senate Comm. on Interior and Insular Affairs, also publ. as Bull. 87, New Mexico Bur. Mines and Mineral Resources and New Mexico Inst. Mining and Technology, pp. 309–311.

O-5 Carter, M.D., 1965, Gem materials in mineral and water resources of New Mexico, New Mexico Bur. Mines and Mineral Resources, New Mexico Inst. Mining and Technology, Bull, 87, p. 274.

O-6 Corey, A.F., 1960, Kyanite occurrence in the Petaca district, Rio Arriba County, New Mexico, New Mexico Bur. Mines and Mineral Resources, New Mexico Inst. Mining and Technology, Bull. 47, 70p.

O-7 Cunningham, J.E., 1974, Geologic map and sections of Silver City quadrangle, New Mexico, New Mexico Bur. Mines and Mineral Resources and New Mexico Inst. Mining and Technology, Socorro, N.M., Geologic Map 30, scale: 1:24,000 (map).

O-8 Davis, G.H., and Keller, G.R., 1978, Subsurface structure of San Luis Valley, in guidebook to Rio Grande rift in New Mexico and Colorado: New Mexico Bur. Mines and Mineral Resources, Circ. 163, p. 28.

O-9 Durham, K.C., 1934, The geology of the Organ Mountains, with an account of the geology and mineral resources of Dona Ana County, New Mexico, New Mexico Bur. Mines and Mineral Resources, Bull. 11, 272p.

O-10 File, L. and Northrup, S.A., 1966, County, township and range locations of New Mexico's mining districts, New Mexico Bur. Mines and Mineral Resources and New Mexico Inst. Mining and Technology, Circ. 84, p. 26.

O-11 Fischer, R. P., 1965, Vanadium, in Mineral and water resources of New Mexico, New Mexico Bur. Mines and Mineral Resources, and New Mexico Inst. Mining and Technology, Bull. 87, p. 227.

O-12 Gillerman, E., 1964, Mineral deposits of western Grant County, New Mexico, New Mexico Bur. Mines and Mineral Resources and New Mexico Inst. Mining and Technology, Bull. 83, 213p.

O-13 Griswold, G.B., 1961, Mineral deposits of Luna County, New Mexico, New Mexico Bur. Mines and Mineral Resources of New Mexico Inst. Mining and Technology, Bull. 72, pp. 95–117, 129–132.

O-14 Hawley, J.W., ed. (with 42 coauthors), 1978, Guidebook to Rio Grande rift in New Mexico and Colorado, (prepared for symposium on tectonics and magmatism of Rio Grande rift, Santa Fe, N.M., Oct. 8–17, 1978); New Mexico Bur. Mines and Mineral Resources Circ. 163, 241p., 2 maps.

    Tweto, O., Northern rift guide 1, Denver–Alamosa, Colo., pp. 13–27.

    Davis, G. H., and Keller, G.R.,

    Subsurface structure of San Luis Valley, p. 28.

    Burroughs, R.L., Lipman, P.W., Muehlberger, W.R., and Hawley, J.W., Northern rift guide 2, Alamosa, Colo.–Santa Fe, N.M., pp. 33–55.

    Lovejoy, E.M.P., Hawley, J.W., Seager, W.R., Keller, G.R., Graham, R.G., Roy, R.F., Morgan, P., Mueller, J., Chapin, C.E., Osburn, G.R., Thompson, S., III, and Deal E.G., Southern rift guide 1, El Paso, Texas–Socorro, N.M., pp. 56–111.

    Sanford, A.R., Chapin, C.E., Chamberlin, R. M., Hawley, J.W., Machette, M.N., Lambert, P.W., Kelley, V.C., Cordell, L., Kottlowski, F.E., and Galusha, T., Southern rift guide 2, Socorro–Santa Fe, N.M., pp. 115–182.

    Bailey, R.A., Smith, R.L., Budding, A.J., Aubele, J.C., and Manley, K., Guide to Jemez mountains and Espanola Basin, pp. 184–210.

    Baltz, E.H., Resume of Rio Grande depression in north-central New Mexico, pp. 210–226.

    Bridwell, J., Physical behavior of upper mantle beneath northern Rio Grande Rift, pp. 228–230.

    Renault, J., Overview of Rio Grande basalts with special reference to T_1O_2 variation, pp. 230–233.

    Reiter, M., Edwards, C.L., Mansure, A.J., and Shearez, C., Heat-flow data and major geologic features along the Rio Grande Rift in New Mexico, p. 234.

    ———, Heat-flow data and major geologic features in central Colorado, p. 235.

    Tweto, O., Tectonic map of Rio Grande Rift system in Colorado (U.S. Geol. Survey, 1978) scale: 1:1,000,000.

    Woodward, L.A., Callender, J.R., Seager, W.R., Chapin, C.E., Gries, J.C., Shaffer, W.L., and Zilinski, R.E., 1978, Tectonic map of Rio Grande Rift region in New Mexico, Chihuahua, and Texas, scale: 1:1,000,000 (approx.) (map).

O-15 Hewitt, C.H., 1959, Geology and mineral deposits of the northern Big Burro mountains—Redrock area, Grant County, New Mexico, New Mexico Bur. Mines and Mineral Resources and New Mexico Inst. Mining and Technology, Bull. 60, 151p.

O-16 Jahns, R.H., 1946, Mica deposits of the Petaca district, Rio Arriba County, New Mexico, New Mexico Bur. Mines and Mineral Resources, Bull. 25, pp. 102–103, 256–274.

O-17 James, H.L., 1971, Southwestern New Mexico Lordsburg, Silver City, Deming, Las Cruces, scenic trips to the geologic past no. 10, New Mexico Bur. Mines and Mineral Resources and New Mexico Inst. Mining and Technology, 80p.

O-18 Jicha, H.L., Jr., 1954 and second reprint 1969, Geology and mineral deposits of Lake Valley quadrangle, Grant, Luna and Sierra Counties, New Mexico, New Mexico Bur. Mines and Mineral Resources and New Mexico Inst. Mining and Technology, Bull. 37, pp. 68–74.

O-19 Jones, W.R., 1965, Copper, in Mineral and water resources of New Mexico, New Mexico Bur. Mines and Mineral Resources and New Mexico Inst. Mining and Technology, Socorro, N.M., Bull. 87, pp. 172–173.

O-20 Kaufman, W.H., and others, 1972, Stratiform copper mineralization in the Nacimiento region, New Mexico Target Exploration Report E-1, New Mexico Bur. Mines and Mineral Resources, 9p.

O-21 Kelley, V.C., 1974, Albuquerque, its mountains, valley, water, and volcanoes: scenic trips to the geologic past no. 9, New Mexico Bur. Mines and Mineral Resources, 106p.

O–22   ——— 1978, Geology of Espanola Basin, New Mexico, New Mexico Bur. Mines and Mineral Resources and New Mexico Inst. Mining and Technology, Geologic map 28, scale: 1:125,000, (map).

O–23   Kelley, V.C. and Kudo, A.M., 1978, Volcanoes and related basalts of Albuquerque Basin, New Mexico, New Mexico Bur. Mines and Mineral Resources and New Mexico Inst. Mining and Technology, Circ. 156, 30p.

O–24   Kottlowski, F.E., 1953, Geology and ore deposits of a part of the Hansonburg mining district, Socorro County, New Mexico, New Mexico Bur. Mines and Mineral Resources, Circ. 23.

O–25   Lasky, S.G., 1932, The ore deposits of Socorro County, New Mexico, New Mexico Bur. Mines and Mineral Resources, Bull. 8, pp. 63–69.

O–26   McAnulty, W.N., Sr., 1972, Fluorspar in silicified rocks in New Mexico, Target Exploration Report E–7, New Mexico Bur. Mines and Mineral Resources, 3p.

O–27   McKinlay, P.F., 1957, Geology of Questa quadrangle, Taos County, New Mexico, New Mexico Bur. Mines and Mineral Resources and New Mexico Inst. Mining and Technology, Bull. 53, 23p and map, scale 1:48,000.

O–28   Rothrock, H.E., and others, 1946, Fluorspar resourcs of New Mexico, New Mexico Bur. Mines and Mineral Resources, Bull. 21, pp. 69–71, 148–165, 175–176.

O–29   Sanford, A.R. and Cash, D.J., 1967, An instrumental study of New Mexico earthquakes, July 1, 1964 through December 31, 1967, New Mexico Bur. Mines and Mineral Resources and New Mexico Inst. Mining and Technology, Circ. 102, 7p.

O–30   Sanford, A.R. and others, 1972, Seismicity of the Rio Grande in New Mexico, New Mexico Bur. Mines and Mineral Resources, Circ. 120, 19p.

O–31   Schilling, J.H., 1956, Geology of the Questa molybdenum (moly) mine area, Taos County, New Mexico, New Mexico Bur. Mines and Mineral Resources and New Mexico Inst. Mining and Technology, Bull. 51, 87p.

O–32   ——— 1960, Mineral resources of Taos County, New Mexico, New Mexico Bur. Mines and Mineral Resources and New Mexico Inst. Mining and Technology, Bull. 21, 97–102.

O–33   ——— 1967, Silver City-Santa Rita-Hurley, New Mexico, scenic trips to the geologic past, no. 5, New Mexico Bur. Mines and Mineral Resources and New Mexico Inst. Mining and Technology, 36p.

O–34   Seager, W.R., 1973, Geologic map and sections of Biship Cap-Organ Mountains area, New Mexico, New Mexico Bur. Mines and Mineral Resources and New Mexico Inst. Mining and Technology, Geologic Map 29. (map)

O–35   Summers, W.K., 1965, A preliminary report on New Mexico's geothermal energy resources, New Mexico Bur. Mines and Mineral Resources and New Mexico Inst. Mining and Technology, Circ. 80, 41p.

O–36   ——— 1968, Geothermics, New Mexico's untapped resource, reprinted from: A New Mexico Business, Aug., 1968, publ. by Bur. of Business Research, Univ. of New Mexico, Albuquerque, N.M., Circ. 98, 9p.

O–37   Talmage, S.B. and Wooton, T.P., 1937, The nonmetallic mineral resources of New Mexico and their economic futures, New Mexico Bur. Mines and Mineral Resources, Bull. 12, pp. 51, 52, 86.

O–38   Thompson, A.J., 1965, Silver, in Mineral and water resources of New Mexico, New Mexico Bur. Mines and Mineral Resources and New Mexico Inst. Mining and Technology, Bull. 87, pp. 139–159.

O–39   ——— 1965, Lead and zinc chapters in Mineral and water resources of New Mexico, New Mexico Bur. Mines and Mineral Resources and New Mexico Inst. Mining and Technology, Bull. 87, pp. 149–159.

O–40   Wells, E.H., 1918, Manganese in New Mexico, New Mexico School of Mines, Bull. 2, no. 2, pp. 35–39, 61–65, 76–81.

O–41   Zalinski, E.R., 1907, Turquoise in the Burro mountains, New Mexico Econ. Geology, v. 2, pp. 464–492, quoted in New Mexico Bur. Mines and Mineral Resources, Bull. 12, 1937, pp. 87–88.

New Mexico Geological Society

P-1   Johnson, R.B., and Read, C.B., editors, 1952, Guidebook of the Rio Grande country, central New Mexico, third field conf.,
    Kelley, V.C., 1952, Tectonics of the Rio Grande depression in central New Mexico, pp. 92–105.

P-2   Rosenzweig, A., editor, 1956, Guidebook of southwestern Sangre de Cristo mountains, New Mexico, seventh field conf.,
    Kelley, V.C., 1956, The Rio Grande depression from Taos to Santa Fe, pp. 109–114.
    Baldwin, B., 1956, The Santa Fe group of north-central New Mexico, pp. 115–121.

P-3   Baldwin, B., editor, 1957, Guidebook of southwestern San Juan mountains, Colorado, eighth field conf.,
    Kottlowski, F.E. Baldwin, B., and Bejnar, W., 1957, Geology along the million dollar highway, pp. 14–26. Smith, C.T., 1957, Road log Albuquerque to Durango, p. 31.
    Wengerd, S.A. and Baars, D.L., 1957, Road log Durango to Silverton, pp. 42–52.
    Kelley, V.C., Hillebrand, J.R., Luedke, R.G. and Burbank, W.S., 1957, Road log Silverton to Ouray, Ridgeway and return to Silverton, pp. 53–74.
    Silver, C., 1957, Silverton to Durango via railroad, pp. 75–90.
    Baars, D.. and Knight, R.L., 1957, Pre-Pennsylvanian stratigraphy of the San Juan mountains and four corners area, chart, p. 110
    Kelley, V.C., 1957, General geology and tectonics of the western San Juan mountains, Colorado, pp. 154–162.
    Bejnar, W., 1957, Lithologic control of ore deposits in the southwestern San Juan mountains, pp. 167–173.
    Kelley, V.C., 1957, Vein and fault systems of the western San Juan mountains mineral belt, Colorado, pp. 173–176.
    Hillebrand, J.R., 1957, The Idarado mine, pp. 176–188.
    Hillebrand, J.R., and Kelley, V.C., 1957, Mines and ore deposits from Red Mountain Pass to Ouray, Ouray, County, Colorado, pp. 188–199.
    Rosenzweig, A., 1957, Mineralogical notes on the Silverton quadrangle, Colorado, pp. 199–202.
    Kelley, V.C., 1957, Geology of Ouray and environs, pp. 203–207.

P-4   Kuellmer, F.J., editor, 1963, Guidebook of the Socorro region, New Mexico, fourteenth field conf.,
    Weber, R.H., 1963, Cenozoic volcanic rocks of Socorro County, pp. 139–142.
    Sanford, A.R., 1963, Seismic activity near Socorro, p. 146.

P-5   Shomaker, J., editor, 1968, Guidebook of San Juan–San Miguel–La Plata region, New Mexico and Colorado, 19th field conf.,
    Molenaar, C.M. and Werts, L., 1968, Road log from Farmington, New Mexico, La Plata mining area and Mancos, pp. 19–20. Eckel, E.F., Williams, J.S., Galbraith, F.W., and others, Geology and ore deposits of the La Plata district, Colorado, (a digest of U.S. Geol. Survey Prof. Paper 219, prepared by F.D. Trauger), pp. 60–62.
    Chapin, C.E. and others, 1968, Road log from Cortez, Colorado to Ouray, Colorado via Dolores, Rico, Lizard Head Pass, Telluride, Placerville, Dallas Divide and Ridgeway, pp. 67–69, 71–74, 77.
    Pratt, W.P., 1968, Summary of the geology of the Rico region, Colorado, pp. 83–87.
    Engel, C.M., 1968, Rico, Colorado: a century of historic adventures in mining, pp. 88–93.
    Molenaar, C.M. and others, 1968, Road log from Ouray, Colorado, pp. 107, 110, 113–115, 117.

P-6   Woodward, L.A., editor, 1970, Guidebook of the Tyrone—Big Hatchet mountains–Florida mountains region, 21st field conf.,
    Gillerman, E., 1970, Mineral deposits and structural pattern of the Big Burro mountains, New Mexico, pp. 115–121.

Kolessar, J., 1970, Geology and copper deposits of the Tyrone district, pp. 127–132.

Nielsen, R.L., 1970, Mineralization and alteration in calcareous rocks near the Santa Rita stock, New Mexico, pp. 133–139.

Kelley, V.C., 1970, Highlights of the Rio Grande depression, abs. of tech. paper presented at 24th annual meeting, Albuquerque, April 17, 1970, p. 157.

Elston, W.E., 1970, Structural control of pre-20 million year volcanic centers: clue to early evolution of Rio Grande trough, abs. of tech. paper presented at 24th annual meeting, Albuquerque , April 17, 1970, pp. 157–158.

Knepper, D.H., Jr., 1970, Structural framework of the Rio Grande Rift zone: Poncha Springs to Mineral Hot Springs, Colorado, abs. of tech. paper presented at 24th annual meeting, Albuquerque, April 17, 1970, pp. 158–159.

Budding, A.J., and Toppozada, T.R., 1970, Late cenozoic faulting in the Rio Grande Rift valley near Socorro, New Mexico, abs. of tech. paper presented at 24th annual meeting, Albuquerque, April 17, 1970, p. 161.

P–7   James H.L., editor, 1971, Guidebook of the San Juan basin, Colorado, 22nd field conf.,

Calkins, W.S., Kendall, R. and Lipman, P.W., 1971, Road log from Alamosa to the eastern San Juan mountains, Colorado, pp. 7–11.

Bruns, D. and others, 1971, Road log from Alamosa to the Great Sand Dunes National Monument, Poncha Pass, Salida, Howard, and return via Saguache and Monte Vista, pp. 20–37.

Lochman-Balk, C., and Bruning, J.E., 1971, Lexicon of stratigraphic names used in south-central Colorado and northern New Mexico, San Luis basin, pp. 101–111.

Upson, J.E., 1939, Physiographic subdivisions of the San Luis Valley, southern Colorado, reprint of 1971 from Journal of Geology, vol. XLVII, no. 7, 1939, pp. 113–122.

Bruns, D.L., Epis, R.C., Weimer, R.J., and Steven, T.A., 1971, Stratigraphic relations between Bonanza center and adjacent parts of the San Juan volcanic field, south-central Colorado, pp. 183–190.

Chapin, C.E., 1971, The Rio Grande rift, part 1: modifications and additions, pp. 191–201.

Lipman, P.W., Steven, T.A., 1971, Reconnaissance geology and economic significance of the Platoro caldera, southern San Juan mountains, Colorado, pp. 221–230.

Bauer, C.B., 1971, Minerals of the San Luis Valley and adjacent areas of Colorado, pp. 231–234.

Buchanan, R.H., 1971, The San Luis Valley—a land of paradox, pp. 243–245.

Knepper, D.H., Jr., and Marrs, R.W., Geological development of the Bonanza–San Luis Valley–Sangre de Cristo Range area, south-central Colorado, pp. 249–264.

Burroughs, R.L., 1971, Geology of the San Luis hills, south-central Colorado, pp. 277–287.

Butler, A.P., Jr., 1971, Tertiary stratigraphy of the eastern Tusas mountains, southwest of the San Luis Valley, Colorado-New Mexico, pp. 289–300.

Mickelson. M.B., 1971, History, location and development of the Johns-Manville perlite deposit, No Aqua, New Mexico, p. 321.

Maps

De Voto, Peel, Pierce, 1971, Geologic map of the Sangre de Cristo range, Colorado.

Knepper, Mars, 1971, Geologic map of the Bonanza–San Luis Valley–Sangre de Cristo range area, south-central Colorado, plate 1.

P–8   Kelley, V.C., and Trauger, F.D., 1972, Guidebook of east-central New Mexico, 23rd field conf.,

Northrop, S.A. and Sanford, A.R., 1972, Earthquakes of northeastern New Mexico and the Texas panhandle, pp. 148–160.

P-9   Siemers, C.B., editor, Woodward, L.A. and Callender, J.F., assoc. editors, Silver anniversary guidebook, Ghost Ranch, central-northern New Mexico, 1974, 25th field conf.,

Woodward, L.A. and others, 1974, Precambrian rocks of the southern Sierra Nacimiento, New Mexico, pp. 95–99.

Long, P.E., 1974, Contrasting types of Precambrian grantic rocks in the Dixon-Penasco area, northern New Mexico, pp. 101–108.

Wooodward, L.A., 1974, Tectonics of central-northern New Mexico, pp. 123–129.

Jiracek, G.A., 1974, Geophysical studies in the Jemez mountains region, New Mexico, pp. 137–144.

Judo, A.M., 1974, Outline of the igneous geology of the Jemez mountains volcanic field, pp. 287–289.

Burroughs, R.L., 1974, Neogene volcanism in the southern San Luis basin, pp. 291–294.

Woodward, L.A. and others, 1974, Sandstone copper deposits of the Nacimiento regions, New Mexico, pp. 295–299.

Talbott, L.W., 1974, Nacimiento pit, a Triassic strata-bound copper deposit, pp. 301–303.

La Point, D.J., 1974, Possible source areas for sandstone copper deposits in northern New Mexico, pp. 305–308.

Chenoweth, W.L., 1974, Uranium in the Petaca, Ojo Caliente and Bromide districts, Rio Arriba County, New Mexico, p. 315.

Jahns, R.H., 1974, Structural and petrogenic relationships of pegmatites in the Petaca district, New Mexico, pp. 371–375.

Newspapers and Special Articles

Information from Western Collection Clipping Files of the Western History Dept., Denver Public Library, Denver, Colorado; Durango Public Library, Durango, Colorado; and other sources.

Q-1   Albuquerque Journal, Geo-thermal steam well, May 5, 1964.

Q-2   —— Assoc. press. Mancos, Colo., Oct. 31, (1933?).

Q-3   —— Aztec Independent, Jan. 18, 1935.

Q-4   Christian Science Monitor, July 26, 1949 (Tues.), by Olga Edit Gunkle.

Q-5   Bluemel, Elinor, 1973, One hundred years of Colorado women.

Q-6   Cortez, Colo.,—Records of the County Clerk, Montezuma County.

Q-7   Craig Empire-Courier, Jan. 16, 1935.

Q-8   The Denver Post, June 14, 1936, Dec. 31, 1939.

Q-9   —— Aug. 8, 1948.

Q-10 —— Dec. 8, 1949.

Q-11 —— Sept. 9, 1970, p. 64.

Q-12 —— Apr. 11, 1973, news item.

Q-13 —— Empire Section, Sept. 11, 1977, Curtis, Olga, 1977, New light on the Molly Brown legend.

Q-14 —— Dec. 25, 1977, p. 2, 46.

Q-15 —— July 19, 1978, Cunningham, Alan, Historic Idarado mine will close indefinitely.

Q-16 —— Nov. 2, 1980, Chronis, P., (oil edition) p. 61, New Mexico uranium activity sounds testimonial to mining.

Q-17 Denver Times, Nov. 19, 1898, p. 3. C3.

Q-18 —— Dec. 31, 1889, p. 23, C6.

Q-19 —— Jan. 4, 1901.

Q-20 —— May 2, 1901.

Q-21 —— May 15, 1901.

Q-22 —— June 9, 1901.

Q-23 Durango Herald Democrat, Durango, Colo., Jan. 21, 1934.

Q–24 —— Jan. 14, 1935.
Q–25 —— Jan. 21, 1935.
Q–26 —— Feb. 4, 1935.
Q–27 —— Feb. 11, 1935.
Q–28 —— Feb. 18, 1935.
Q–29 —— May 13, 1935.
Q–30 —— Aug. 12, 1935.
Q–31 —— Sept. 3, 1935.
Q–32 —— Oct. 9, 1937.
Q–33 —— Oct, 11, 1937.
Q–34 El Paso Times, Steam well may produce electricity, July 16, 1964.
Q–35 Great Divide, January, 1892.
Q–36 Leadville Herald Democrat, Feb. 28, 1950.
Q–37 —— Dec. 31, 1953.
Q–38 —— Oct. 31, 1957.
Q–39 The New Mexican, Hottest drilling target tests underway at Jemez Springs, Aug. 19, 1964.
Q–40 Republican, Leadville, July 12, 1902.
Q–41 —— Oct. 26, 1903.
Q–42 —— Dec. 30, 1905.
Q–43 —— Jan. 1, 1907.
Q–44 Rocky Mountain News, March 7, 1882, p. 3, c.3.
Q–45 —— April 22, 1882, p. 5, c.1.
Q–46 —— May 8, 1882, p. 3, c.2, as reprinted from St. Elmo Mountaineer.
Q–47 —— September 13, 1882, p. 1, c.4.
Q–48 —— February 16, 1883, p. 6. c.4.
Q–49 —— November 10, 1883, p. 6, c.3.
Q–50 —— December 12, 1883.
Q–51 —— January 7, 1885.
Q–52 —— September 8, 1885.
Q–53 —— January 30, 1916.
Q–54 —— November 10, 1933.
Q–55 —— June 3, 1934.
Q–56 —— August 18, 1935.
Q–57 —— September 1, 1935.
Q–58 Telluride Journal, Apr. 27, 1935.
Q–59 Leadville Times, February 19, 1899.
Q–60 —— February 23, 1899.
Q–61 —— May 7, 1891.
Q–62 —— March 10, 1899.
Q–63 —— May 7, 1901.
Q–64 —— June 4, 1902.
Q–65 Bear Pause, v. IV, no. 5, Feb., 1977, publication of the Denver Museum of Natural History, Denver, Colo.
Q–66 Unpublished report, Denver, Colorado, from Western History Department, Denver Public Library, Denver, Colo., Schwartz, T.E., Cons. M.E., June 15, 1897, Alicante and John Reed mines, Denver, Colorado, (June 15, 1897, U.S. Survey, Alicante Mine Pat. No. 948, John Reed Mine adjoins U.S. Survey No. 11682 on south end line, John Reed nos. 1–3–5, plus Millsite, Grace, May Queen, Maud Hope no. 1, Maud Hope, Cleveland no. 2.)
Q–67 Annotated catalogue of unpublished engineering and geologic reports on mineral resources of Colorado, Dec. 1936, Colorado State Planning Commission, Denver, Colo. Report on the Red Arrow gold discovery in the La Plata mountains; Nov. 1933, U.S. Geol. Survey, press release no. 81670 (as quoted in the above reference).
Q–68 Silverton Standard and the Miner; June 8, 1978, pp. 1–3 (Lake Emma drains through Sunnyside).

Q-69 Durango Herald; June 5, 1978, p. 1 (Flood forces mine closure).
Q-70 —— June 6, 1978, p. 1 (Witness says mine flood roared).

United States Bureau of Mines

R-1   Apell, G.A. and others, 1947, Lake Valley manganese deposits, Sierra County, New Mexico, U.S. Bur. Mines, R-I-4099, 9p, 30 figs.
R-2   Belser, Carl, 1956, Tungsten potential in Chaffee, Fremont, Gunnison, Lake, Larimer, Park and Summit Counties, Colorado, U.S. Bur. Mines, I.C. 7748, p. 7.
R-3   —— 1956, Tungsten potential in the San Juan area, Ouray, San Juan and San Miguel Counties, Colorado, U.S. Bur. Mines, I.C. 7731, pp. 13, 14, 17.
R-4   Berliner, M.H., 1949, Investigation of the Harding tantalum–lithium deposits, Taos County, New Mexico, U.S. Bur. Mines, R.I. 4607, 7p.
R-5   Deshayes, E.V. and Young, W.E., 1948, Camp Bird lead-zinc deposit, Ouray County, Colorado, U.S. Bur. Mines, R.I. 4230, 11p.
R-6   Ebberly, N.E., Jr., and Schumacher, J.T., 1949, Examination, mapping and sampling of mine shafts and underground workings, Leadville, Lake County, Colorado, U.S. Bur. Mines, R.I. 4518, 115p.
R-7   —— 1949, Investigation of the Fairview hill area manganese deposits, Leadville, Lake County, Colorado, U.S. Bur. Mines, R.I. 4589, 18p.
R-8   Elgin, R.A., Volin, M.E., and Townsend, J.W., 1949, The Leadville drainage tunnel, Lake County, Colorado, U.S. Bur. Mines, R.I. 4493, 37p.
R-9   Gardner, E.D., Jonson, C.H., and Butler, B.S., 1938, Copper mining in North America, U.S. Bur. Mines, Bull. No. 405, 300p.
R-10 Hamilton, W.H. and McLellan, R.R., 1955, Investigation of the Kokomo zinc deposits, Summit County, Colorado, U.S. Bur. Mines, R.I. 5138, p. 28.
R-11 Harrer, C.M. and Tesch, W.J., Jr., 1959, Reconnaissance of iron ore occurrences in Colorado, U.S. Bur. Mines, I.C. 7918, pp. 14–17.
R-12 Harrer, C.M. and Kelly, F.J., 1963, Reconnaissance of iron resources in New Mexico, U.S. Bur. Mines, I.C. 8190, p. 65.
R-13 Hazen, Scott W., Jr., 1949, Lead–zinc silver in the Poughkeepsie district, and part of the upper Uncompahgre and Mineral Point districts, Ouray and San Juan County, Colorado, U.S. Bur. Mines, R.I. 4508, 110p.
R-14 King, W.H. and Allsman, P.T., 1950, Reconnaissance of metal mining in the San Juan region, Ouray, San Juan and San Miguel Counties, Colorado, U.S. Bur. Mines, I.C. 7554, 109p.
R-15 MacDonald, D.F. and Enzian, C., 1916, Prospecting and mining of copper ore at Santa Rita, New Mexico, U.S. Bur. Mines, Bull. no. 107, 122p.
R-16 McCulloch, R.B., and Huleatt, W.P., 1946, Exploration of the Big Four zinc-silver mine, Summit County, Colorado, U.S. Bur. Mines, R.I. 3884, 6p.
R-17 Meeves, H.C., 1966, Nonpegmatitic beryllium occurrences in Arizona, Colorado, New Mexico, Utah, and four adjacent states, U.S. Bur. Mines, R.I. 6828, pp. 25–28.
R-18 Meeves, H. and others, 1966, Reconnaissance of beryllium-bearing pegmatite deposits in six western states, U.S. Bur. Mines, I.C. 8298, pp. 14–15.
R-19 Meeves, H.C. and Darnell, R.P., 1968, Study of the silver potential, Creede district, Mineral County, Colorado, U.S. Bur. Mines. I.C. 8370, 58p.
R-20 —— 1970, Silver potential and economic aspects of the Leadville district, Lake County, Colorado, U.S. Bur. Mines, I.C. 8464, pp. 21, 30–36.
R-21 Redman, D.E., 1961, Reconnaissance of selected pegmatite districts of north-central New Mexico, U.S. Bur. Mines, I.C. 8013, pp. 50–55, 64–65.
R-22 Salsbury, M.H., 1956, Leadville drainage tunnel second project, Lake County, Colorado, U.S. Bur. Mines, R.I. 5284, 50p.
R-23 Soule', J.H., 1946, Exploration of Harding tantalum-lithium deposits, Taos County, New Mexico, U.S. Bur. Mines, R.I. 3986, 10p.

R-24 ——— 1956, Reconnaissance of the ''red bed'' copper deposits in southeastern Colorado and New Mexico, U.S. Bur. Mines, I.C. 7740, pp. 42-57.

R-25 Storms, W.R., 1947, Iron mountain beryllium deposits, Sierra and Socorro Counties, New Mexico, U.S. Bur. Mines, R.I. 4024, 13p.

R-26 ——— 1947, Iron mountain tungsten deposits, Sierra County, New Mexico, U.S. Bur. Mines, R.I. 4035, 5p.

R-27 Thorne, H.A., 1931, Mining practice at the Chino mines, Nevada Consolidated Copper Company, Santa Rita, New Mexico, U.S. Bur. Mines, I.C. 6412, March, 1931, 29p.

United States Geological Survey

S-1 Adams, J.W., 1953, Beryllium deposits of the Mount Antero region, Chaffee County, Colorado, U.S. Geol. Survey, Bull. 982-D, pp. D. 95, D. 119.

S-2 ——— 1959, Mount Antero area: in Warner, L.A., and others, Occurrence of nonpegmatic beryllium in the United States, U.S. Geol. Survey, Prof. Paper 318, pp. 163-164.

S-3 Atwood, W.W. and Mather, K.F., 1932, Physiography and Quaternary geology of the San Juan mountains, Colorado, U.S. Geol. Survey, Prof. paper 166, pp. 11-25, 67-68, 176.

S-4 Bailey, R.A. and others, 1963, Stratigraphic nomenclature of volcanic rocks in the Jemez mountains, New Mexico, U.S. Geol. Survey, Bull. 1274-P, pp. P-1, P-19.

S-5 Bastin, E.S., 1923, Silver enrichment in the San Juan mountains, Colorado, U.S. Geol. Survey, Bull. 735, pp. 65-129.

S-6 Beekly, A.L., 1915, Geology and coal resources of North Park, Colorado, U.S. Geol. Survey, Bull. 596, pp. 116-118.

S-7 Behre, C.H., Jr., 1953, Geology and ore deposits of the west slope of the Mosquito Range, U.S. Geol. Survey, Prof. Paper 235, 176p.

S-8 Bergendahl, M.H., 1963, Geology of the northern part of the Tenmile Range, Summit County, Colorado, U.S. Geol. Survey, Bull. 1162-D 19p.

S-9 Bergendahl, M.H. and Koschmann, A.H., 1971, Ore deposits of the Kokomo-Tenmile district, Colorado, U.S. Geol. Survey, Prof. Paper 652, 53p.

S-10 Brady, B.T., 1975, Fluorspar deposits of Colorado, U.S. Geol. Survey, Map MR-70, scale: 1:500,000 (map).

S-11 Burbank, W.S., 1932, Geology and ore deposits of the Bonanza mining district, Colorado, U.S. Geol. Survey, Prof. Paper 169, 166p.

S-12 ——— 1940, Structural control of ore deposition in the Uncompahgre district, Ouray County, Colorado, U.S. Geol. Survey, Bull. 906-E, pp. E-189-E-265.

S-13 Burbank, W.S. and Luedke, R.G., 1961, Origin and evolution of ore and gangue forming solutions, Silverton caldera, San Juan mountains, Colorado, U.S. Geol. Survey, Prof. Paper 424-C, pp. C-7-C-11.

S-14 ——— 1964, Geology of the Ironton quadrangle, Colorado, scale: 1:24,000 (map).

S-15 ——— 1969, Geology and ore deposits of the Eureka and adjoining districts, San Juan mountains, Colorado, U.S. Geol. Survey, Prof. Paper 535, 73p.

S-16 Burbank, W.S., Luedke, R.G. and Ward, F.N., 1972, Arsenic as an indictor element of mineralized volcanic pipes in the Red Mountain area, western San Juan mountains, Colorado, U.S. Geol. Survey, Bull. 1364, p. 31.

S-17 Butler, B.S. and Vanderwilt, J.W., 1933, The Climax molybdenum deposit, U.S. Geol. Survey, Bull. 840-C, pp. C-195-C-237.

S-18 Capps, S.R., Jr., 1909, Pleistocene geology of the Leadville quadrangle, Colorado, U.S. Geol. Survey, Bull. 386, p. 80-84.

S-19 Creasey S.C. and Granger, A.E., 1953, Geologic map of the Lake Valley manganese district, Sierra County, New Mexico, U.S. Geol. Survey, MF-9 (map).

S-20 Cross, W., Howe, E., and Irving, J.D., 1907, Description of the Ouray quadrangle, Colorado, U.S. Geol. Survey, Geologic Atlas, Folio 153, 20p.

S-21   Cross, W. and Hole, A.D., 1910, Geologic Atlas, Engineer mountain, Colorado, U.S. Geol. Survey, Folio 171, 14p.

S-22   Cross, W. and Larsen, E.S., 1935, A brief review of the geology of the San Juan region of southwestern Colorado, U.S. Geol. Survey, Bull. 843, 138p.

S-23   Cross, W., Spencer, A.C. and Purington, C.W., 1899, LaPlata, Colorado, U.S. Geol. Survey, Geologic Atlas, Folio 60, 14p.

S-24   Cross, W., and Purington, C.W., 1899, Telluride quadrangle, Colorado, U.S. Geol. Survey, Geologic Atlas, Folio 57, 19p.

S-25   Cross, W. and Ransome, F.L., 1905, Rico, Colorado, U.S. Geol. Survey, Geologic Atlas, Folio 130, 20p.

S-26   Darton, N.H., 1928, "Red beds" and associated formations in New Mexico, U.S. Geol. Survey, Bull. 794, pp. 155–177.

S-27   Dings, M.G., and Robinson, C.S., 1957, Geology and ore deposits of the Garfield quadrangle, Colorado, U.S. Geol. Survey, Prof. Paper 289, pp. 54–55, 98–99.

S-28   Eckel, E.B. and others, 1949, (1950) Geology and ore deposits of the LaPlata district, Colorado, U.S. Geol. Survey, Prof. Paper 219, 179p.

S-29   Emery, P.A. and others, 1971, Hydrology of the San Luis Valley, south-central Colorado, U.S. Geol. Survey, Hydrologic investigations, Atlas HA–381, scale: 1:25,000 (map).

S-30   Emmons, S.F., 1882, Abstract of report on geology and mining industry of Leadville, Lake County, Colorado, second annual report, director, U.S. Geol. Survey, for 1880–1882, U.S. Geol. Survey, pp. 201–290.

S-31   —— 1886, Geology and mining industry of Leadville, Colorado, with Atlas, U.S. Geol. Survey, Monographs, vol. XII, 770 p. 70pl.

S-32   —— 1898, Description of Tenmile district quadrangle, Colorado, U.S. Geol. Survey, Geologic Atlas, Folio 48.

S-33   Emmons, S.F. and Irving, J.D., 1907, The downtown district of Leadville, Colorado, U.S. Geol. Survey, Bull. 320, 72p.

S-34   Emmons, W.H., and Larsen, E.S., 1911, A preliminary report on the geology and ore deposits of Creede, Colorado: in Contributions to economic geology, U.S. Geol. Survey, Bull. 530, pt. 1, pp. 42–65.

S-35   —— 1923, Geology and ore deposits of the Creede district, Colorado, U.S. Geol. Survey, Bull. 718, 195p.

S-36   Emmons, S.F., Irving, J.D. and Loughlin, G.F., 1927, Geology and ore deposits of the Leadville mining district, Colorado, U.S. Geol. Survey, Prof. Paper 148, 368p.

S-37   Endlich, F.M., 1877, Geologic report on the southeastern disctrict, U.S. Geol. Survey, Terr., 9th Ann. Rept., pp. 103–235.

S-38   —— 1878, On the erupted rocks of Colorado, U.S. Geol. Survey, Terr., 10th Ann. Rept., pp. 199–272.

S-39   Epis, R.C., and Chapin, C.E., 1974, Stratigraphic nomenclature of the Thirty-nine Mile volcanic field, Central, Colorado, U.S. Geol. Survey, Bull. 1395–C, pp. C–1–C–23.

S-40   Fisher, R.P., 1946, Map showing metallic mineral deposits of Colorado, scale: 1:1,000,000 (map), Missouri River Basin studies, no. 8, Metallic mineral deposits of Colorado, U.S. Geol. Survey in cooperation with the Colorado State Geol. Surv. Board and Colorado Metal Mining Fund.

S-41   Fisher, R.P. and others, 1968, Mineral resources of the Uncompahgre primitive area, Colorado, U.S. Geol. Survey, Bull. 1261–C, 60p.

S-42   Fisher, F.S. and Leedy, W.P., 1973, Geochemical characteristics of mineralized breccia pipes in the Red Mountain district, San Juan mountains, Colorado, U.S. Geol. Survey, Bull. 1381, 43p.

S-43   Freeman, V.L., 1971, Permian deformation in the Eagle Basin, Colorado, U.S. Geol. Survey, Prof. Paper 750–D, pp. D–80–D–83.

S-44   Gillerman, E., 1952, Fluorspar deposits of Burro mountains and vicinity, New Mexico, U.S. Geol. Survey, Bull. 973–F, pp. F–261–F–288.

S-45 Granger, H.C., 1953, Radioactive spring deposits, Perry Robb property, Jemez Springs: in Lovering, T.G., 1956, Radioactive deposits in New Mexico, U.S. Geol. Survey, Bull. 1009-L, pp. L-358-L-361.

S-46 —— 1962, Clays in the Morrison formation and their spatial relation to the uranium deposits at Ambrosia Lake, New Mexico, U.S. Geol. Survey, Prof. Paper 450-D, pp. D-15-D-20.

S-47 Granger, H.C. and Bauer, H.L., Jr., 1956, White Signal district: in Lovering, T.G., 1956, Radioactive deposits in New Mexico, U.S. Geol. Survey, Bull. 1009-L, pp. L-329-L-349.

S-48 Granger, H.C. and Ingram, B.L., 1966, Occurrence and identification of jordisite at Ambrosia Lake, New Mexico, U.S. Geol. Survey, Prof. Paper 550-B, pp. B-120-B-124.

S-49 Hail, W.J., Jr., 1965, Geology of northwestern North Park, Colorado, U.S. Geol. Survey, Bull. 1188, 128p.

S-50 Handley, J.B., Heinrich, E.W., and Paige, L.R., 1950, Pegmatite investigations in Colorado, Wyoming and Utah, 1942-1944, U.S. Geol. Survey, Prof. Paper 227, pp. 21-22.

S-51 Hawley, C.C., and Wobus, R.A., 1977, General geology and petrology of the Precambrian crystalline rocks, Park and Jefferson Counties, Colorado; U.S. Geol. Survey, P.P. 608-B, 77p.

S-52 Henderson, C. W., 1926, Mining in Colorado, U.S. Geol. Survey, Prof. Paper 138, 263p.

S-53 Hess, F.L., 1911, Vanadium in the Sierra de los Caballos, New Mexico, U.S. Geol. Survey, Bull. 530, pp. 157-130.

S-54 —— 1917, Tungsten minerals and deposits, U.S. Geol. Survey, Bull. 652, 85p.

S-55 Heyl, A.V., 1964, Oxidized zinc deposits of the United States, Part 3, Colorado, U.S. Geol. Survey, Bull. 1135-C, pp. C-6-C-83.

S-56 Hillebran, W.F., 1905, Two tellurium minerals from Colorado: in Contributions to mineralogy, U.S. Geol. Survey, Bull. 262, p. 57.

S-57 Irving, J.D., 1905, Ore deposits in the vicinity of Lake City, Colorado, U.S. Geol. Survey, Bull. 260, pp. 78-84.

S-58 Irving, J.D. and Cross, W., 1907, Economic geology of the Ouray quadrangle: in Geologic Atlas, Ouray, Colorado, U.S. Geol. Survey, Folio 153, pp. 16-18.

S-59 Irving, J.D. and Bancroft, H., 1911, Geology and ore deposits near Lake City, Colorado, U.S. Geol. Survey, Bull. 478, 128p.

S-60 Izett, G.A., 1966, Tertiary extrusive volcanic rocks in Middle Park, Grand County, Colorado, U.S. Geol. Survey, Prof. Paper 550-B, pp. B-42-B-46.

S-61 Johnson, R.B., 1964, Walsen composite dike near Walsenburg, Colorado, U.S. Geol. Survey, Prof. Paper 501-B, pp. B-69-B-73.

S-62 ——1967, The great sand dunes of southern Colorado, U.S. Geol. Survey, Prof. Paper 575-C, pp. C-177-C-183.

S-63 —— 1968, Geology of the igneous rocks of the Spanish Peaks region, Colorado, U.S. Geol. Survey, Prof. Paper 594-G, pp. G-1-G-47.

S-64 Jones, W.R. and others, 1961, Geologic events culminating in primary metallization in the Central mining district, Grant County, New Mexico, U.S. Geol. Survey, Prof. Paper 424-C, pp. C-11-C-16.

S-65 —— 1967, General geology of Santa Rita quadrangle, Grant County, New Mexico, U.S. Geol. Survey, Prof. paper 555, 144p.

S-66 —— 1970, Geologic map of the Fort Bayard quadrangle, Grant County, New Mexico, U.S. Geol. Survey, Quad. Map. GQ-865, scale: 1:24,000/4 sheets of text (map).

S-67 —— 1973, Ore deposits and rock alteration of the Santa Rita quadrangle, Grant County, New Mexico, U.S. Geol. Survey, PB-214, 371, N.T.I.S. U.S. Dept. of Commerce, 96p.

S-68 Karig, D.E., 1965, Geophysical evidence of a caldera at Bonanza, Colorado, U.S. Geol. Survey, Prof. Paper 525-B, pp. B-9-B-12.

S-69 Larsen, E.S., 1929, Recent mining developments in the Creede district, Colorado, U.S. Geol. Survey, Bull. 811, Contributions to economic geology, Pt. 1, pp. 89-112.

S–70   Larsen, E.S., 1942, Alkalic rocks of Iron Hill, Gunnison County, Colorado; U.S.G.S. Prof. Paper 197–A, 64p.

S–71   Larsen, E.S., Jr., and Cross, W., 1956, Geology and petrology of the San Juan region, southwestern Colorado, U.S. Geol. Survey, Prof. Paper 158, pp. 52–303.

S–72   Lindgren, W., 1908, Notes on the copper deposits in Chaffee, Fremont and Jefferson Counties, Colorado, U.S. Geol. Survey, Bull. 340, pp. 161–169.

S–73   Lindgren, W., Graton, L.C. and Gordon, C.H., 1910, The ore deposits of New Mexico, U.S. Geol. Survey, Prof. Paper 68, pp. 80–81, 170–175, 241–258, 284–285.

S–74   Lipman, P.W. and Steven, T.A., 1970, Reconnaissance geology and economic significance of the Platoro caldera, southeastern San Juan mountains, Colorado, U.S. Geol. Survey, Prof. Paper 700–C, pp. C–19–C–29.

S–75   Lipman, P.W., Stevens, T.A., Luedke, R.G., and Burbank, W.S., 1973, Revised volcanic history of the San Juan, Uncompahgre, Silverton and Lake City calderas in the western San Juan mountains, Colorado, Journal Research, U.S. Geol. Survey, v. 1, no. 6, pp. 627–642.

S–76   Lipman, P.W., 1974, Geologic map of the Platoro caldera area, southeastern San Juan mountains, southwestern Colorado, U.S. Geol. Survey, Map I–828, scale: 1:48,000 (map).

S–77   Lipman, P.W. and Steven, T.A., 1976, Geologic map of the South Fork area, eastern San Juan mountains, southwestern Colorado, U.S. Geol. Survey, Map I–966, scale: 1:48,000 (map).

S–78   Lipman, P.W., and Mehnert, H.H., 1980, Potassium–Argon ages from the Mount Taylor volcanic field, New Mexico; U.S. Geol. Survey, Shorter Contributions to Min. and Pet., 1979, pp. B–1–B–8.

S–79   Loughlin, G.F., 1918, The oxidized zinc ores of Leadville, Colorado, U.S. Geol. Survey, Bull. 681, 91p.

S–80   ——— 1926, Guides to ores in the Leadville district, U.S. Geol. Survey, Bull. 779, 36p.

S–81   Lovering, T.S., and Goddard, E.N., 1950, Geology and ore deposits of the Front Range Colorado; U.S. Geol. Survey, Prof. Paper 223, 319p.

S–82   Lovering, T.G., 1956, Radioactive deposits in New Mexico, U.S. Geol. Survey, Bull. 1009–L, pp. L–372–L–380.

S–83   Lovering, T.G., and Mallory, W.W., 1962, The Eagle Valley evaporite and its relation to the Minturn and Maroon formations, northwest Colorado, U.S. Geol. Survey, Prof. Paper 450–D, pp. D–45–D–48.

S–84   Luedke, R.G. and Burbank, W.S., 1963, Tertiary volcanic stratigraphy in the western San Juan mountains, Colorado, U.S. Geol. Survey, Prof. Paper 475–C, pp. C–33–C–44.

S–85   Luedke, R.G. and Hosterman, J.W., 1971, Zoning in chimney ore deposits, Red Mountain mining district, Colorado, U.S. Geol. Survey, Prof. Paper 750–A, p. A–40.

S–86   ——— 1971, Clay minerals, Longfellow mine, San Juan County, Colorado, U.S. Geol. Survey, Prof. Paper 750–C, pp. C–104–C–111.

S–87   Lustig, L.K., 1969, Trend-surface analysis of the Basin and Range Province and some geomorphic implications, U.S. Geol. Survey, Prof. Paper 500–D, 70p.

S–88   MacDonald, D.F. and Enzian, C., 1916, Prospecting and mining of copper ore at Santa Rita, New Mexico, U.S. Geol. Survey, Bull. 107, 122p.

S–89   Mallory, W.W., 1971, The Eagle Valley evaporite, northwest Colorado, U.S. Geol. Survey, Bull. 1311–E. 37p.

S–90   Moench, R.H. and Schlee, J.S., 1967, Geology and uranium deposits of the Laguna district, New Mexico, U.S. Geol. Survey, Prof. Paper 519, 117p.

S–91   Nash, J.T., 1976, Fluid inclusion petrology—data from porphyry copper deposits and applications to exploration, U.S. Geol. Survey, Prof. Paper 907–D, 16p.

S–92   Neuerburg, G.J. and others, 1974, Molybdenite in the Montezuma District of Central Colorado; U.S. Geol. Survey, Circ. 704, 21p.

S–93   Newman, W.L., 1976, Geologic time, the age of the earth, U.S. Geol. Survey, Information Pamphlet, pp. 18–19.

S–94 —— 1976, Geologic time, in Denver's geologic setting, U.S. Geol. Survey, Info. 70–1, R–8.

S–95 Olson, J.C., and Wallace, S.R., 1956, Thorium and rare-earth minerals in Powderhorn District, Gunnison County, Colorado; U.S. Geol. Survey Bull. 1027–O, pp. 693–723.

S–96 Plouff, D., and Pakiser, L.C., 1972, Gravity study of the San Juan mountains, Colorado, U.S. Geol. Survey, Prof. Paper 800–B, pp. B–183–B–190.

S–97 Powell, W.J., 1958, Ground water resources of the San Luis Valley, Colorado, U.S. Geol. Survey, Water-Supply Paper 1379, 284p.

S–98 Purington, C.W., 1898, Preliminary report on the mining industries of the Telluride quadrangle, Colorado, 18th annual report, Director of the U.S. Geol. Survey for 1896–1897, pp. 745–861.

S–99 Ransome, F.L., 1901, Economic geology of the Silverton quadrangle, U.S. Geol. Survey, Bull. 182, 265p.

S–100 —— 1901, The ore deposits of the Rico mountains, Colorado, 22nd annual report, Director of the U.S. Geol. Survey for 1900–1901, Pt. 2, pp. 229–397.

S–101 Sanders, G.F., Jr., Scott, G.R. and Naeser, C.W., 1976, The Buffalo Peaks andesite of central Colorado, U.S. Geol. Survey, Bull. 1405–F, 8p.

S–102 Sanford, S. and Stone, R.W., 1914, Useful minerals of the United States, U.S. Geol. Survey, Bull. 585, 250p.

S–103 Schaller, W.T., 1905, Mineralogical notes, No. 17: IN Contributions to mineralogy, U.S. Geol. Survey, Bull. 262, pp. 133–135.

S–104 —— 1905, Mineralogical notes, No. 19: In Contributions to mineralogy, U.S. Geol. Survey, Bull. 262, pp. 139–140.

S–105 Scott, G.R., 1970, Quaternary faulting and potential earthquakes in east-central Colorado, U.S. Geol. Survey, Prof. Paper 700–C, pp. C–11–C–18.

S–106 Sharp, W.N., 1976, Geologic map and details of beryllium and molybdenum, Mount Antero, Chaffee County, Colorado, U.S. Geol. Survey, MF 810, scale: 1:24,000/2 sheets (map).

S–107 Singewald, Q.D. and Butler, B.S., 1941, Ore deposits in the vicinity of the London Fault of Colorado, U.S. Geol. Survey, Bull. 911, 74p.

S–108 Smith J.A., 1883, Biennial report of State Geologist of Colorado for years 1881–1882, U.S. Geol. Survey, 151p.

S–109 Smith, R.L., Bailey, R.A. and Ross, C.S., 1970, (reprint 1976), Geologic map of the Jemez mountains, New Mexico, U.S. Geol. Survey, Map I–571, scale: 1:125,000 (map).

S–110 Snyder, G.L. and Hedge, C.E., 1978, Intrusive rocks northeast of Steamboat Springs, Park Range, Colorado, U.S. Geol. Survey, Prof. Paper 1041, 42p.

S–111 Spencer, A.C., and Paige, S., 1935, Geology of Santa Rita mining area, New Mexico, U.S. Geol. Survey, Bull. 859.

S–112 Staatz, M.H. and others, 1980 Thorium Resources of selected regions in the United States; U.S.G.S. Circ. 824, pp. 22–25.

S–113 Sterret, D.B., 1911, Gems and precious stones: in Mineral resources for 1909, Pt. 2, pp. 791–795: in Lasky, S.G., 1947, Geology and ore deposits of the Little Hatchet Mountains, Hidalgo and Grant Counties, New Mexico, U.S. Geol. Survey, Prof. Paper 208, pp. 81–82.

S–114 Steven, T.A., 1968, Critical review of the San Juan peneplane, southwestern Colorado, U.S. Geol. Survey, Prof. Paper 594–I, pp. I–11, I–19, I–110, I–119.

S–115 Steven, T.A. and Lipman, P.W., 1973, Geologic map of the Spar City Quadrangle, Mineral County, Colorado, U.S. Geol. Survey, Map GQ–1052, scale: 1:62,500 (map).

S–116 —— 1976, Calderas of the San Juan volcanic field, southwestern Colorado, U.S. Geol. Survey, Prof. Paper 958, 35p.

S–117 Steven, T.A., Mehnert, H.H. and Obradovich, J.D., 1967, Age of volcanic activity in the San Juan mountains, Colorado, U.S. Geol. Survey, Prof. Paper 575–D, pp. D–47–D–55.

S–118 Steven, T.A. and Ratte, J.C., 1960, Geology and ore deposits of the Summitville district, San Juan mountain, Colorado, U.S. Geol. Survey, Prof. Paper 343, 70p.

S-119 —— 1960, Relation of mineralization to caldera subsidence in the Creede district, San Juan mountains, Colorado, U.S. Geol. Survey, Prof. Paper 400–B, pp. B–14–B–17.

S-120 —— 1965, Geology and structural control of ore depositions in the Creede district, San Juan mountains, Colorado, U.S. Geol. Survey, Prof. Paper 487, 90p.

S-121 —— 1973, Geologic map of the Creede quadrangle, Mineral and Saguache Counties, Colorado, U.S. Geol. Survey, Map GQ–1053, scale: 1:62,500 (map).

S-122 Steven, T.A. and others, 1969, Mineral resources of the San Juan primitive area, Colorado, U.S. Geol. Survey, Bull. 1261–F, pp. F–1–F–120.

S-123 —— 1977, Mineral resources of the LaGarita wilderness, San Juan mountains, Southwestern Colorado, U.S. Geol. Survey, Bull. 1420, 65p.

S-124 Thomas, H.E. and others, 1963, Effects of drought in the Rio Grande Basin: in Drought in the Southwest, 1942–1956, by McLaughlin, T.C., U.S. Geol. Survey, Prof. Paper 372–D, p. D–6.

S-125 Towle, J.N., 1980, Polarization of geomagnetic bay-type disturbances in the Rio Grande rift, U.S. Geol. Sur. open file report 80–377, 67p.

S-126 Tweto, O., 1960, Precambrian ore age of faults at Leadville, Colorado: in Short papers in Geol. Sci., U.S. Geol. Survey, Prof. Paper 400–B, pp. B–10–B–11.

S-127 —— 1961, Late Cenozoic events of the Leadville district and upper Arkansas Valley, Colorado, U.S. Geol. Survey, Prof. Paper 424–B, pp. B–133–B–135.

S-128 —— 1977, Tectonic map of the Rio Grande rift system in Colorado, U.S. Geol. Survey, open file report 77–750, scale 1:1,000,000.

S-129 Tweto, O. and Pearson, R.C., 1964, St. Kevin granite, Sawatch Range, Colorado, U.S. Geol. Survey, Prof. Paper 475–D, pp. D–28–D–32.

S-130 Tweto, O. and others, 1970, Mineral resources of the Gore Range-Eagles Nest primitive area and vicinity, Summit and Eagle Counties, Colorado, U.S. Geol. Survey, Bull. 1319–C, 125p.

S-131 Tweto, O. and Lovering, T.C., 1971, Geologic resources, U.S. Geol. Survey, Prof. Paper 750–A, pp. A–39–A–40 (abs.).

S-132 Tweto O., and Case, J.E., 1972, Gravity and magnetic features as related to geology in the Leadville 30-minute quadrangle, Colorado, U.S. Geol. Survey, Prof. Paper 726–C, 31p.

S-133 Tweto, O., 1977, Nomenclature of Precambrian rocks of Colorado, U.S. Geol. Survey, Bull. 1422–D, 22p.

S-134 Van Alstine, R.E., 1968, Tertiary trough between the Arkansas and San Luis Valleys, Colorado, U.S. Geol. Survey, Prof. Paper 600–C, pp. C–158–C–160.

S-135 —— 1969, Geology and mineral deposits of the Poncha Springs N.W. quadrangle, Chaffee County, Colorado, U.S. Geol. Survey, Prof. Paper 626, 52p.

S-136 —— 1970, Allochthonous paleozoic blocks in the Tertiary San Luis-Upper Arkansas graben, Colorado, U.S. Geol. Survey, Prof. Paper 700–B, pp. B–43–B–51.

S-137 —— 1971, Amphibolites near Salida, Colorado, U.S. Geol. Survey, Prof. Paper 750–B, pp. B–74–B–81.

S-138 —— 1974, Geology and mineral deposits of the Poncha Springs S.E. quadrangle, Chaffee County, Colorado, U.S. Geol. Survey, Prof. Paper 829, 19p.

S-139 Van Alstine, R.E., and Lewis, G.E., 1960, Pliocene sediments near Salida, Chaffee County, Colorado, U.S. Geol. Survey, Prof. Paper 400–B, p. B–245, (article III).

S-140 Van Alstine, R.E., and Schruben, P.G., 1980, Fluorspar resources of Africa; U.S.G.S. Bull. 1487, 25p.

S-141 Varnes, D.J., 1963, Geology and ore deposits of south Silverton mining area, San Juan County, Colorado, U.S. Geol. Survey, Prof. Paper 378–A, p. A–35.

S-142 Vhay, J.S., 1962, Geology and mineral deposits of the area south of Telluride, Colorado, U.S. Geol. Survey, Bull. 1112–G and plates, pp. G–209–G–310.

S-143 Vine, J.D., 1974, Geologic map and cross sections of the La Veta Pass, and Ritter Arroyo quadrangles, Huerfano and Costilla Counties, Colorado, U.S. Geol. Survey, Map I–833, scale: 1:48,000 (map).

S–144 Warner, L.A. and others, 1959, Occurrence of nonpegmatic beryllium in the U.S., U.S. Geol. Survey, Prof. Paper 318, pp. 118–119, 129, 177.

S–145 Wilmarth, V.P., 1953, Placerville hydrocarbons, Colorado: in Search for and geology of radioactive deposits, U.S. Geol. Survey TEI–330, pp. 107–110.

S–146 Wrucke, C.T., 1974, The Whitehorn granodiorites of the Arkansas Valley in central Colorado, U.S. Geol. Survey, Bull. 1394–H, 8p.

S–147 Young, E.J. and Lovering, T.G., 1960, Jasperoids of the Lake Valley mining district, New Mexico, U.S. Geol. Survey, Bull. 1222–D, pp. D–1–D–27.

S–148 Reported occurrence of selected minerals in Colorado, U.S. Geol. Survey, Map MR–57, 1971 (map).

S–149 Volcanoes of the United States, Pamphlet of U.S. Geol. Survey, 1969, 19p.

MAPS: Oil and Gas

OM–21, 1944
Read, C.B., Wilpolt, R.H., Andrews, D.A. and others
Geologic map and stratigraphic sections of Permian and Pennsylvanian rocks of parts of San Miguel, Santa Fe, Sandoval, Bernalillo, Torrance and Valencia Counties, north-central, New Mexico, scale 1 inch to 3 miles (1:190,080)

OM–54, 1946
Northern, S.A., Sullwold, Jr., H.H., MacAlpin, A.J. and Rogers, Jr., C.P.
Geology maps of a part of the Las Vegas Basin and of the foothills of the Sangre de Cristo Mountains, San Miguel and Mora Counties, New Mexico, scale 1 inch to 3 miles (1:190,080) and 1 inch to 2/3 mile (1:42.240)

OM–57, 1946, reprinted 1951
Wood, G.H. and Northrop, S.A.
Geology of Nacimiento Mountains, San Pedro Mountain and adjacent plateaus in parts of Sandoval and Rio Arriba Counties, New Mexico, Scale 1 inch to 1 1/2 miles (1:95,040)

OM–61, 1946, reprinted 1954
Wilpolt, R.H., MacAlpin, A.J., Bates, R.L. and Vorbe, Georges
Geologic map and stratigraphic sections of Paleozoic rocks of Joyita Hills, Los Pinos Mountains and northern Chupadera Mesa, Valencia, Torrance and Socorro Counties, New Mexico, scale 1 inch to 1 mile (1:63,360).

OM–121, 1951
Wilpolt, R.H. and Wanek, A.A.
Geology of the region from Socorro and San Antonio east to Chupadera Mesa, Socorro County, New Mexico, scale 1:63,360.

Geophysical Investigations

GP–840, 1972
Aeromagnetic map of the Ridgeway-Pagosa Springs area, southwestern Colorado, scale 1:250,000

Special Quadrangle Map

Leadville mining district, Colorado, 1911, scale 1:9,600
Tenmile mining district, Colorado, north half 1927-40, south half 1927-39, scale 1:12,000

MAPS: Field Study

MF–12, 1953
Tweto, O.
Geologic map of the Pando area, Eagle and Summit Counties, Colorado, scale 1:14,400

MF-34, 1956
Tweto, O.
Geologic map of the Treasure Pass area, Eagle and Lake Counties, Colorado, scale 1:14,400
MF-130, 1958
Osterwald, F.W. and Dean, B.G.
Preliminary tectonic map of northern Colorado and northeastern Utah showing the distribution of uranium deposits, scale 1:500,000.
MF-291, 1964
Izett, G.A. and Barclay, C.S.
Preliminary geologic map of the Hot Sulfur Springs SW quadrangle, Grand County, Colorado, scale 1:24,000
MF-556, 1974
Tweto, O.
Geologic map of the Mount Lincoln quadrangle, Eagle, Lake, Park and Summit Counties, Colorado, scale 1:62,500
MF-649, 1975
Johnson, R.
Geologic structure map of the southernmost Sangre de Cristo Mountains, San Miguel and Santa Fe Counties, New Mexico, scale 1:125,000
MF-666, 1975
Tweto, O.
Preliminary geologic map of the Craig 1° × 2° quadrangle, NW colorado, scale 1:250,000
MF-682, 1975
Lipman, P.W. and Hail, Jr., W.J.
Reconnaissance geologic map of the Chama Peak quadrangle, Conejos and Archuleta Counties, Colorado, scale 1:48,000
MF-688, 1976
Tweto, O.
Preliminary geologic map of Colorado, scale 1:500,000
MF-760, 1976
Tweto, O. and others
Preliminary geology, Leadville 1° × 2° quadrangle, Colorado, scale 1:250,000
1:250,000
MF-761, 1976
Geology, Montrose 1° × 2° quadrangle, Colorado, scale 1:250,000
MF-775, 1976
Scott, G.R. and others
Geology, Pueblo 1° × 2° quadrangle, Colorado, scale 1:187,500
MF-805, 1976
Wobus, R.A., Epis, R.C. and Scott, G.R.
Geologic map of Cripple Creek-Pikes Peak area, Colorado, scale 1:48,000
MR-819, 1976
Luedke, R.G.
Snow avalanche, Telluride quadrangle, scale 1:24,000
MF-823, 1977
Booth, F.O., III
Geologic map of Galisteo Creek area, New Mexico, scale 1:12,000

MAPS: Misc. Geologic Investigations

I-224, 1957
Dane, C.H. and Bachman, G.O.
Preliminary geologic map of the northwestern part of New Mexico, scale 1:380,160
I-256, 1958

Dane, C.H. and Bachman, G.O.
Preliminary geologic map of the southeastern part of New Mexico, scale 1:380,160
I-299, 1959
Finch, W.I., Parrish, I.S. and Walker, G.W.
Epigenetic uranium deposits in the United States, scale 1:5,000,000
I-344, 1961
Dane, C.H. and Bachman, G.O.
Preliminary geologic map of the southwestern part of New Mexico, scale 1:380,160
I-358, 1962
Dane, C.H. and Bachman, G.O.
Preliminary geologic map of the northeastern part of New Mexico, scale 1:380,160
I-374, 1963
Bachman, G.O. and Myers, D.A.
Geology of the Bear Peak NE quadrangle, Dona Ana County, New Mexico, scale 1:31,680
I-408, 1964
Scott, G.R.
Geology of the northwest and northeast Pueblo quadrangle, Colorado, scale 1:24,000
I-558, 1969
Johnson, R.B.
Geologic map of the Trinidad quadrangle, south-central Colorado, Scale 1:250,000
I-563, 1969
Bergendahl, M.H.
Geologic map and sections of the southwest quarter of the Dillon quadrangle, Eagle and Summit
Counties, Colorado, scale 1:24,000
I-673, 1972
Baltz, E.H.
Geologic map and cross sections of the Gallinas Creek area, Sangre de Cristo Mountains, San
Miguel Counties, New Mexico, scale 1:24,000
I-750, 1972
Neuerburg, G.J. and Botinelly, T.
Map showing geologic and structural control of ore deposits, Montezuma district, central Col-
orado, scale 1:31,680
I-764, 1974
Steven, T.A., Lipman, P.W., Hail, Jr., W. J., Barker, F. and Leudke, R.G.
Geologic map of the Durango quadrangle, southwestern Colorado, scale 1:250,000
I-830, 1974
Tweto, O.
Geologic map and sections of the Holy Cross quadrangle, Eagle, Lake, Pitkin and Summit
Counties, Colorado, scale 1:24,000
I-886, 1975
Ratte, J.C. and Gaskill, D.L.
Reconnaissance geologic map of the Gila Wilderness study area, southwestern New Mexico,
scale 1:62,500
I-901, 1975
Lipman, P.W.
Geologic map of the lower Conejos River Canyon area, southeastern San Juan Mountains, Col-
orado, scale 1:48,000
I-952, 1976
Lipman, P.W.
Geologic map of the Del Norte area, eastern San Juan Mountains, Colorado, scale 1:48,000
I-962, 1976
Lipman, P.W.
Geologic map of the Lake City caldera area, western San Juan Mountains, southwestern Col-
orado, scale 1:48,000

I-966, 1976
Lipman, P.W. and Steven, T.A.
Geologic map of the South Fork area, eastern San Juan Mountains, southwestern Colorado, scale 1:48,000
I-973,A, 1976
Luedke, R.G. and Burbank, W.S.
Map showing types of bedrock and surficial deposits in the Telluride quadrangle, San Miguel, Ouray and San Juan Counties, Colorado, scale 1:24,000

MAPS: Geologic Quadrangle

GQ-152, 1962
Luedke, R.G. and Burbank, S.
Geology of the Ouray quadrangle, Colorado, scale 1:24,000
GQ-504, 1966
Burbank, W.S. and Luedke, R.G.
Geologic map of the Telluride quadrangle, southwestern Colorado, scale 1:24,000
GQ-551, 1966
Myers, D.A.
Geologic map of the Tajique quadrangle, Torrance and Bernalillo Counties, New Mexico, scale 1:24,000
GQ-631, 1967
Steven, T.A.
Geologic map of the Bristol Head quadrangle, Mineral and Hinsdale Counties, Colorado, scale 1:62,500
GQ-797, 1969
Pratt, W.P., McKnight, E.T. and DeHon, R.A.
Geologic map of the Rico quadrangle, Dolores and Montezuma Counties, Colorado, Scale 1:24,000
GQ-952, 1972
Brock, M.R. and Barker, F.
Geologic map of the Mount Harvard quadrangle, Chaffee and Gunnison Counties, Colorado, scale 1:62,500
GQ-956, 1971
Johnson, R.B.
Geologic map of the Laguna Ortiz quadrangle, San Miguel County, New Mexico, scale 1:24,000
GQ-1007, 1972
Johnson, R.B.
Geologic map of the north San Ysidro quadrangle, San Miguel County, New Mexico, scale 1:24,000
GQ-1011, 1972
Luedke, R.G.
Geologic map of the Wetterhorn Peak quadrangle, Colorado, scale 1:24,000
GQ-1036, 1972
Johnson, R.B.
Geologic map of the Rowe quadrangle, San Miguel and Santa Fe Counties, New Mexico, scale 1:24,000
GQ-1077, 1973
Johnson, R.B.
Geologic map of the Bull Canyon quadrangle, Santa Fe County, New Mexico, scale 1:24,000
GQ-1134, 1974
Hedlund, D.C. and Olson, J.C.
Geologic map of the Iris NW quadrangle, Gunnison and Saguache Counties, Colorado, scale 1:24,000

GQ-1163, 1974
Johnson, R.B.
Geologic map of the Apache Springs quadrangle, San Miguel, County, New Mexico, scale 1:62,500
GQ-1177, 1974
Olson, J.C.
Geologic map of the Rudolph Hills quadrangle, Gunnison, Hinsdale and Saguache Counties, Colorado, scale 1:24,000
GQ-1234, 1975
Johnson, R.B.
Geologic map of the Galisteo quadrangle, Santa Fe County, New Mexico, scale 1:24,000
GQ-1268, 1975
Bachman, G.O.
Geologic map of the Madrid quadrangle, Santa Fe and Sandoval Counties, New Mexico, scale 1:62,500

General Quadrangle Maps

Colorado:
Alma, 1970, scale 1:24,000
Antero Reservoir, 1959, scale 1:62,500
Bonanza, 1959, scale 1:62,500
Buena Vista, 1955, scale 1:62,500
Cameron Mountain quadrangle, 1956, scale 1:62,500
Como quadrangle, 1937, 1947 reprinted, scale 1:62,500
Craig quadrangle, 1916, 1949 reprinted, scale 1:125,000
Creede quadrangle, 1916, 1939 reprinted, scale 1:125,000
Creede and vicinity, 1927, 1961 reprinted, scale 1:24,000
Crested Butte, surveyed 1883–188, 1927, 1956 revised, scale 1:62,500
Daton Peak quadrangle, (Hayden), 1920, scale 1:62,500
Dillon quadrangle, 1934, 1944 revised, scale 1:62,500
Durango quadrangle, October, 1980, 1946 reprinted, scale 1:62,500
Durango, 1963, scale 1:250,000
Durango, 1966, scale 1:250,000
Engineer Mountain, 1908, 1942 reprinted, scale 1:62,500
Holy Cross quadrangle, 1951, scale 1:62,500
Igancio quadrangle (LaPlata), 1980, 1939 reprinted, sale 1:125,000
Lake City quadrangle, 1927, 1961 reprinted, scale 1:62,500
LaPlata quadrangle, 1908, 1946 reprinted, scale 1:62,500
Leadville Sheet, 1891, 1947 reprinted, scale 1:125,000
Leadville Mining Distrit, June, 1913, scale 1:9,600
Leadville, 1964, scale 1:250,000
Minturn quadrangle, 1934, 1944 reprinted, scale 1:62,500
Montrose, November, 1911, 1948 reprinted scale 1:125,000
Montrose, 1956, 1962 reprinted, scale 1:250,000
Mount Harvard, 1955, scale 1:62,500
Mount Lincoln quadrangle, 1945, scale 1:62,500
Needle Mountains, 1902, 1946 reprinted, scale 1:62,500
Needle Mountains, 1900 survey, 1965 reprinted scale 1:62,500
Ouray, 1902, scale 1:62,500
Pagosa Springs, quadrangle, 1927, 1949 reprinted, scale 1:125,000
Poncha Springs, 1956, scale 1:62,500
Red Mesa quadrangle (LaPlata), September, 1913, 1949 reprinted, scale 1:62,500
Rico District, Dolores County, 1899, 1916 reprinted, scale 1:23,600

Rico quadrangle, 1899, 1951 reprinted, 1:62,500
Saguache 1 quadrangle (south Poncha Springs), advance proof map, scale 1:48,000
Silverton quadrangle, 1901, 1946 reprinted, scale 1:62,500
Silverton quadrangle (Topo. 15 foot series), 1955, scale 1:62,500
Summitville quadrangle, October, 1915, 1949 reprinted, scale 1:500,000
Taylor Park quadrangle, 1949 reprinted, scale 1:62,500
Telluride quadrangle, 1904, 1922 reprinted, scale 1:125,000
Tenmile District, August, 1897, 1945 reprinted, scale 1:31,680
Trinidad, 1954, Ltd. Rev. 1962, scale 1:250,000
Uncompahgre, April, 1911, 1944 reprinted, scale 1:125,000
New Mexico:
Albuquerque topographic map, 1963, scale 1:250,000
Aztec, 1962, scale 1:250,000
Bingham, 1948, sale 1:62,500
Jemez Springs/Frijoles quadrangle, 1952–1953, scale 1:62,500
Magdalena District, 1932, 1948 reprinted, scale 1:12,000
Raton, New Mexico, Colorado, 1954, scale 1:250,000
San Antonio quadrangle, 1948, scale 1:62,500
San Cristobal quadrangle, surveyed 1904–1905, 1927, 1963 reprinted, scale 1:125,000
Santa Fe, 1962, scale 1:250,000
Socorro quadrangle, 1906, 1948 reprinted, scale 1:62,500
Colorado–Utah:
Cortez, 1966, scale 1:250,000
Colorado–Wyoming:
Craig, 1964, scale 1:250,000
Kings Canyon quadrangle, 1950, scale 1:24,000

Base Maps, General Maps and Western U.S. Maps

Colorado Base Map, 1956, 1959 reprinted, scale 1:500,000 Ouray, Colorado Chamber of Commerce, 2/21/57, scale 1 inch = 3 miles Western United States, 1962, scale 1:250,000
All pertinent Forest Service maps of the entire rift area.
Tectonic Map of the United States of America: 1961, U.S. Geol. Survey

National Geographic Society Maps

National Geographic Maps of the Ocean, Floors Based on Bathmetric studies by Heezen, B.C., and Tharp, M.
Pacific Ocean Floor, 1969, Scale 575 mi/in at equator
Atlantic Ocean Floor, 1968, scale 480 mi/in at equator
Indian Ocean Floor, 1967, scale not given

INDEX

INDEX